Principles of Military Communication Systems

Principles of Military Communication Systems

Don J. Torrieri

Artech

To Nancy

Contents

PREFACE

1 COMMUNICATION WARFARE 1

1.1 Power and Propagation 1
1.2 Analog Communications 6
1.3 Digital Communications: Frequency-Shift Keying 11
1.4 Pulsed Jamming 17

References 21

2 PSEUDONOISE SPREAD-SPECTRUM SYSTEMS 23

2.1 Principles 23
2.2 Pseudonoise Sequences 30
2.3 Concealment of Pseudonoise Waveforms 36
2.4 Error Probabilities in Presence of Interference 41
2.5 Jamming 52
2.6 Code Synchronization 53
2.7 Pseudonoise Networks 56
2.8 Burst-Communication System 60

References 62

3 FREQUENCY HOPPING 65

3.1 Introduction 65
3.2 Fast Hopping and Slow Hopping with Bit Interleaving 70
3.3 Slow Hopping without Interleaving 74
3.4 Conditional Bit Error Probabilities 75
3.5 Effect of Coding 78
3.6 Partial-Band Jamming 79
3.7 Repeater Jamming 85
3.8 Other Data Modulations 89
3.9 Code Synchronization 94
3.10 Hybrid System 96
3.11 Comparison of Frequency-Hopping Systems and Pseudonoise Systems 98
3.12 Frequency-Hopping Networks 100

References 122

4 INTERCEPTION 125

4.1   Introduction 125
4.2   Detection 126
4.3   Frequency Estimation 147
4.4   Direction Finding 167
4.5   Countermeasures to Interception 188

References 189

5 ADAPTIVE ANTENNA SYSTEMS 191

5.1   Introduction 191
5.2   Sidelobe Canceller 192

    5.2.1   Steady State Operation 194
    5.2.2   Adaptive Null Steering 203

5.3   Classical Theory 205

    5.3.1   Signal-to-Noise Ratio Criterion 209
    5.3.2   Mean-Square Error Criterion 211
    5.3.3   Steepest Descent 213

5.4   Adaptive Noise Cancelling 217
5.5   Constrained Minimum Power Criterion 219
5.6   Convergence of Widrow-Hoff Algorithm 223
5.7   Adaptive Polarization Discrimination 225

References 229

6 CRYPTOGRAPHIC DIGITAL COMMUNICATIONS 231

6.1   Ciphers and Cryptanalysis 231
6.2   Error Probability Bounds and Ensemble Averages for Stream Ciphers 243
6.3   Error Probability Bounds and Ensemble Averages for Block Ciphers 249
6.4   Degradation due to Cryptography 250
6.5   Error Correction 253
6.6   Synchronization and Jamming 256
6.7   Security 261

References 262

APPENDIX A:

DERIVATIONS OF CONDITIONAL BIT ERROR PROBABILITIES FOR FREQUENCY-SHIFT KEYING 265

References 272

APPENDIX B:

NONCENTRAL CHI-SQUARED DISTRIBUTION 275

References 278

APPENDIX C:

THE DISCRETE FOURIER TRANSFORM AND THE SIGNAL SPECTRUM 281

APPENDIX D:

MATRIX ANALYSIS 285

D.1   Elementary Results 285
D.2   Hermitian and Quadratic Forms 288
D.3   The Gradient 292
D.4   Linear Discrete-Time Equations 293

References 293

INDEX

Preface

In contrast to ordinary communication systems, military communication systems must be designed with the presumption that they will operate in hostile environments. Consequently, special techniques that might be irrelevant or even harmful in ordinary communication systems are needed for communication systems that are to be viable on the battlefield. This book is devoted to an analytical study of those aspects of communication theory that have special relevance to military systems. These aspects are not thoroughly treated in any other single textbook.

This book concentrates on principles, concepts, and systems-level analysis. Specific implementations and hardware, which are more susceptible to obsolescence due to the relentless progress of technology, are given much less emphasis.

This book is intended for graduate students and practicing engineers with a background in communication theory such as that offered in Ziemer and Tranter, *Principles of Communications* (1976). In addition, a knowledge of basic matrix analysis is needed for parts of Chapter 5. Although an adequate mathematical background is necessary for a full appreciation of the issues, the reader can often skip the mathematical detail and concentrate on the final results without a great loss of understanding.

The plethora of jargon and acronyms that fill the military literature has been carefully avoided. A reasonably simple terminology is available to those inclined to use it. In general, only the most useful and interesting references have been listed, with preference given to readily accessible textbooks and articles.

The fundamental issues of power and propagation are presented in Chapter 1. The effectiveness of various types of jamming against amplitude-modulation, frequency-modulation, phase-modulation, and frequency-shift-keying systems is assessed.

Chapters 2 and 3 explore spread-spectrum systems, which potentially resist both interception and jamming. Chapter 2 examines the basic characteristics of various pseudonoise systems. A necessary condition is derived for the concealment of a pseudonoise waveform from detection. The bit error probability in the presence of various types of interference is determined. Methods of reducing the mutual interference in a network of pseudonoise systems, jamming strategies, and acquisition techniques are discussed.

Chapter 3 considers the response of frequency-hopping systems to various types of jamming. Fast and slow hopping are defined in terms of the symbols per hop. The impacts of coding, bit interleaving, and channel selections on the jamming susceptibilities of frequency-hopping systems are analyzed. The conditions for effective partial-band jamming and effective repeater jamming are established. Different types of data modulation, the acquisition problem, and hybrid frequency-hopping pseudonoise systems are considered. Differences in performance between frequency-hopping systems and pseudonoise systems are illustrated. Error probabilities are derived for a frequency-hopping system that operates in a network of similar systems.

Whatever its ultimate purpose, an interception system nearly always must achieve the three basic functions of detection, frequency estimation, and direction finding. In Chapter 4, the fundamental concepts and issues of these three elements of interception are presented at the systems level, assuming that little is known about the signals to be intercepted. The capabilities of radiometers and cross correlators for detection are determined. Channelized, discrete Fourier transform, acousto-optical, instantaneous frequency measurement, scanning superheterodyne, and microscan receivers for frequency estimation are described and analyzed. Direction finding by energy comparison systems and interferometers is examined. Throughout the chapter, the special aspects of spread-spectrum interception are investigated.

Chapter 5 is devoted to adaptive antenna systems for interference rejection. The first part of the chapter contains a heuristic development of the basic principles. The operation of the sidelobe canceller is interpreted in terms of noise cancelling, adaptive beam forming, and null steering. In the remainder of the chapter, the classical theory of adaptive systems is derived using more advanced mathematics. The results can be applied to both tapped-delay-line and frequency-domain array-processing filters. The general theory of adaptive noise cancelling is linked to the sidelobe canceller, the classical theory of adaptive elements, and the adaptive notch filter. An adaptive antenna system is derived from the constrained minimum power criterion, which limits the accidental cancellation of the desired signal. Adaptive polarization discrimination is shown to provide a useful supplementary method of interference rejection.

Cryptography is used to ensure the secrecy of messages when hostile personnel have the technical capability of intercepting and correctly interpreting a message. In Chapter 6, the basic types of ciphers for digital communications are defined and compared. The chapter focuses on the examination of the increased error rates caused by the use of ciphers in communication systems. Synchronization and jamming problems in cryptographic digital communications are explained.

The knowledge and motivation required to write this book were acquired during my employment at the U.S. Army Electronics Research and Development Command (ERADCOM) Headquarters. Much of the material has been drawn from the reports, memoranda, and notes prepared in the course of my work.

I am thankful to many friends in ERADCOM and Harry Diamond Laboratories, particularly Della Whittaker, Sandy Herrmann, Hal Harrelson, Joseph Kirshner, and William Pepper, for their direct and indirect assistance in this effort. I am grateful to my wife and daughter, who endured all the pressures and inconveniences that accompanied the writing of this book.

1

Communication Warfare

1.1 POWER AND PROPAGATION

Communication warfare is an element of warfare that pits potential communicators against hostile personnel who seek to intercept and/or disrupt their communications. Since the development of covert communication techniques has severely curtailed the possibility of intercepting and interpreting communications, it seems inevitable that military communications in the battlefield will be forced to operate in a jamming environment. However, to conserve power, the potential jammer usually must first intercept the communications and perhaps locate the receivers.

To reduce communication susceptibility to interception and jamming, various general measures may be adopted. If transmission frequencies exceed 30 MHz, ionospheric reflections are small, thereby reducing long-range interception and jamming possibilities. Highly directional laser beams or millimeter waves are difficult to intercept. Their receivers are difficult to jam because of the narrow radiation patterns of the receiving antennas. Although atmospheric attenuation may hinder interception and jamming, attenuation and acquisition problems may limit the use of optical or millimeter transmissions through the air to special applications such as satellite communications.

Cable communications by metallic wires, coaxial cables, and waveguides and by optical fibers provide advantages similar to those of directional beams, but without the acquisition problem. The main problems with cables are their impracticality in mobile, rapidly changing tactical environments and their susceptibility to damage.

Because optical fibers do not emit a significant amount of electromagnetic energy, they are very effective in preventing the interception of communications by an opponent. Tapping is more difficult than it is for a metallic cable. Since ambient electromagnetic energy does not interfere significantly with the propagation of optical waves in fibers, communication by means of optical fibers is nearly invulnerable to jamming. Other advantages of optical fibers are their light weight, resistance to fire, lack of crosstalk among fibers, and freedom from short circuits. Although it may not be necessary in many military communication systems, optical fibers can carry a much higher message density than metallic cables of comparable dimensions. For military applications, the major disadvantage of optical fibers relative to metallic cables appears to be the difficulty of rapidly replacing damaged fibers.

The use of relays increases the jamming resistance of a communication network. However, network management problems and equipment costs limit the number of relays in a network. If the communicators store, compress, and rapidly transmit all messages, effective jamming becomes less likely.

Ordinarily, the jammer cannot ascertain the effectiveness of the jamming. However, effective jamming may force communicators to change the operating frequency. If the jammer can detect this change in frequency, he has an important indication that the jamming is indeed disrupting communications. The jammer may then attempt to change the center frequency of the jamming signal accordingly.

To deny the jammer this opportunity to confirm his effectiveness, communication systems can be designed to change operating frequency periodically. Another tactic is to relocate one or more elements of a disrupted communication network to establish a line-of-sight path between the transmitters and the receivers and, if the jammer's location is known, to mask the receivers from the jammer by means of terrain obstacles.

If the communication frequencies can be accurately estimated, narrowband jamming can be used against the communicators. This type of jamming not only allows economical use of power, but also makes it easy for the jammer to avoid jamming his own communications. If frequency-estimation equipment is not used, or if accurate frequency estimation is impossible because of rapid frequency changes or other unfavorable conditions, the jammer can employ wideband jamming. In this case, the jamming energy is spread over large spectral regions to increase the probability that some jamming energy interferes with the enemy communications.

The jamming-to-signal ratio at the receiver is a basic quantity that is needed in the assessment of communication system performance. To relate this power ratio to other quantities, we examine the power relations at the receiver.

If two communicators are separated by a distance D_T, the average power of a transmitted signal at the input of a receiver is

$$R_s = \frac{P_T G_{TR} G_{RT} \lambda^2}{(4\pi)^2 D_T^2 L_{TR}}, \qquad (1.1)$$

where P_T is the average transmitter power, G_{TR} is the gain of the transmitter antenna in the direction of the receiver, G_{RT} is the gain of the receiver antenna in the direction of the transmitter, and λ is the wavelength. The loss factor, L_{TR}, is a measure of the deviation of the propagation from ideal free-space propagation. If the communication elements are airborne and atmospheric attenuation is negligible, $L_{TR} \approx 1$. Otherwise, L_{TR} may be a function of D_T.

If one or both of the communication elements are on the ground, an accurate calculation of R_s must allow for the curvature of the spherical earth, the dielectric constant, the antenna heights, the presence of obstacles, multipath, and other effects. Many modern propagation models are based upon the *Longley-Rice model* [1], which gives computerized predictions of the transmission loss, $L = L_{TR} D_T^2$, over irregular terrain.

Measurements of L or R_s for different paths of the same length often show great variation due to path-to-path differences in terrain profiles. Values recorded for a single path over a long period of time sometimes exhibit comparable ranges. The Longley-Rice model can be used to calculate the median and the standard deviation of L in a geographical region. Experimental results suggest that L usually has a distribution that is approximately lognormal. The standard deviation of L increases with frequency and terrain irregularity, but is relatively insensitive to path length and antenna heights [2].

For mobile communicators, the received signal power exhibits additional variation over short periods of time. This variation, which is called fading, is caused by time-varying multipath effects.

Because of the computational complexity of propagation models, an approximate power-law equation for the median value of the received signal is desirable for analytical purposes. If R_s in Equation (1.1) is interpreted as the median received signal power and the range of values of D_T is appropriately restricted, it is often possible to write

$$L = L_{TR} D_T{}^2 \cong \frac{D_T{}^n}{K_T} \quad , \tag{1.2}$$

where K_T is independent of D_T, but is a function of other parameters such as the heights of the antennas above the earth. Substituting Equation (1.2) into Equation (1.1) yields

$$R_s = \frac{K_T P_T G_{TR} G_{RT} \lambda^2}{(4\pi)^2 D_T{}^n} \quad . \tag{1.3}$$

To use this equation, we need specific values for K_T and n. These values can be determined from experimental data or data calculated from a propagation model. Equation (1.3) indicates that n satisfies

$$n = \frac{\partial \log R_s}{\partial \log D_T} \quad . \tag{1.4}$$

Thus, a consistent way to estimate n is to calculate this partial derivative from a graph of R_s in decibels versus D_T in decibels. If n varies with D_T, the range must be subdivided into small enough pieces that each piece can be associated with a nearly constant value of n. Once n is determined for a range of D_T, the corresponding value of K_T can be calculated by fitting Equation (1.3) to a single point of the R_s versus D_T curve within that range.

For very high frequency (VHF) ground communications, experimental data indicate that n = 4 is often approximately valid over a wide range of values of D_T.

At optical and millimeter frequencies, the severe atmospheric attenuation can be more accurately modeled by replacing Equation (1.3) with

$$R_s = \frac{K_T P_T G_{TR} \, G_{RT} \lambda^2}{(4\pi)^2 \, D_T^{\,n}} \exp\left(-\alpha D_T\right) , \qquad (1.5)$$

where $\alpha \geqslant 0$. The parameters K_T, n, and α are probably best estimated by regression analysis.

The jamming power that enters a receiver may be reduced by two factors. First, there is a *polarization loss* due to the fact that the jammer may not be emitting radiation with the appropriate polarization. This relative polarization loss may be described by a coefficient p, which has the range $0 \leqslant p \leqslant 1$. A second jamming power reduction may be caused by the receiver bandpass filtering. The effect of this filtering usually may be described by a function $f(B_R, B_J)$, where B_R is the bandwidth of the effective receiver bandpass filter, and B_J is the bandwidth of the jamming signal. If the entire jamming spectrum is included in the receiver passband, we may write

$$f(B_R, B_J) = 1 \; ; \qquad (1.6)$$

if the jamming spectrum includes the entire receiver passband, we have

$$f(B_R, B_J) = \frac{B_R}{B_J} . \qquad (1.7)$$

The median value of the net jamming power affecting the receiver is

$$R_j = \frac{K_J P_J G_{JR} G_{RJ} \lambda^2 p \, f(B_R, B_J)}{(4\pi)^2 \, D_J^{\,m}} \exp\left(-\beta D_J\right) , \qquad (1.8)$$

where D_J is the distance between the jammer and the receiver, P_J is the average jammer transmitter power, G_{JR} is the gain of the jamming antenna in the direction of the receiver, and G_{RJ} is the gain of the receiver antenna in the direction of the jammer. It is assumed that the average wavelength of the jamming signal is approximately equal to that of the intended signal. The parameters K_J, m, and β are defined analogously to K_T, n, and α, respectively.

An approximate median value of the jamming-to-signal ratio is determined from Equations (1.5) and (1.8) to be

$$\frac{R_j}{R_s} = \frac{P_J K_J G_{JR} G_{RJ} \, pf \, (B_R, B_J)}{P_T K_T G_{TR} G_{RT}} \frac{D_T^{\,n}}{D_J^{\,m}} \exp\left(\alpha D_T - \beta D_J\right) . \qquad (1.9)$$

This equation gives the relation between the median jamming-to-signal ratio and other quantities. Even if the right-hand side of Equation (1.9) has a fixed value, the jamming-to-signal ratios for particular locations of the communicators and the jammer differ because of the particular terrain profiles.

According to information theory, the most destructive type of additive noise in a communication channel is white Gaussian noise. Thus, it is often desirable for a jammer to produce a facsimile of bandlimited white Gaussian noise. However, in practice it is difficult to synthesize a waveform with the large random voltage swings of this type of noise. To the extent that the jamming can be modeled as white Gaussian noise, well-known theoretical formulas can often be used to determine the impact of the jamming on communications.

Non-Gaussian jamming waveforms usually are studied through computer simulations. However, in certain cases, an approximate mathematical analysis is possible. Although such analyses are necessarily limited in scope, they provide valuable insight into the general characteristics of jamming and the countermeasures against it. In the next two sections, examples of the jamming of analog and digital communication systems are analyzed.

Reference [3] provides many examples of the uses and problems of military communication systems. A number of papers on interference analysis, some of which apply to jamming, are included in reference [4].

1.2 ANALOG COMMUNICATIONS

We consider a general received waveform, which includes amplitude-modulation (AM), phase-modulation (PM), and frequency-modulation (FM) waveforms as special cases. This waveform is

$$s(t) = A(t) \cos [\omega_1 t + \phi_1(t)] , \tag{1.10}$$

where $A(t)$ is the amplitude modulation, ω_1 is the carrier frequency, and $\phi_1(t)$ is the angle modulation. The receiver possesses an initial bandpass filter that passes $s(t)$ with negligible distortion. A general form for a jamming waveform may be written as

$$J(t) = B(t) \cos [\omega_2 t + \phi_2(t)] . \tag{1.11}$$

It is assumed that $J(t)$ passes the receiver bandpass filter with negligible distortion. Alternatively, we may view $J(t)$ as the description of the jamming waveform at the filter output.

Throughout the subsequent analysis, we neglect the effect of thermal noise for simplicity. Consequently, the signal at the output of the bandpass filter is $X(t) = s(t) + J(t)$. Using a trigonometric identity to expand the cosine term of Equation (1.11), we obtain

$$X(t) = \left\{ A(t) + B(t) \cos [\omega_3 t + \phi_3(t)] \right\} \cos [\omega_1 t + \phi_1(t)]$$

$$- B(t) \sin [\omega_3 t + \phi_3(t)] \sin [\omega_1 t + \phi_1(t)] , \quad (1.12)$$

where $\omega_3 = \omega_2 - \omega_1$ and $\phi_3 = \phi_2 - \phi_1$. Further trigonometry yields

$$X(t) = R(t) \cos [\omega_1 t + \phi_1(t) + \theta(t)] , \quad (1.13)$$

where

$$R(t) = \left\{ A^2(t) + B^2(t) + 2A(t)B(t) \cos [\omega_3 t + \phi_3(t)] \right\}^{\frac{1}{2}}$$

$$(1.14)$$

and

$$\theta(t) = \tan^{-1} \left\{ \frac{B(t) \sin [\omega_3 t + \phi_3(t)]}{A(t) + B(t) \cos [\omega_3 t + \phi_3(t)]} \right\} . \quad (1.15)$$

AM Systems

When an AM signal is transmitted, we have $\phi_1(t) = 0$ and $\phi_3(t) = \phi_2(t)$. The message is carried by $A(t)$. Consider a noncoherent system in which the receiver demodulates by means of an envelope detector. An ideal envelope detector produces an output proportional to the instantaneous amplitude, $R(t)$, if it is slowly varying relative to $\omega_1 t$. Assuming this ideal operation, the envelope detector output is proportional to

$$y(t) = A(t) \left\{ 1 + 2 \frac{B(t)}{A(t)} \cos [\omega_3 t + \phi_2(t)] + \frac{B^2(t)}{A^2(t)} \right\}^{\frac{1}{2}} . \quad (1.16)$$

We expand the square root as a Taylor series in the parameter $B(t)/A(t)$ about the origin. Only the first three terms of the expansion are retained. This truncation gives a reasonably small error if $A(t) \geqslant 2 B(t)$ for most times of interest. The use of a trigonometric identity in the expansion yields

$$y(t) = A(t) + B(t) \cos [\omega_3 t + \phi_2(t)] + B(t)$$

$$\times \left\{ \frac{B(t)}{4\,A(t)} - \frac{B(t)}{4\,A(t)} \cos [2\omega_3 t + 2\phi_2(t)] \right\} . (1.17)$$

If we set $\phi_2(t)$ equal to a constant, the effectiveness of the interference is not greatly impaired unless $\omega_3 \approx 0$ and $\phi_2 \approx \pi/2$. Furthermore, the spectral bandwidth of the jamming signal is decreased, so that the receiver bandpass filter can block less jamming power before it reaches the envelope detector. Thus, an AM signal is usually a suitable choice of jamming waveform for jamming AM communications. If both $\phi_2(t)$ and B(t) are constants, the energy in the interference terms of Equation (1.17) can be significantly reduced by a blocking capacitor when $\omega_3 \approx 0$. Consequently, a *tone* (unmodulated carrier) is not a satisfactory jamming signal.

Ideal coherent demodulation of the intended signal is accomplished when X(t) is multiplied by $2 \cos [\omega_1 t + \phi_1(t)]$ and the double-frequency terms are removed by a filter. From Equation (1.12), the output is

$$y(t) \approx A(t) + B(t) \cos [\omega_3 t + \phi_2(t)] . \qquad (1.18)$$

This expression can be compared with Equation (1.17) to see the effects of the highly nonlinear operation of envelope detection. The main problem with coherent demodulation is the need for a locally generated phase-coherent reference. The carrier synchronization system of the receiver is subject to degradation due to jamming. If the carrier component is transmitted, it is susceptible to detection by the enemy, who can produce more effective jamming once the carrier frequency has been determined.

PM Systems

When a PM signal is transmitted, we have A(t) = A, a constant. The message is carried by $\phi_1(t)$. The output of an ideal PM discriminator with X(t) as an input is proportional to $\phi_1(t) + \theta(t)$ if the instantaneous amplitude, R(t), is slowly varying as a function of time, which is often true if the discriminator is preceded by a bandpass limiter. From Equation (1.15), the ideal discriminator output is proportional to

$$y(t) = \phi_1(t) + \tan^{-1} \left\{ \frac{B(t) \sin [\omega_3 t + \phi_3(t)]}{A + B(t) \cos [\omega_3 t + \phi_3(t)]} \right\} .$$

$$(1.19)$$

We expand the arctangent as a Taylor series in the parameter $B(t)/A$ about the origin and retain the first three terms. This truncation gives a reasonably small error if $A \geq 2 B(t)$ for most times of interest. Simple trigonometry yields

$$y(t) \approx \phi_1(t) + \frac{B(t)}{A} \sin[\omega_3 t + \phi_3(t)]$$

$$- \frac{1}{2}\left[\frac{B(t)}{A}\right]^2 \sin[2\omega_3 t + 2\phi_3(t)] . \qquad (1.20)$$

If ω_3 exceeds the message bandwidth, the postdetection filter removes most of the power in the last two terms. Thus, although the bandwidth of the initial bandpass filter may be greater than in the AM case, it is important for the jammer to accurately estimate the receiver center frequency. Assuming that ω_3 does not exceed the message bandwidth, there appears to be little loss in jamming effectiveness if $\phi_2(t)$ is a constant, since the interference terms in Equation (1.20) are still phase modulated by $\phi_1(t)$. (Recall that $\phi_3 = \phi_2 - \phi_1$.) We conclude that a PM jamming waveform offers no particular advantage in the jamming of a PM communication system.

If we set both $B(t)$ and $\phi_2(t)$ equal to constants, the jamming effectiveness does not appear to be seriously impaired. Thus, a tone is often a satisfactory jamming signal against a PM communication system, although ineffective against an AM system.

FM Systems

An FM transmission may be described by Equation (1.10) with $A(t) = A$, a constant. The message is carried by the derivative of the phase function, which is denoted by $\phi_1'(t)$. Under the same assumptions made in the PM case, the output of an ideal FM discriminator is proportional to $\phi_1'(t) + \theta'(t)$, where the second term is the derivative of Equation (1.15). A straightforward calculation yields

$$y(t) = \phi_1' + \frac{[\omega_3 + \phi_3'(t)]\{AB(t)\cos[\omega_3 t + \phi_3(t)] + B^2(t)\}}{A^2 + B^2(t) + 2AB(t)\cos[\omega_3 t + \phi_3(t)]} .$$

$$(1.21)$$

As usual, we approximate the second term in this expression by the first three terms of a Taylor series, assuming $A \geq 2B(t)$ for most times of interest. The result is

$$y(t) \approx \phi_1'(t) + [\omega_3 + \phi_3'(t)] \left. \frac{B(t)}{A} \right\} \cos[\omega_3 t + \phi_3(t)]$$

$$- \frac{B(t)}{A} \left. \cos[2\omega_3 t + 2\phi_3(t)] \right\} . \qquad (1.22)$$

By reasoning similar to that used in the PM case, we draw analogous conclusions. An FM jamming waveform offers no compelling advantage in the jamming of an FM communication system; a tone is often satisfactory.

Equation (1.22) indicates that the interference at the receiver output increases with the frequency offset ω_3. Comparing Equation (1.20) and (1.22) reveals that the jamming is more effective against FM systems than PM systems when the frequency offset is large but less than the bandwidth of the postdetection filter.

To combat the potentially severe effects of jamming on FM systems, we may adopt the tactics employed against environmental interference [5]. Specifically, if we use a *deemphasis filter* with a transfer function that decreases as ω^{-1} for large frequencies, the effect of the jamming does not increase with frequency offset. To compensate for the distortion of the message due to the presence of the deemphasis filter, the message should be modified by a *preemphasis filter* before transmission, as shown in Figure 1.1. The preemphasis filter should have a transfer function equal to the reciprocal of the transfer function of the deemphasis filter so that the demodulated message is unchanged.

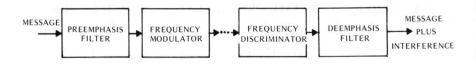

Figure 1.1/FM system that resists interference.

Careful design is required when this pair of filters is used. The pre-emphasis filter amplifies high-frequency spectral components of the message, thereby increasing the bandwidth required for transmission.

As the jamming power is increased, angle-modulation systems and noncoherent AM systems are susceptible to sudden disruptions due to well-known threshold effects [5]. When the jamming has the appropriate form and its power is so great that the receiver responds to the jamming rather than to the intended signal, the receiver is said to have been *captured*. Generally, complete disruption of angle-modulation systems requires less power than complete disruption of AM systems. Panter [6] gives examples of the distortion caused by interference in FM reception.

It has been shown that jamming effectiveness against analog communications is not dependent upon a similarity between the intended signal and the jamming waveform. An AM jamming waveform is usually effective against AM, PM, and FM systems. A tone is often a satisfactory choice for jamming PM and FM systems.

Analog communication systems are declining in importance relative to digital communication systems for military applications. The two most important reasons are probably the proliferation of the digital computer and the increased security provided by cryptographic digital communications.

1.3 DIGITAL COMMUNICATIONS: FREQUENCY-SHIFT KEYING

There are two basic ways in which a digital communication system is disrupted by jamming. Either the bit error rate is increased to an intolerable level or the synchronization system is upset. In this section, the bit error rate degradation due to jamming is investigated for a binary frequency-shift-keying (FSK) communication system.

A standard noncoherent FSK receiver is illustrated in Figure 1.2. At the receiver, the two possible intended signals are represented by

$$s_1(t) = A \cos \omega_1 t , \quad 0 \leqslant t \leqslant T_b , \qquad (1.23)$$

$$s_2(t) = A \cos \omega_2 t , \quad 0 \leqslant t \leqslant T_b , \qquad (1.24)$$

where A is a constant amplitude, T is the bit period, and ω_1 and ω_2 are the center frequencies of bandpass filter 1 and bandpass filter 2, respectively. Each of these spectrally disjoint filters has a bandwidth that is large enough to accommodate a received signal without distortion. The passband of each filter is called a channel.

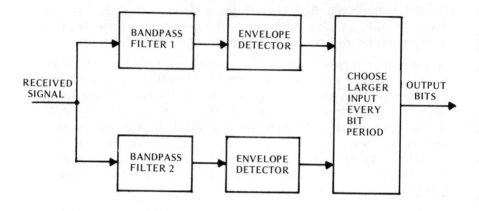

Figure 1.2/Noncoherent frequency-shift-keying demodulator.

Let N_1 represent the power of bandlimited white Gaussian noise at the output of bandpass filter 1, and let N_2 be defined similarly. Some of the noise power, denoted by N_t, is due to thermal and background noise that is common to both channels. The remainder is due to *noise jamming*, which is jamming that approximates bandlimited white Gaussian noise. Since the noise jamming is statistically independent of the thermal noise,

$$N_1 = N_t + N_{j1} , \qquad (1.25)$$

$$N_2 = N_t + N_{j2} , \qquad (1.26)$$

where N_{j1} and N_{j2} are jamming powers.

The probability of a bit error in the presence of noise jamming is given by Equation (A.32) of Appendix A. Using Equations (1.25) and (1.26), we obtain the bit error probability

$$P_b = \frac{1}{2} \exp\left(- \frac{R_s}{2N_t + N_{j1} + N_{j2}} \right) , \qquad (1.27)$$

where R_s represents the average power in the intended transmission at the receiver. Since P_b is a function of the sum $N_{j1} + N_{j2}$, the distribution of the noise jamming power between the two channels is irrelevant. Figure 1.3 plots P_b versus the jamming-to-signal ratio, $(N_{j1} + N_{j2})/R_s$, for various fixed values of the signal-to-noise ratio, R_s/N_t.

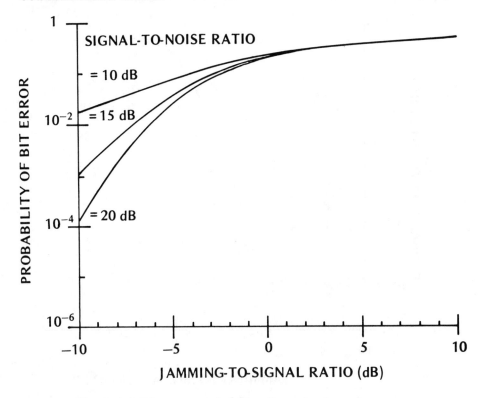

Figure 1.3/Bit error probability for noise jamming.

Let R_j represent the average power at the receiver in a narrowband, angle-modulated jamming signal of the form

$$J(t) = \sqrt{2R_j} \cos\left[\omega t + \phi(t)\right] . \tag{1.28}$$

The jamming is assumed to be narrowband compared to the receiver bandpass filters. If the narrowband jamming, which may be a tone, passes through one of the filters without significant distortion and $N_1 = N_2 = N_t$, then Equation (A.29) of Appendix A indicates that the bit error probability is

$$S_1 = \frac{1}{2} Q\left(\sqrt{\frac{R_j}{N_t}}, \sqrt{\frac{R_s}{N_t}}\right), \tag{1.29}$$

where the function $Q(\alpha, \beta)$ is defined by

$$Q(\alpha, \beta) = \int_{\beta}^{\infty} x \exp\left(-\frac{x^2 + \alpha^2}{2}\right) I_0\,(\alpha x)\,dx . \tag{1.30}$$

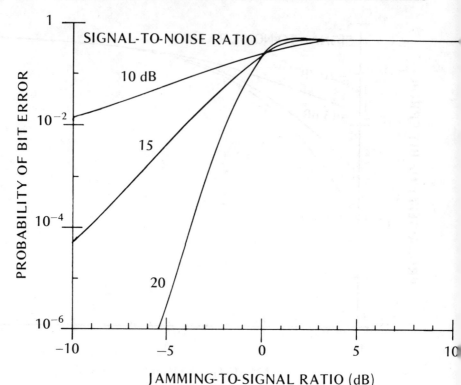

Figure 1.4/Bit error probability for narrowband jamming of single channel.

Figure 1.4 depicts S_1 versus the jamming-to-signal ratio, R_j/R_s. If narrowband jamming signals of equal power, R_j, pass undistorted through both receiver bandpass filters and $N_1 = N_2 = N_t$, then Equation (A.27) indicates that the bit error probability is

$$S_2 = \frac{1}{2\pi} \int_0^{2\pi} dx \left\{ Q\left[\sqrt{\frac{R_j}{N_t}}, \frac{D(x)}{\sqrt{2N_t}} \right] \right.$$

$$\left. - \frac{1}{2} \exp\left[-\frac{2R_j + D^2(x)}{4N_t} \right] I_0\left[\frac{\sqrt{2R_j}\, D(x)}{2N_t} \right] \right\},$$

$$(1.31)$$

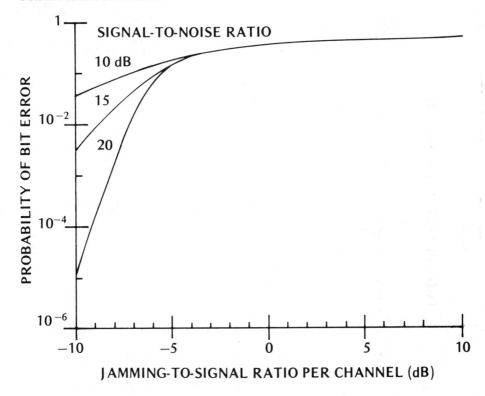

Figure 1.5/Bit error probability for narrowband jamming of both channels.

where
$$D^2(x) = 2R_s + 2R_j + 4\sqrt{R_s R_j} \cos x .$$

Figure 1.5 depicts S_2 versus the jamming-to-signal ratio per channel, R_j/R_s.

Figures 1.3 to 1.5 indicate that noise jamming is more effective than narrowband jamming unless the bit error probability is on the order of 10^{-1} or more. Since most practical communication systems do not operate satisfactorily when the bit error probability exceeds 10^{-1}, it is usually not necessary for a jammer to drive the bit error rate beyond this point. Thus, noise jamming is usually preferable to the jammer who does not know the jamming-to-signal ratio at the receiver. Figures 1.6 and 1.7 compare the effects of noise jamming and narrowband jamming when a single channel or both channels are jammed, respectively.

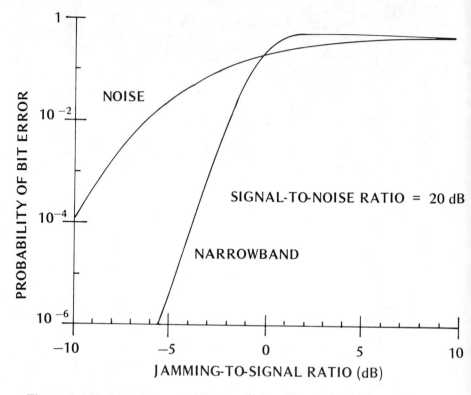

*Figure 1.6/Comparison of bit error probabilities for noise jamming
and narrowband jamming when single channel is jammed.*

A comparison of Figures 1.4 and 1.5 indicates that for narrowband
jamming of fixed total power, the jamming of both channels is usually
preferable to the jamming of a single channel. Only when the bit
error probability is on the order of 10^{-1} or more is the jamming of
·a single channel more efficient. Figure 1.8 compares the jamming of
a single channel and of both channels as a function of the total jamming-to-signal ratio when R_s/N_t = 20 dB.

The bit error probability is not the ultimate performance measure of
digital communication systems. For data communications, the probability of a data word error is usually a more significant figure of merit.
For voice communications, the message intelligibility is the performance measure of greatest interest to the user. However, the exact method of measuring intelligibility is somewhat controversial. Whatever the

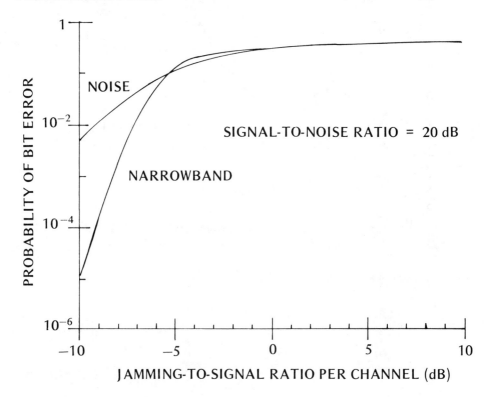

Figure 1.7/Comparison of bit error probabilities for noise jamming and narrowband jamming when both channels are jammed.

method, intelligibility is a sensitive function of the experience and ability of the listener. Thus, at least for the comparison of different digital voice communication systems, the bit and data word error probabilities are often the most useful performance measures.

1.4 PULSED JAMMING

In attempting to disrupt digital communications, it is often advantageous to concentrate the jamming energy in short pulses. *Pulsed jamming* can cause a substantial increase in the bit error probability relative to continuous jamming with the same average power. *Swept-frequency jamming*, which results from periodically sweeping the center frequency of a jamming signal over a frequency range, produces pulsed jamming in communication systems operating over part of the frequency range.

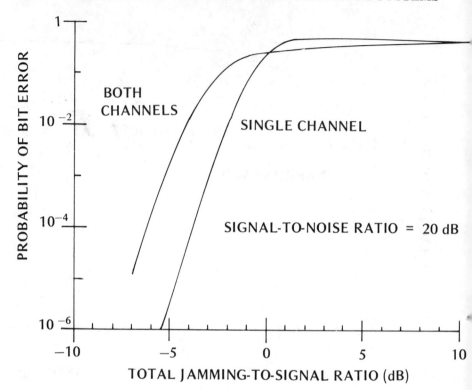

Figure 1.8/Comparison of bit error probabilities for narrowband jamming of single channel and both channels.

The bit error probability of most communication systems operating in white Gaussian noise is a function $f(E_b/N_0)$, where E_b is the energy in a received bit, and $N_0/2$ is the two-sided noise power spectral density. Suppose that during a pulse the jamming can be modeled as an independent white Gaussian process. If the jamming pulse duration is a fraction r of the pulse repetition period, then the jamming power spectral density during a pulse is $J_0/2r$, where $J_0/2$ is the power spectral density of continuous jamming with the same average power as the pulsed jamming. If the pulse duration exceeds a bit duration, it is reasonable to approximate the bit error probability by

$$P_b = r\, f\!\left(\frac{E_b}{N_0 + r^{-1}J_0}\right) + (1-r)\, f\!\left(\frac{E_b}{N_0}\right) ,$$

$$0 < r \leqslant 1 . \quad (1.32)$$

The optimum value of r to maximize P_b when J_0 is fixed can be determined from Equation (1.32). Many noncoherent and differentially coherent systems have bit error probabilities of the form

$$f\left(\frac{E_b}{N_0}\right) = b\,\exp\left(-\frac{dE_b}{N_0}\right) , \qquad (1.33)$$

where b and d are constants that depend on the modulation type. In this case, the approximate optimum value of r is easily determined. If $J_0 \gg N_0$, then

$$f\left(\frac{E_b}{N_0 + r^{-1}J_0}\right) \cong b\,\exp\left(-\frac{dr\,E_b}{J_0}\right) . \qquad (1.34)$$

Substituting Equations (1.33) and (1.34) into Equation (1.32), differentiating with respect to r, and equating to zero, we obtain

$$\exp\left(-\frac{dr\,E_b}{J_0}\right) - \exp\left(-\frac{d\,E_b}{N_0}\right) = \frac{dr\,E_b}{J_0}\,\exp\left(-\frac{dr\,E_b}{J_0}\right).$$
$$(1.35)$$

Since $J_0 \gg N_0$ and $r \leqslant 1$, the second term on the left-hand side is much smaller than the first term and can be ignored. It is then a simple matter to obtain

$$r_0 \approx \begin{cases} \dfrac{J_0}{d\,E_b} , & J_0 < d\,E_b , \\[3mm] 1 , & J_0 \geqslant d\,E_b , \end{cases} \qquad (1.36)$$

as the optimum value. Thus, a continuous jamming waveform is preferable to pulsed jamming if $J_0 \geqslant d\,E_b$.

By substituting $r = r_0$ in Equation (1.32), we obtain an equation for the bit error probability caused by optimal jamming. The latter equation may be solved to determine the minimum value of J_0 needed to cause a specified bit error probability.

The bit errors induced by pulsed jamming are clustered. Suppose that the communication system employs an error-correcting code. If the jamming pulse duration is comparable to the duration of a code word, the error-correcting code may not be able to decrease the word error probability significantly. To reduce the clustering of bit errors, code bits from various words can be interleaved before transmission. After deinterleaving at the receiver, a burst of errors is spread over a number of different code words. The decoding may then remove the errors. Alternatively, special codes for correcting bursts of errors can be used.

As an illustration of the implementation of bit interleaving, consider the matrix representing m code words of n bits:

$$
\begin{array}{ccccc}
x_{11} & x_{12} & x_{13} & \cdots & x_{1n} \\
x_{21} & x_{22} & x_{23} & \cdots & x_{2n} \\
\cdot & \cdot & \cdot & & \cdot \\
\cdot & \cdot & \cdot & & \cdot \\
\cdot & \cdot & \cdot & & \cdot \\
x_{m1} & x_{m2} & x_{m3} & \cdots & x_{mn}
\end{array}
$$

where x_{ij} represents bit j of code word i. Without bit interleaving, successive rows are transmitted. With bit interleaving, successive columns are transmitted so that the transmitted stream of symbols is

$$x_{11}\ x_{21}\ \cdots\ x_{m1}\ x_{12}\ x_{22}\ \cdots\ x_{m2}\ x_{13}\ x_{23}\ \cdots\ x_{mn}\ .$$

When a burst of errors occurs in m or fewer consecutive symbols and there are no other errors in the stream, each code word after deinterleaving has at most one error. Thus, a single-error-correcting code can eliminate all the errors. Similarly, a double-error-correcting code can be used to correct a single burst of errors spanning as many as 2m symbols.

REFERENCES

[1]   A.G. Longley and P.L. Rice, *Prediction of Tropospheric Radio Transmission Loss over Irregular Terrain, A Computer Method*, Environmental Sciences Administration ERL 79-ITS67, National Technical Information Service, AD-676 874, 1968.

[2]   A.G. Longley, *Location Variability of Transmission Loss—Land Mobile and Broadcast Systems*, Office of Telecommunications OTR 76-87, National Technical Information Service PB-254 472, 1976.

[3]   *Special Issue on Military Communications, IEEE Trans. Comm.* COM-28 (September 1980).

[4]   P. Stavroulakis, ed., *Interference Analysis of Communication Systems*. New York: IEEE Press, 1980.

[5]   R.E. Ziemer and W.H. Tranter, *Principles of Communications*. Boston: Houghton Mifflin, 1976.

[6]   P.F. Panter, *Modulation, Noise, and Spectral Analysis*. New York: McGraw-Hill, 1965.

2

Pseudonoise Spread-Spectrum Systems

2.1 PRINCIPLES

A *spread-spectrum system* is a system that produces a signal with a bandwidth much wider than the message bandwidth. Because a spread-spectrum system distributes the transmitted energy over a wide bandwidth, the signal-to-noise ratio at the receiver input is low. Nevertheless, the receiver is capable of operating successfully because the transmitted signal has distinct characteristics relative to the noise.

The generic forms of the transmitter and the receiver in a spread-spectrum system are shown in Figure 2.1. The spreading waveform is controlled by a *pseudonoise code*, which is a binary sequence that is apparently random, but can be reproduced deterministically by intended users. The pseudonoise code gives spread-spectrum systems identification and selective calling capabilities.

Spread-spectrum systems [1 − 4] are useful for military communications because they make it difficult to detect the transmitted waveform, extract the message, or jam the intended receiver. Constraints, such as those on transmitter peak power and linearity, limit the variety of practical spread-spectrum systems. The most widely used spread-spectrum methods are *pseudonoise modulation, frequency hopping,* and *hybrids* of these two methods.

In this chapter and the next, we examine the most important aspects of spread-spectrum systems for military digital communications. We

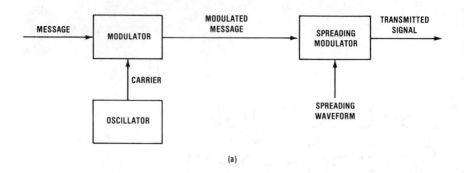

(a)

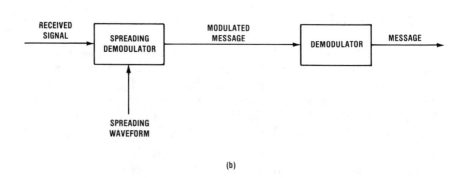

(b)

Figure 2.1/Generic spread-spectrum system: (a) transmitter and (b) receiver.

consider idealized system models and neglect many second-order effects. Even then, a number of approximations are necessary to obtain analytical results.

Pseudonoise spread-spectrum systems usually spread the transmitted spectrum by phase modulation. Figure 2.2 shows the generic form of the transmitter in a pseudonoise system with binary phase-shift keying (PSK) or quadriphase-shift keying (QPSK).

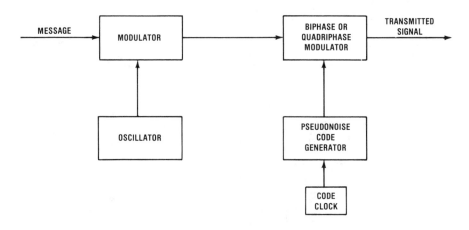

Figure 2.2/Generic form of pseudonoise system transmitter with biphase or quadriphase modulation for spectrum spreading.

Message privacy is provided by a pseudonoise system if a transmitted message cannot be recovered without knowledge of the pseudonoise code. If message privacy is required, most analog message modulations cannot be used [1, 2]. If the message is in digital form, but the data bits are asynchronous with the code clock, the data bit transitions do not coincide with the pseudonoise code transitions, and separation is possible. Thus, message privacy requires synchronization of the data bit transitions with the code clock. This synchronization may be accomplished by either feeding the code clock back to the data source or providing for bit storage. Since the data and the code are synchronized at the transmitter, code synchronization in the receiver automatically gives data bit synchronization.

Figure 2.3 is a functional block diagram of a pseudonoise system with message privacy. This system, often called a *direct-sequence system*, is the most widely used implementation in practice. Synchronized data bits and pseudonoise code bits, which are called *chips*, are modulo-two added before the phase modulation. A coherent PSK demodulator may be used in the receiver. Alternatively, if the uncertainty in the carrier frequency is sufficiently small, a differential phase-shift keying demodulator may be used in the receiver.

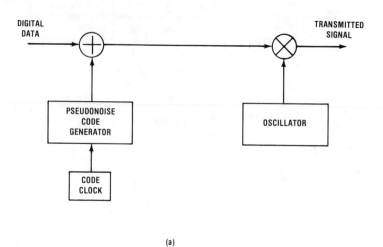

(a)

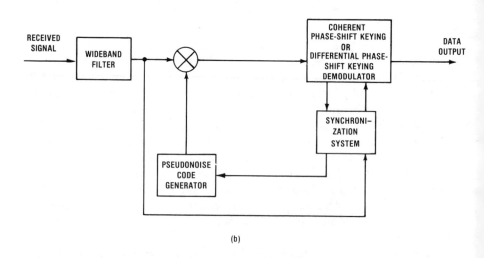

(b)

Figure 2.3/Direct-sequence pseudonoise system: (a) transmitter and (b) receiver. Configuration of code synchronization system is one of several possibilities.

The received signal can be represented by

$$s(t) = Am(t)p(t) \cos(\omega_0 t + \theta) ,\qquad(2.1)$$

where A is the amplitude, m(t) is the binary message sequence, p(t) is the binary pseudonoise code sequence, ω_0 is the carrier frequency, and θ is the phase angle. For simplicity, we assume that m(t) and p(t) have rectangular waveforms. Thus, m(t) = ±1 and p(t) = ±1. The message bits have a duration of T_b, and the chips have a shorter duration of T_p. Since the message bit and chip transitions coincide on both sides of a message bit, the ratio of T_b to T_p is an integer. If W is the bandwidth of s(t) and B is the bandwidth of m(t) cos $\omega_0 t$, the spreading due to p(t) gives W $\gg$ B.

Assuming code synchronization has been established, the received signal passes through the wideband filter and is multiplied by a local code replica of p(t). Since $p^2(t) = 1$, this multiplication yields

$$s_1(t) = Am(t) \cos(\omega_0 t + \theta)$$

at the input of the demodulator. Since $s_1(t)$ has the form of a PSK signal, the corresponding demodulation extracts m(t).

The receiver reduces interference as qualitatively illustrated in Figure 2.4; quantitative results are given subsequently. Figure 2.4(a) shows

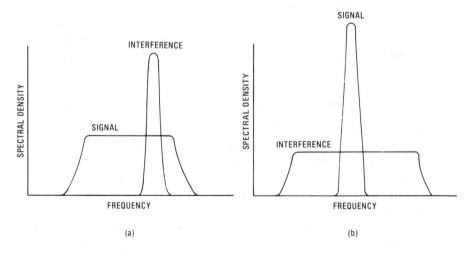

Figure 2.4/Spectra of desired signal and interference: (a) wideband filter output and (b) demodulator input.

the relative spectra of the desired signal and interference at the output of the wideband filter. Multiplication by the pseudonoise code produces the spectra of Figure 2.4(b) at the demodulator input. The signal bandwidth is reduced to B, while the interference energy is spread over a bandwidth exceeding W. The filtering action of the demodulator removes most of the interference spectrum that does not overlap the signal spectrum. Thus, most of the original interference energy is eliminated and does not affect the receiver performance. The ratio W/B, which is called the *processing gain*, is a measure of the interference rejection.

Two other pseudonoise systems with potential message privacy are diagrammed in Figures 2.5 and 2.6. For simplicity, the figures omit depictions of the synchronization systems.

Figure 2.5 shows a *quadriphase pseudonoise system*, which uses QPSK modulation. Two pseudonoise codes, which may be derived from a single generator, are used with two quadrature carriers. Each member of each successive pair of data bits is combined with one of the pseudonoise codes and one of the quadrature carriers. Thus, the received signal can be represented by

$$s(t) \; = \; Am_1(t)p_1(t) \cos (\omega_0 t + \theta) + Am_2(t)p_2(t) \sin (\omega_0 t + \theta),$$

$$(2.2)$$

where $m_1(t)$ and $m_2(t)$ are the binary sequences derived from the data bits, and $p_1(t)$ and $p_2(t)$ are the pseudonoise codes. In each branch of the receiver, one of the codes is removed, followed by coherent PSK demodulation. The output bits of the two branches are alternately sampled to reconstruct the data stream.

Figure 2.6 shows a pseudonoise system with binary *code-shift keying* (CSK). Depending upon the logical state of the digital data, one or the other of two nearly orthogonal pseudonoise codes is transmitted. In the receiver, each code creates a significant output in only one of the two parallel branches. Thus, the data are recovered by comparing the branch outputs. In a pseudonoise system with M-ary CSK, each group of n data bits is encoded as one of $M = 2^n$ codes chosen to have small cross correlations. Binary CSK systems exhibit a relatively poor bit error probability in white Gaussian noise, whereas M-ary systems have improved bit error probabilities, but require complex implementations. An application of binary CSK is presented in Section 2.8.

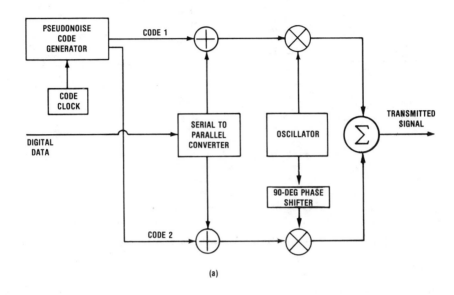

(a)

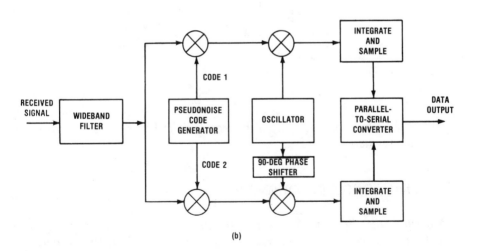

(b)

Figure 2.5/Quadriphase pseudonoise system: (a) transmitter and (b) receiver.

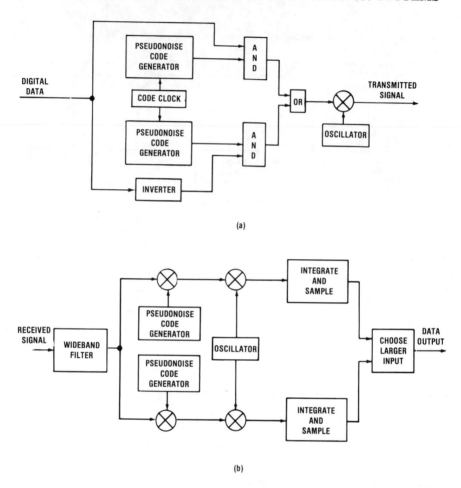

Figure 2.6/Pseudonoise system with code-shift keying: (a) transmitter and (b) receiver.

2.2 PSEUDONOISE SEQUENCES

A *pseudonoise* or *pseudorandom sequence* is a periodic binary sequence with an autocorrelation that resembles, over one period, the autocorrelation of bandlimited white noise. Although it is deterministic, a pseudonoise sequence has many characteristics, such as a nearly even balance of *zeros* and *ones*, similar to those of a random binary sequence.

In general, pseudonoise sequences are generated by combining the outputs of *feedback shift registers.* A feedback shift register, which is diagrammed in Figure 2.7, consists of consecutive two-state memory or storage stages and feedback logic. Binary sequences are shifted through the shift register in response to clock pulses. The contents of the stages are logically combined to produce the input to the first stage. The initial contents of the stages and the feedback logic determine the successive contents of the stages. A feedback shift register is called *linear* when the feedback logic consists entirely of modulo-two adders (Exclusive OR gates).

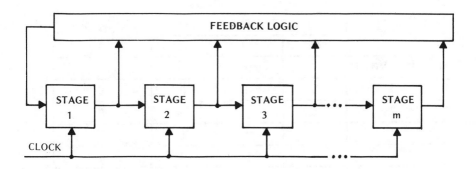

Figure 2.7/General feedback shift register with m stages.

An example of a linear feedback shift register with three stages is shown in Figure 2.8(a). The input to the first stage is the modulo-two sum of the contents of the second and third stages. The successive contents of the third stage provide the output sequence of the shift register. After each clock pulse, the contents of the first two stages are shifted to the right, and the input to the first stage becomes its content. If the initial contents of the shift-register stages are 0 0 1, the subsequent contents after successive shifts are listed in Figure 2.8(b). After seven shifts, the shift register returns to its initial state. Thus, the periodic output sequence has a length of seven bits before repeating.

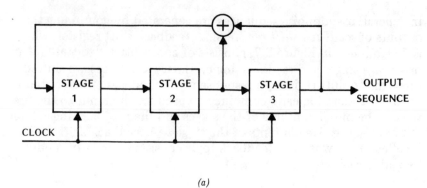

(a)

SHIFTS	CONTENTS			OUTPUT SEQUENCE
	STAGE 1	STAGE 2	STAGE 3	
INITIAL CONTENTS	0	0	1	1
1	1	0	0	0
2	0	1	0	0
3	1	0	1	1
4	1	1	0	0
5	1	1	1	1
6	0	1	1	1
7	0	0	1	1
8	1	0	0	0
9	0	1	0	0
10	1	0	1	1

(b)

Figure 2.8/(a) Three-stage linear feedback shift register and (b) contents and output after successive shifts.

Consider a linear feedback shift register with the output sequence provided by the final stage. The contents of the shift register stages uniquely determine the subsequent output sequence. If the stages all contained *zeros* at some point, the output sequence would sub-sequently be all *zeros*. An m-stage linear feedback shift register can contain each *nonzero* m-tuple only once before the output sequence begins to repeat itself. Since there are exactly $2^m - 1$ nonzero m-tuples, and the period of the output sequence is equal to the minimum number of output bits before repetition, the period of a linear m-stage shift register output sequence cannot exceed $2^m - 1$. A sequence of period $2^m - 1$ generated by a linear feedback shift register is called a *maximal-length* or *maximal sequence*.

Out of the 2^m possible m-tuples, the last bit in the m-tuple is *zero* in 2^{m-1} cases. Thus, out of the *nonzero* m-tuples, the last bit is *zero* in $2^{m-1} - 1$ cases. Since maximal sequence bits are the last bits of a succession of the *nonzero* m-tuples, we conclude that the maximal sequence contains exactly $2^{m-1} - 1$ *zeros* and 2^{m-1} *ones* per period. Thus, in one period of $K = 2^m - 1$ bits of the output sequence, there are $(K - 1)/2$ *zeros* and $(K + 1)/2$ *ones*.

Let x_i denote the state of bit i in a maximal sequence. Since each bit was once the output of the feedback logic, we can express x_i as a modulo-two summation

$$x_i = \sum_{k=1}^{m} a_k x_{i-k} , \qquad (2.3)$$

where the coefficients a_k equal either 1 or 0, depending upon which stages feed the modulo-two adders. For example, Figure 2.8 gives $x_i = x_{i-2} \oplus x_{i-3}$, where $\oplus$ denotes modulo-two addition. Let $\{x_i\}$ denote a maximal sequence. We form a new sequence, $\{z_i\}$, such that $z_i = x_i \oplus x_{i+j}$. Using Equation (2.3) and modulo-two arithmetic, we obtain

$$z_i = \sum_{k=1}^{m} (a_k x_{i-k} \oplus a_k x_{i+j-k})$$

$$= \sum_{k=1}^{m} a_k (x_{i-k} \oplus x_{i+j-k})$$

$$= \sum_{k=1}^{m} a_k z_{i-k} . \qquad (2.4)$$

This result indicates that the sequence $\{z_i\}$ can be generated by the same feedback logic as the original sequence $\{x_i\}$. If $j \neq 0$, modulo K, the sequences $\{x_i\}$ and $\{x_{i+j}\}$ are not equal so that $\{z_i\}$ is not the sequence of all *zeros*. It follows that $\{z_i\}$ must be some permutation of $\{x_i\}$. We conclude that the modulo-two sum of a maximal sequence and a cyclic shift of itself by j digits, where $j \neq 0$, modulo K, produces another cyclic shift of the original sequence. This property is succinctly written as

$$\{x_i\} \oplus \{x_{i+j}\} = \{x_{i+k}\} , \quad j \neq 0 \text{ (modulo K)} . \quad (2.5)$$

Using the above properties, we derive the autocorrelation of a maximal sequence. The autocorrelation of a periodic function x(t) with period T is defined as

$$R_x(\tau) = \frac{1}{T} \int_{-T/2}^{T/2} x(t) \; x(t + \tau) \, dt , \quad (2.6)$$

where τ is the relative delay variable. The maximal sequence serves as a modulation and is transmitted as a binary waveform, p(t), taking the values of +1 or −1 over each successive interval of duration T_p. For this waveform, the autocorrelation, $R_p(\tau)$, varies linearly between the values that it assumes at the points $\tau = jT_p$, where j is an integer. Thus, only the latter points need to be considered. If y_i is the value of bit i of the binary waveform representing a maximal sequence of length K, then Equation (2.6) yields the algebraic sum

$$R_p(jT_p) = \frac{1}{K} \sum_{i=1}^{K} y_i \, y_{i+j} = \frac{A_j - D_j}{K} , \quad (2.7)$$

where A_j denotes the number of terms with $y_i y_{i+j} = +1$ and D_j is the number of terms with $y_i y_{i+j} = -1$. Let the logical variable x_i be *one* when $y_i = +1$ and *zero* when $y_i = -1$. Then A_j equals the number of *zeros* in a period of $\{x_i \oplus x_{i+j}\}$. From Equation (2.5), it follows that A_j equals the number of *zeros* in a maximal sequence if $j \neq 0$, modulo K. Thus, $A_j = (K - 1)/2$; similar reasoning gives $D_j = (K + 1)/2$ if $j \neq 0$, modulo K. We conclude that

$$R_p(jT_p) = -\frac{1}{K} , \quad j \neq 0 \text{ (modulo K)} . \quad (2.8)$$

When $j = 0$, modulo K, $R_p(jT_p) = 1$. Therefore, over the interval

$$|\tau| \leqslant \frac{KT_p}{2} \;,$$

we have

$$R_p(\tau) = \begin{cases} 1 - \left(\dfrac{K + 1}{K}\right)\dfrac{|\tau|}{T_p} \;, & |\tau| \leqslant T_p \;, \\[3mm] -\dfrac{1}{K} \;, & |\tau| > T_p \;. \end{cases} \tag{2.9}$$

Since $R_p(\tau)$ has period KT_p, it is completely specified by this equation. The autocorrelation is plotted in Figure 2.9.

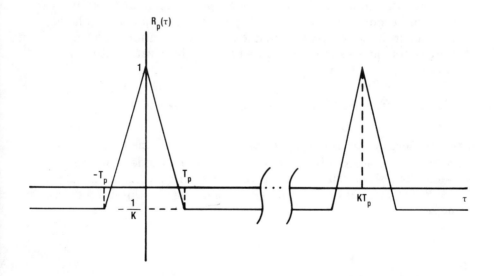

Figure 2.9/Autocorrelation of maximal sequence.

Some nonmaximal sequences have nearly even balances of *zeros* and *ones* and have autocorrelations roughly similar to that of Figure 2.9. Thus, these sequences can be considered pseudonoise sequences. However, the autocorrelations of most nonmaximal sequences have minor peaks in addition to the major ones.

The autocorrelation of maximal sequences is sharply peaked for zero delay, but relatively small for other delays. Consequently, these sequences are desirable for code synchronization in the receiver. The minor peaks of nonlinear sequences and linear nonmaximal sequences hinder rapid code synchronization.

The autocorrelation characteristics of maximal sequences enable the receiver to discriminate against delayed signal replicas caused by multipath effects. Thus, if the multipath delay exceeds T_p, the resulting receiver performance degradation is usually negligible.

Linear pseudonoise codes are inherently susceptible to mathematical cryptanalysis. Thus, if message security is desired, the message must be enciphered before it is added to the pseudonoise code.

Although cryptographic integrity may be lacking, long pseudonoise codes make it more difficult for hostile personnel to deduce the code and produce effective jamming, or to extract an unenciphered message from intercepted pseudonoise communications. However, long codes increase the time needed for synchronization at the receiver.

2.3 CONCEALMENT OF PSEUDONOISE WAVEFORMS

In this section, we derive a condition under which the transmitted output of a pseudonoise system using a maximal code is difficult to detect by a simple spectrum analyzer. To write a compact equation for $R_p(\tau)$, it is convenient to use the following notation for a triangular pulse:

$$\Lambda\left(\frac{t}{T}\right) = \begin{cases} 1 - \dfrac{|t|}{T} , & |t| \leqslant T , \\ \\ 0 , & |t| > T . \end{cases} \tag{2.10}$$

We then may write

$$R_p(\tau) = -\frac{1}{K} + \frac{K+1}{K} \sum_{i=-\infty}^{\infty} \Lambda\left(\frac{t - iKT_p}{T_p}\right) . \quad (2.11)$$

The Fourier transform of a function x(t) is defined by

$$\mathcal{F}\left\{x(t)\right\} = \int_{-\infty}^{\infty} x(t)e^{-j2\pi ft} \, dt \,, \quad (2.12)$$

where f is the frequency variable and $j = \sqrt{-1}$. A straightforward calculation or Fourier transform tables give

$$\mathcal{F}\left\{\Lambda\left(\frac{t}{T}\right)\right\} = T \, \text{sinc}^2 \, fT \,, \quad (2.13)$$

where it is convenient to define

$$\text{sinc } x = \frac{\sin \pi x}{\pi x} \,. \quad (2.14)$$

Since the summation on the right-hand side of Equation (2.11) is a periodic function, it can be expressed as a complex exponential Fourier series. We take the Fourier transform of this series, express the Fourier coefficients as Fourier transforms, and use Equation (2.13). The result is

$$\mathcal{F}\left\{\sum_{i=-\infty}^{\infty} \Lambda\left(\frac{t - iKT_p}{T_p}\right)\right\} = \frac{1}{K} \sum_{i=-\infty}^{\infty} \text{sinc}^2\left(\frac{i}{K}\right) \delta\left(f - \frac{i}{KT_p}\right),$$

$$(2.15)$$

where $\delta(\ )$ is the Dirac delta function. We use the preceding results to determine $S_p(f)$, the power spectral density of p(t), which is defined as the Fourier transform of $R_p(\tau)$. Taking the Fourier transform of Equation (2.11), substituting Equation (2.15), noting that the Fourier transform of a constant is a delta function, and rearranging the result, we obtain

$$S_p(f) = \frac{K+1}{K^2} \sum_{\substack{i=-\infty \\ i \neq 0}}^{\infty} \text{sinc}^2\left(\frac{i}{K}\right) \delta\left(f - \frac{i}{KT_p}\right) + \frac{1}{K^2} \delta(f) \,.$$

$$(2.16)$$

This function is plotted in Figure 2.10. It consists of delta functions separated by $1/KT_p$.

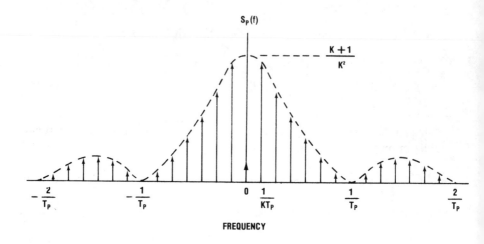

Figure 2.10/Power spectral density of pseudonoise code.

The autocorrelation of a stochastic process $x(t)$ is defined by

$$R_x(t,\tau) = E[x(t)x(t + \tau)] , \qquad (2.17)$$

where $E[y]$ is the expected value of y. If $x(t)$ is a stationary process, then $R_x(t,\tau)$ is a function of τ alone, and we denote the autocorrelation by $R_x(\tau)$. The power spectral density of a stationary process is defined as the Fourier transform of its autocorrelation. We define the *average autocorrelation* of $x(t)$ as

$$\overline{R}_x(\tau) = \lim_{T \to \infty} \frac{1}{2T} \int_{-T}^{T} R_x(t,\tau)\, dt \qquad (2.18)$$

The limit exists and may be non-zero if $x(t)$ has finite power and infinite duration. If $x(t)$ is stationary, $\overline{R}_x(\tau) = R_x(\tau)$. The *average power spectral density*, denoted by $\overline{S}_x(f)$, is defined as the Fourier transform of the average autocorrelation.

We assume that the message, $m(t)$, is a stationary stochastic process with an autocorrelation $R_m(\tau)$. We assume that θ in Equation (2.1) is a random variable uniformly distributed over the interval $[0, 2\pi]$ and statistically independent of $m(t)$. The autocorrelation of

$$m_1(t) = m(t) \cos(\omega_0 t + \theta) \qquad (2.19)$$

is determined by applying Equation (2.17) and using trigonometry. The result is independent of t, so we write

$$R_{m1}(\tau) = \frac{1}{2} R_m(\tau) \cos \omega_0 \tau . \qquad (2.20)$$

Thus, the power spectral density of $m_1(t)$ is

$$S_{m1}(f) = \frac{1}{4} [S_m(f - f_0) + S_m(f + f_0)] , \qquad (2.21)$$

where $f_0 = \omega_0/2\pi$ and $S_m(f)$ is the power spectral density of $m(t)$.

By using Equation (2.1) and (2.17) and noting that $p(t)$ is deterministic, the autocorrelation of $s(t)$ is determined to be

$$R_s(t,\tau) = A^2 p(t)p(t + \tau)R_{m1}(\tau) , \qquad (2.22)$$

which indicates that $s(t)$ is a nonstationary process. Since $p(t)$ is periodic, the definitions of Equations (2.6) and (2.18) yield

$$\overline{R}_s(\tau) = A^2 R_p(\tau)R_{m1}(\tau) . \qquad (2.23)$$

Consequently, $\overline{S}_s(f)$, the average power spectral density of $s(t)$, is the convolution of $A^2 S_p(f)$ with $S_{m1}(f)$. Using Equation (2.16), we get

$$\overline{S}_s(f) = A^2 \frac{K + 1}{K^2} \sum_{\substack{i = -\infty \\ i \neq 0}}^{\infty} \text{sinc}^2 \left(\frac{i}{K}\right) S_{m1} \left(f - \frac{i}{KT_p}\right)$$

$$+ \frac{A^2}{K^2} S_{m1}(f) . \qquad (2.24)$$

Substituting Equation (2.21), we obtain

$$\overline{S}_s(f) = \frac{A^2}{4K^2} S_m(f - f_0) + A^2 \frac{K+1}{4K^2} \sum_{\substack{i=-\infty \\ i \neq 0}}^{\infty} \text{sinc}^2\left(\frac{i}{K}\right)$$

$$\times S_m\left(f - f_0 - \frac{i}{KT_p}\right) + \frac{A^2}{4K^2} S_m(f + f_0) + A^2 \frac{K+1}{4K^2}$$

$$\times \sum_{\substack{i=-\infty \\ i \neq 0}}^{\infty} \text{sinc}^2\left(\frac{i}{K}\right) S_m\left(f + f_0 + \frac{i}{KT_p}\right). \qquad (2.25)$$

This equation gives the average power spectrum of a transmitted signal in a pseudonoise system that uses a maximal sequence.

If a transmission has a low power spectral density compared with thermal and environmental noise, and if the spectrum is nearly flat, then it is difficult to detect the presence of the signal with a simple spectrum analyzer. To ensure that the spectrum is flat, the spectral contributions of the terms in the summations of Equation (2.25) must overlap. The center of the spectral contribution of a term is separated from the center of the spectral contribution of an adjacent term by $1/KT_p$. Thus, $B \geqslant 2/KT_p$ is required if $\overline{S}_s(f)$ is to be approximately flat. Since $B \cong 2/T_b$, an approximate necessary condition for communication concealment from spectrum analysis is

$$KT_p \geqslant T_b \, , \qquad (2.26)$$

which states that the pseudonoise code period must equal or exceed a data bit duration. Spectral envelope smoothing may also be necessary.

Since messages tend to be nearly random in character, it is plausible to model $m(t)$ as a random binary sequence. This stationary process has a mean value of zero. The autocorrelation of a random binary sequence of bit period T_b is [5]

$$R_m(\tau) = \Lambda\left(\frac{\tau}{T_b}\right). \qquad (2.27)$$

Equation (2.13) gives the corresponding power spectral density:

$$S_m(f) = T_b \, \text{sinc}^2 \, f \, T_b \, . \qquad (2.28)$$

The fact that a pseudonoise signal is concealed does not mean that it cannot be detected. Suppose that s(t) enters a wideband receiver and is squared. Since $m^2(t) = p^2(t) = 1$, the output of the squaring device is

$$s^2(t) = A^2 \cos(\omega_0 t + \theta)$$

$$= \frac{A^2}{2} + \frac{A^2}{2} \cos(2\omega_0 t + 2\theta) . \tag{2.29}$$

If $s^2(t)$ is applied to an integrator or a narrowband filter, the energy of the signal can often be detected, even if $\overline{S}_s(f)$ is far below the noise power spectral density. The double-frequency term of Equation (2.29) can be applied to a separate device for estimation of the carrier frequency of the pseudonoise signal (see Chapter 4). However, an interceptor cannot demodulate s(t) without knowledge of p(t).

For a quadriphase pseudonoise system, the average power spectral density has the same form as Equation (2.25). The energy of a quadriphase signal can be detected in the same manner as the energy of a biphase signal. A device that raises the received signal of Equation (2.2) to the fourth power produces a sinusoidal term with frequency $4\omega_0$. Thus, $s^4(t)$ can be used for the estimation of the carrier frequency of a quadriphase pseudonoise signal. To demodulate s(t), an interceptor must be able to produce both $p_1(t)$ and $p_2(t)$.

2.4 ERROR PROBABILITIES IN PRESENCE OF INTERFERENCE

A pseudonoise receiver with an ideal correlation demodulator for PSK signals is diagrammed in Figure 2.11. Suppose that interference, which may be jamming, accompanies the desired pseudonoise signal at the receiver. After passage through the wideband filter, the total received signal is represented by

$$r(t) = A m(t) p(t) \cos(\omega_0 t + \theta) + j(t) + n(t) , \tag{2.30}$$

where j(t) denotes the interference and n(t) denotes the bandlimited white Gaussian noise. Assuming that code synchronization has been established, the input to the demodulator is

$$r_1(t) = A m(t) \cos(\omega_0 t + \theta) + j(t) p(t) + n(t) p(t) . \tag{2.31}$$

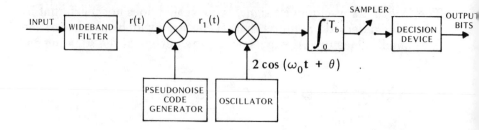

*Figure 2.11/Basic elements of ideal coherent receiver for pseudonoise
    system.*

The factor p(t) in this equation ensures that the interference energy
is spread over a bandwidth at least equal to W. Assuming perfect
phase synchronization, the input to the decision device at the end of the
bit interval $0 \leqslant t \leqslant T_b$ is

$$L = \int_0^{T_b} 2 r_1(t) \cos(\omega_0 t + \theta) \, dt \ . \tag{2.32}$$

We assume that $f_0 = \omega_0/2\pi \gg W \geqslant 1/T_p \geqslant 1/T_b$. Therefore, Equations (2.31) and (2.32) yield approximately

$$L = A \int_0^{T_b} m(t) \, dt + L_1 + L_2$$

$$= \pm AT_b + L_1 + L_2 \ , \tag{2.33}$$

where $m(t) = +1$ represents a logical *one*, $m(t) = -1$ represents a
logical *zero*, and

$$L_1 = \int_0^{T_b} 2 j(t) p(t) \cos(\omega_0 t + \theta) \, dt \ , \tag{2.34}$$

$$L_2 = \int_0^{T_b} 2 n(t) p(t) \cos(\omega_0 t + \theta) \, dt \ . \tag{2.35}$$

We assume that j(t) is a zero-mean, stationary stochastic process that is independent of n(t), p(t), and θ. The expected value of L is

$$E[L] = \pm A T_b . \tag{2.36}$$

The variance of L is equal to the sum of the variances of L_1 and L_2. Assuming that n(t) approximates ideal white noise, a straightforward calculation gives $VAR(L_2) = N_0 T_b$, where $N_0/2$ is the power spectral density of the thermal noise. Thus,

$$VAR(L) = VAR(L_1) + N_0 T_b. \tag{2.37}$$

The decision device produces a logical *one* if $L > 0$ and a logical *zero* if $L < 0$. An error occurs if $L < 0$ when m(t) = +1 or if $L > 0$ when m(t) = -1.

If L_1 is a zero-mean Gaussian random variable, a simple calculation gives the bit error probability

$$P_b = \frac{1}{2} \operatorname{erfc} \left[\sqrt{\frac{E_b T_b}{N_0 T_b + VAR(L_1)}} \right], \tag{2.38}$$

where $E_b = A^2 T_b/2$ is the received energy per bit, and the complementary error function is defined by

$$\operatorname{erfc} x = \frac{2}{\sqrt{\pi}} \int_x^\infty \exp(-y^2) \, dy . \tag{2.39}$$

If j(t) is a Gaussian process, L_1 is a Gaussian random variable; if j(t) is not, L_1 may still approximate a Gaussian random variable. Assuming that

$$\tag{2.40}$$

$$T_p \ll T_b \ll K T_p ,$$

it is reasonable to approximate p(t) over the interval $[0, T_b]$ by a random binary sequence. Therefore, the integral in Equation (2.34) can be approximated by a summation of weighted binary-valued random variables. Thus, in view of the central limit theorem [6], it is plausible that L_1 is approximated by a Gaussian random variable.

After making the Gaussian assumption, P_b can be calculated from Equation (2.38) once the variance of L_1 has been determined. Since $p(t)$ is approximated by a random binary sequence, its autocorrelation is

$$R_p(\tau) = \Lambda\left(\frac{\tau}{T_p}\right) . \qquad (2.41)$$

We assume that θ is an independent random variable uniformly distributed over $[0, 2\pi]$. Using Equation (2.34) and the independence of $j(t)$ and $p(t)$, we can express the variance of L_1 as a double integral over autocorrelations. We obtain

$$\text{VAR}(L_1) = 2 \int_0^{T_b} \int_0^{T_b} R_j(t_1 - t_2) \Lambda\left(\frac{t_1 - t_2}{T_p}\right)$$

$$\times \cos[\omega_0(t_1 - t_2)] \, dt_1 \, dt_2 , \qquad (2.42)$$

where $R_j(\tau)$ is the autocorrelation of $j(t)$. We change coordinates by using $\tau = t_1 - t_2$, $\sigma = t_1 + t_2$. The Jacobian of the transformation is 2. Evaluating one of the integrals leaves

$$\text{VAR}(L_1) = 2 \int_{-T_b}^{T_b} (T_b - |\tau|) R_j(\tau) \Lambda\left(\frac{\tau}{T_p}\right) \cos \omega_0 \tau \, d\tau .$$

$$(2.43)$$

If we assume that θ is a fixed constant instead of a random variable, we obtain an additional integral in the equation for $\text{VAR}(L_1)$. However, since $\omega_0 \gg 1/T_b$, this integral is negligible . Equation (2.40) and the definition of $\Lambda(\tau/T_p)$ imply that Equation (2.43) is approximately

$$\text{VAR}(L_1) = 2T_b \int_{-T_p}^{T_p} R_j(\tau) \Lambda\left(\frac{\tau}{T_p}\right) \cos \omega_0 \tau \, d\tau .$$

$$(2.44)$$

The limits in this integral can be extended to $\pm \infty$ since the integrand is truncated. Since $R_j(\tau)$ is an even function, we can use the convolution theorem and Equation (2.13) to transform Equation (2.44) into the alternative form

$$\text{VAR}(L_1) = 2T_b T_p \int_{-\infty}^{\infty} S_j(f) \, \text{sinc}^2 \left[(f_0 - f)T_p \right] df ,$$

(2.45)

where $S_j(f)$ is the power spectral density of the interference at the output of the wideband filter. If $S_j'(f)$ is the interference power spectral density at the input and $H(f)$ is the transfer function of the filter, then

$$S_j(f) = S_j'(f) \, |H(f)|^2 .$$

(2.46)

Several special cases are of particular interest. It is convenient to define the *interference parameter*, b, implicitly by the equation

$$\text{VAR}(L_1) = b \, R_j \, T_p \, T_b ,$$

(2.47)

where $R_j = R_j(0)$ is the interference power. Suppose that the interference has a flat spectrum over a band within the passband of the wideband filter so that

$$S_j(f) = \begin{cases} \dfrac{R_j}{2W_1} , & |f - f_1| \leqslant \dfrac{W_1}{2} , \quad |f + f_1| \leqslant \dfrac{W_1}{2} , \\[2ex] 0 , & \text{otherwise} . \end{cases}$$

(2.48)

Since $f_0 \gg 1/T_p$, Equations (2.45), (2.47), and (2.48) yield approximately

$$b = \frac{1}{W_1} \int_{f_1 - W_1/2}^{f_1 + W_1/2} \text{sinc}^2 \left[(f_0 - f) T_p \right] df .$$

(2.49)

Since $\text{sinc}(x) \leqslant 1$, we have $b \leqslant 1$. Similarly, we see that $b \leqslant 1$ for arbitrary $S_j(f)$ if $f_0 \gg 1/T_p$ allows us to completely neglect the integration over negative frequencies in Equation (2.45).

Next, suppose that $j(t)$ has the form

$$j(t) = \sqrt{2R_j} \, q(t) \cos(\omega_1 t + \phi) ,$$

(2.50)

where $q(t)$ is a unit-power stationary process, carrier frequency $f_1 = \omega_1/2\pi$ is within the receiver passband, and ϕ is an independent, uniformly distributed random variable. It follows that

$$R_j(\tau) = R_j R_q(\tau) \cos \omega_1 \tau ,$$
(2.51)

where $R_q(\tau)$ is the autocorrelation of $q(t)$. Combining Equations (2.44), (2.47), and (2.51), and neglecting a double-frequency term that does not contribute significantly to the result, we obtain

$$b = \frac{1}{T_p} \int_{-T_p}^{T_p} R_q(\tau) \Lambda\left(\frac{\tau}{T_p}\right) \cos\left[(\omega_1 - \omega_0)\tau\right] d\tau .$$
(2.52)

For tone (unmodulated-carrier) interference, we have $R_q(\tau) = 1$, which implies

$$b = \text{sinc}^2\left[(f_1 - f_0)T_p\right] .$$
(2.53)

For tone jamming at the carrier or center frequency, we have $f_1 = f_0$ so that $b = 1$. Thus, the interference parameter is a measure of the effectiveness of an interference type relative to optimal tone jamming.

As a third special case, we assume that $q(t)$ in Equation (2.50) is a pseudonoise sequence with bit duration T_q and length K_1. We neglect the effect of the wideband filter. If

$$T_q \ll T_b \ll K_1 T_q ,$$
(2.54)

and the cross correlation of $p(t)$ and $q(t)$ is small for all relative delays, it is reasonable to model $q(t)$ over the interval $[0, T_b]$ as an independent random binary sequence. The autocorrelation of $q(t)$ is

$$R_q(\tau) = \Lambda\left(\frac{\tau}{T_q}\right) .$$
(2.55)

We define the parameters

$$T_0 = \min (T_p, T_q) ,,$$
(2.56)
$$T_1 = \max (T_p, T_q) .$$

Substituting Equation (2.55) into Equation (2.52) and using Equation (2.10), the integral can be evaluated. For $T_0 \neq 0$, we obtain

$$b = \frac{2}{T_p} \left\{ \frac{\cos[2\pi(f_1 - f_0)T_0]}{(2\pi)^2(f_1 - f_0)^2} \left(\frac{1}{T_1} - \frac{1}{T_0}\right) \right.$$

$$\left. - \frac{2\sin[2\pi(f_1 - f_0)T_0]}{(2\pi)^3(f_1 - f_0)^3 T_1 T_0} + \frac{1}{(2\pi)^2(f_1 - f_0)^2}\left(\frac{1}{T_1} + \frac{1}{T_0}\right) \right\} ,$$

$$f_1 \neq f_0 ,$$

$$b = \frac{T_0}{T_p}\left(1 - \frac{T_0}{3T_1}\right) , \quad f_1 = f_0 . \tag{2.57}$$

If $T_p = T_q$, this equation becomes

$$b = \begin{cases} \dfrac{1 - \text{sinc}[2(f_1 - f_0)T_p]}{\pi^2(f_1 - f_0)^2 T_p^{\,2}} , & f_1 \neq f_0 , \; T_p = T_q , \\[3mm] \dfrac{2}{3} , & f_1 = f_0 , \; T_p = T_q . \end{cases} \tag{2.58}$$

Equation (2.52) indicates that b is greatest when $f_1 = f_0$.

If more than one statistically independent source of interference is present, the linearity of the demodulation allows calculation of the appropriate value of b. If R_j is interpreted as the total interference power,

$$b = \frac{1}{R_j} \sum_i b_i R_{ji} , \tag{2.59}$$

where R_{ji} is the interference power due to source i, and b_i is the corresponding interference parameter. Since the $b_i \leqslant 1$, we still have $b \leqslant 1$.

Substituting Equation (2.47) into Equation (2.38) yields the bit error probability for a pseudonoise system with ideal coherent PSK demodulation. Using $E_b = R_s T_b$, where R_s is the average power in the intended transmission, we obtain

$$P_b = \frac{1}{2} \, \text{erfc}\left[\left(\frac{bR_j}{GR_s} + \frac{N_0}{E_b}\right)^{-\frac{1}{2}}\right] , \tag{2.60}$$

where

$$G = \frac{T_b}{T_p} = \frac{W}{B} \qquad (2.61)$$

is the processing gain. Other calculations of the bit error probability using different approximations can be found in the literature.

Increasing the processing gain is helpful against interference for which R_j is fixed. Increasing the processing gain by increasing W is not helpful against interference for which R_j increases proportionately with W.

Figures 2.12 and 2.13 illustrate the dependence of b for pseudonoise interference on the *normalized frequency offset,*

$$\Delta = |(f_1 - f_0) T_p| , \qquad (2.62)$$

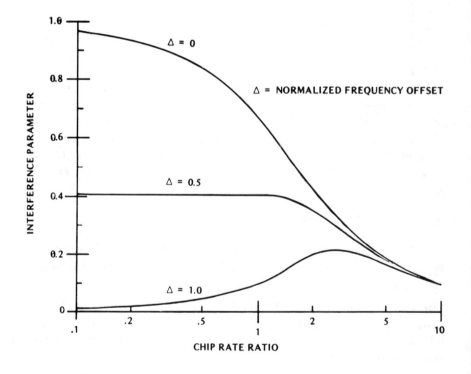

Figure 2.12/Interference parameter versus chip rate ratio.

and the *chip rate ratio*

$$\rho = \frac{1/T_q}{1/T_p} = \frac{T_p}{T_q} \quad . \tag{2.63}$$

Figure 2.13 also shows b for tone interference.

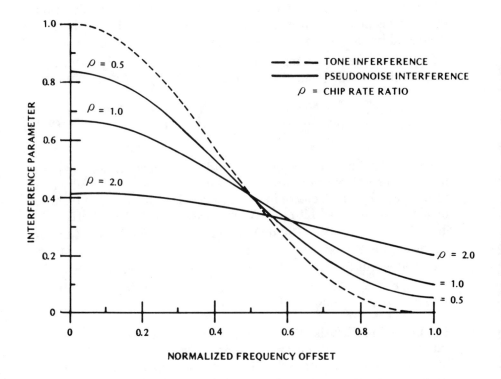

Figure 2.13/Interference parameter versus normalized frequency offset.

Both block codes and convolutional codes can significantly improve the performance of spread-spectrum systems. In this chapter and the next, we consider the effects of block codes.

Suppose that words of w data bits are block encoded so that c bits are transmitted for each word. Depending upon the code, r or more bits per code word must be in error for a word error to occur at the receiver output. Assuming that bit errors occur independently, the probability of a word error is [6]

$$P_w = \sum_{m=r}^{c} \binom{c}{m} (1 - P_b)^{c-m} P_b^m , \qquad (2.64)$$

where P_b is the probability of an error in a code bit. If the duration of a word is preserved after encoding, the duration of a code bit is decreased by the factor w/c. Thus, the energy per code bit is $E_b = wE_{bu}/c$, and the processing gain is $G = wG_u/c$, where E_{bu} and G_u refer to the uncoded bits. From Equation (2.60), we obtain

$$P_b = \frac{1}{2} \text{erfc}\left[\left(\frac{cbR_j}{wG_u R_s} + \frac{cN_0}{wE_{bu}} \right)^{-\frac{1}{2}} \right] . \qquad (2.65)$$

When the total bandwidth and the word duration are fixed, the potential improvement in performance due to encoding is partially counterbalanced by the decrease in processing gain, which results from the increased transmitted bit rate. As an illustration of the net effect, let $b = 1$ and $G_u = 1000 \, (30 \text{ dB})$. Figure 2.14 shows P_w as a function of the signal-to-noise ratio per word, $cE_b/N_0 = wE_{bu}/N_0$, for four-bit uncoded words ($c = w = 4, r = 1$) and a (7,4) block code ($c = 7, w = 4, r = 2$). The interference-to-signal ratio, R_j/R_s, is 10 dB for one pair of curves and 20 dB for the other.

The preceding analysis of a biphase pseudonoise system can easily be extended to the quadriphase pseudonoise system of Figure 2.5. Again, the Gaussian assumption is decisive in simplifying the mathematics. After passage through the wideband filter, the total received signal is represented by

$$r(t) = A m_1(t) p_1(t) \cos(\omega_0 t + \theta) + A m_2(t) p_2(t) \sin(\omega_0 t + \theta)$$

$$+ j(t) + n(t) . \qquad (2.66)$$

We assume that $f_0 = \omega_0/2\pi \gg W \geqslant 1/T_p \geqslant 1/T_s$, where T_p is the common chip duration of $p_1(t)$ and $p_2(t)$, and $T_s = 2T_b$ is the common symbol duration of $m_1(t)$ and $m_2(t)$. The output of the upper integrator

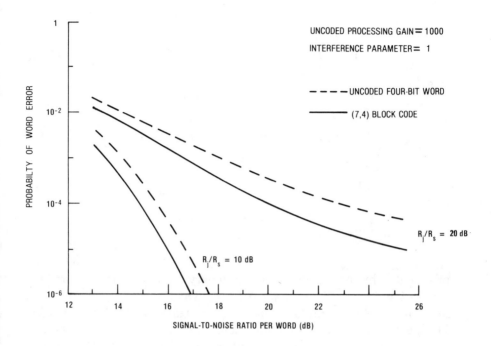

Figure 2.14/Comparison of uncoded and coded word error probabilities in presence of optimal interference.

in Figure 2.5(b) at the end of a symbol interval is approximately

$$L = \pm A T_s + L_1 + L_2 ,$$

(2.67)

where

$$L_1 = \int_0^{T_s} 2 j(t) p_1(t) \cos (\omega_0 t + \theta) \, dt ,$$

(2.68)

$$L_2 = \int_0^{T_s} 2 n(t) p_1(t) \cos (\omega_0 t + \theta) \, dt .$$

(2.69)

Similarly, the output of the lower integrator at the end of a symbol interval is approximately

$$Q = \pm\, AT_s + Q_1 + Q_2 \,, \tag{2.70}$$

where

$$Q_1 = \int_0^{T_s} 2\, j(t)\, p_2(t)\, \sin(\omega_0 t + \theta)\ dt \,, \tag{2.71}$$

$$Q_2 = \int_0^{T_s} 2\, n(t)\, p_2(t)\, \sin(\omega_0 t + \theta)\, dt \,. \tag{2.72}$$

Assuming that the two pseudonoise codes, $p_1(t)$ and $p_2(t)$, can be approximated by independent random binary sequences, then L_i and Q_j, $i = 1, 2$ and $j = 1, 2$, are uncorrelated. The Gaussian assumption then implies that L and Q are independent Gaussian random variables. Thus, errors in L and Q are independent and the probability of an error is the same for both inputs to the parallel-to-serial converter and each bit of the data output. Of the available transmitted power, R_s, half is in each signal term of Equation (2.66). Since $T_s = 2T_b$, the energy per symbol in each term is the same as the energy per bit of the data sequence, E_b. Thus, it is easy to verify that the probability of a bit error in the data output is given by Equation (2.60). We conclude that, within the accuracy of the approximations made, the performance of quadriphase and biphase pseudonoise systems are similar. However, although it is more expensive to implement than a biphase system, a quadriphase pseudonoise system makes some types of signal processing by an interceptor considerably more difficult.

2.5 JAMMING

The jamming resistance of a pseudonoise system depends upon the integrity of its pseudonoise code, since once the code is known, it can be reproduced as a jamming waveform that is not eliminated by the processing gain. To make decipherment time-consuming, the codes should be long. However, since eventual decipherment is inevitable, the pseudonoise code generators in the transmitter and the receiver must be readily programmable.

Assuming that the pseudonoise code is unknown to the jammer, the most effective form of jamming against a pseudonoise system is tone jamming at the center frequency of the pseudonoise spectrum. However, if the processing gain is inadequate to eliminate the jamming, there are a number of specific countermeasures against tone jamming. The tone frequency can be acquired by a phase-locked loop sweeping through the pseudonoise bandwidth. The tone can then be subtracted from the received signal to cancel the interference. Alternatively, an adaptive notch filter can be used as a countermeasure.

If the carrier frequency and the chip rate of a pseudonoise system can be approximately determined by the jammer, then jamming with a pseudonoise signal having a similar carrier frequency and chip rate can be effective. Although the interference parameter is somewhat lower than for ideal jamming, as shown in Figures 2.12 and 2.13, it is difficult to design a specific countermeasure to supplement the processing gain in suppressing pseudonoise jamming.

2.6 CODE SYNCHRONIZATION

For message demodulation to occur in a pseudonoise receiver, the code must be synchronized to within one chip. Range uncertainty and relative clock drifts are the primary sources of synchronization errors, particularly for mobile communicators. Code synchronization consists of two operations, *acquisition* and *tracking*. Acquisition, also called *initial synchronization* or *course synchronization*, is the operation by which the relative timing of the receiver code is brought to within one chip of the transmitted code. After this condition is recognized and confirmed, the tracking system is activated. Tracking, also called *fine synchronization*, is the operation by which synchronization errors are further reduced or at least maintained within one chip.

The acquisition stage is particularly susceptible to hostile actions, whereas the tracking stage [7] is much less sensitive. Thus, we give a brief account of acquisition systems only. There are three requirements of an acquisition system for military applications:

(a) Since successful jamming during acquisition completely disables a communication system, the acquisition system must have a strong capability to reject interference.

(b) The pseudonoise codes used for acquisition must be changeable and sufficiently long for security.

(c) The acquisition operation should be rapid, so that a jammer must operate continuously to ensure jamming during acquisition: continuous operation reduces the amount of jamming power that can be produced.

Because of the first requirement, two acquisition techniques appear to be among the most desirable for military communications: *serial search synchronization* and *matched-filter synchronization*.

Serial Search Synchronization

Serial search synchronization consists of a search over all possible relative time alignments of a received code and a code generated in the receiver. The relative alignments are tested successively until the codes are aligned within a chip. In the *serial acquisition system* of Figure 2.15, the received pseudonoise waveform is multiplied by a code generated in the receiver. The latter code has its rate adjusted until the codes are aligned. With perfect alignment, the input to the envelope detector is a tone and the detector output exceeds a threshold. Under certain conditions determined by the search logic,

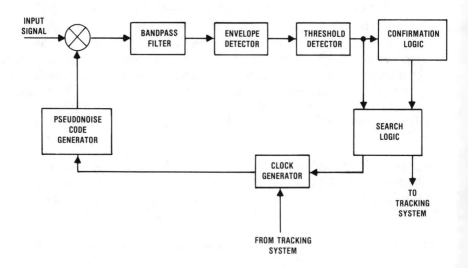

Figure 2.15/Serial acquisition system.

the output of the threshold detector stops the search by stabilizing the clock rate. The two codes are temporarily assumed to be in synchronism so the tracking system immediately begins operation. Acquisition is confirmed by logic circuits that continue to monitor the threshold detector output. If confirmation fails, the search operation is resumed.

The spectrum of the local pseudonoise code is shown in Figure 2.10. If tone jamming is present, the input to the bandpass filter of Figure 2.15 contains discrete frequency components. If the code period is such that only a few of these frequency components pass through the filter, the effect on the envelope detector output can be greater than that due to random noise with the same power. Thus, to reject tone jamming, the code repetition rate must be much less than the bandwidth of the bandpass filter.

To minimize the noise or interference power that enters the envelope detector, the bandwidth of the bandpass filter should be as small as possible. If Doppler shifts and relative oscillator drifts cause a large uncertainty in the carrier frequency to be received, it may be desirable to replace the bandpass filter, the envelope detector, and the threshold detector by an array of similar devices in parallel. In this manner, the bandwidth of each filter can be kept small.

The pseudonoise code used for acquisition does not have to be the same as the code used for communication following acquisition. Once acquisition occurs, the receiver's code generator for communication can be started at a predetermined point. To reduce the acquisition time, the code sequence length during acquisition can be shorter than the code sequence length during communication. However, if the code period is too short, a serial search acquisition system becomes susceptible to tone jamming. Furthermore, the possibility of either false correlations or code reproduction by a jammer increases as the code sequence length is decreased.

Matched-Filter Synchronization

The output of a filter matched to the pseudonoise code can be used to synchronize the receiver code generator. Figure 2.16 diagrams a *matched-filter acquisition system* with protection against interference. The signal matched-filter output is compared with a threshold that is automatically adjusted as a function of a reference matched-filter output. The comparator output activates the tracking system and the confirmation logic. Since the reference matched filter produces a relatively small response to the pseudonoise code being used for acquisition, its output is a measure of the interference and the noise. The level adjustment circuit provides amplification or attenuation of the reference matched-filter output according to the desired probabilities of false alarm and detection.

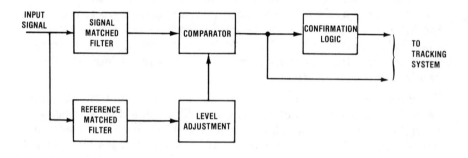

Figure 2.16/Matched-filter acquisition system with protection against interference.

If $KT_p = T_b$ in a direct-sequence system, a matched-filter output can be used for message demodulation, thereby eliminating the need for a separate code synchronization subsystem. However, the code sequence length required is usually too short to provide the protection against false correlations due to pseudonoise jamming and the security desired in a military communication system.

2.7 PSEUDONOISE NETWORKS

A *pseudonoise network* is a communication network in which each element is a pseudonoise system. The set of network codes for acquisition must have small cross correlations to enable a receiver to distinguish between the codes of various transmitters and to expedite the acquisition of the desired code. For practical reasons, all network elements usually have a common carrier frequency and chip rate. If the network elements have different code lengths, cross correlations are usually small if the code lengths do not contain common factors. If, for practical reasons, all network elements have a common code length, it is usually difficult to find large sets of maximal sequences with satisfactory cross-correlation characteristics. However, there are large families of nonmaximal codes with bounded cross correlations [8].

One such family are the Gold codes, which are usually generated by the modulo-two addition of two or more maximal sequences. An example of a Gold code generator is shown in Figure 2.17. If each maximal code generator has m stages, a resulting Gold code sequence is a nonmaximal sequence with a period of $2^m - 1$ bits. Different Gold codes are obtained by selecting the initial contents of the maximal code generators. If n shifts of one of these generators is required to change its initial contents to the initial contents of the other generator, the two generators are said to have a relative displacement of n shifts. Since any relative displacement of the two maximal code generators from 0 to $2^m - 2$ shifts results in a different Gold code, $2^m - 1$ different nonmaximal Gold codes can be produced by the system of Figure 2.17.

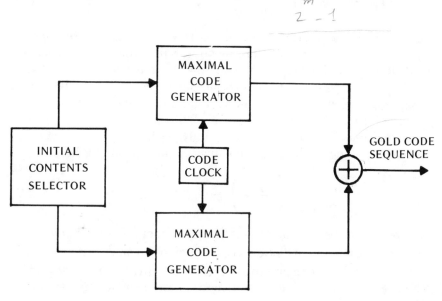

Figure 2.17/Gold code generator.

Assuming that the cross correlations are negligible and the code periods are much longer than T_b, so that the pseudonoise codes can be modeled as independent random binary sequences, we can use Equation (2.60) to calculate P_b in the presence of mutual interference among the network elements. To minimize the interference parameter, the network elements should have different carrier frequencies and different chip rates whenever practical.

One method of counteracting mutual interference is to use time-division multiplexing. If there are N elements in the network, each element is assigned a separate time slot for transmission during each interval of duration T_n. Neglecting propagation time uncertainties, this procedure eliminates the mutual interference, but requires that the transmitted data bit rate be increased by the factor N or more during the allotted time slots if the overall data bit rate is to remain constant. If the transmitted bits have duration T_b/N in a network with time-division multiplexing, the bit error probability in the absence of mutual interference (and other interference) is

$$P_b = \frac{1}{2} \, \text{erfc} \left[\left(\frac{R_s' T_b}{NN_0} \right)^{\frac{1}{2}} \right] , \tag{2.73}$$

where R_s' is the received signal power from a transmitter during one of its time slots. If the transmitters of the pseudonoise systems are not peak-power limited, then increasing the signal power so that $R_s' = NR_s$ preserves the average received power over T_n at the level R_s that would exist without time-division multiplexing. In this case, a comparison of Equations (2.73) and (2.60) for $E_b = R_s T_b$ indicates that the time-division multiplexing is always helpful. If the transmitters are peak-power limited, time-division multiplexing is helpful if

$$N < \frac{R_s'}{R_s} \left(1 + \frac{bR_j T_p}{N_0} \right) , \tag{2.74}$$

where R_j is the power due to interference from the other network elements. If the elements have a common chip rate and carrier frequency, then $b = 2/3$. The main problem with time-division multiplexing is the need for establishing accurate coordination among the network elements.

A *time-hopping system* is a system in which the time slots are selected according to the state of a pseudonoise code generator. Figure 2.18

diagrams a time-hopping pseudonoise system. The data bits are temporarily stored for transmission at a high rate during the slot. After code synchronization has been established at the receiver, only signals corresponding to the desired portion of the frame pass through the initial switch. The pseudonoise nature of the transmitted bursts is useful as a countermeasure to interception or jamming.

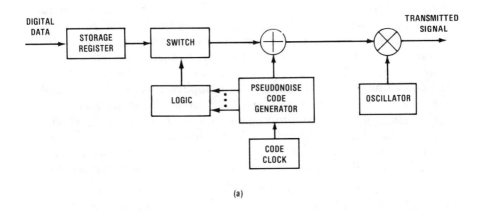

(a)

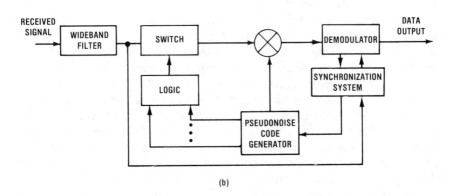

(b)

Figure 2.18/Time-hopping pseudonoise system: (a) transmitter and (b) receiver.

2.8 BURST-COMMUNICATION SYSTEM

Communications for interrogation or identification among network
elements are usually short and infrequent. Systems for these communications can establish synchronization by including a synchronization
preamble in each transmitted burst. However, preambles lengthen the
burst, thereby increasing the probability of interception.

A *pseudonoise burst-communication system* [3] that does not require
preambles is depicted in Figure 2.19. Binary CSK is used as the data
modulation. A programmable switching matrix connects each tap of
a delay line with a pair of code generators or matched filters. In the
transmitter, the delay line is excited by a pulse. As the pulse traverses
the delay line, a corresponding pulse is applied to a different pair of
pseudonoise code generators every bit interval. Depending upon the
logical state of the corresponding data bit, each bit selector, which
may consist of logic circuitry similar to that shown in Figure 2.6(a),
passes either the mark code or the space code to the phase modulator.
Thus, M data bits produce M contiguous pseudonoise code sequences.

If tap i of the transmitter delay line is connected to code generators
j, then tap M − i + 1 of the receiver delay line is connected to
matched filters j. Thus, the received waveform does not produce
significant matched-filter outputs until it completely fills the delay
line. Shortly afterwards, either the mark or the space code output
of each pair of matched filters produces a correlation peak. Each
comparator output becomes the logical state corresponding to a mark
or space code. The correlation peaks are all in phase coherence if the
tap separations correspond to a bit duration and if the matched filters
cause identical propagation delays. If the mark and space codes are
nearly orthogonal to each other, one output of each pair of matched
filters is negligible compared to the other output. Thus, the sum of
the matched-filter outputs is a signal that has a peak amplitude equal
to M times the peak amplitude of the output of a single matched filter. Assuming the noise outputs of the matched filters are nearly uncorrelated with each other, the noise power entering the threshold
detector is 2M times the noise power of the output of a single matched
filter. Thus, the signal-to-noise ratio at the threshold detector input is
M/2 times the signal-to-noise ratio at the output of one of the matched
filters. As a result, the detector output pulses are synchronized to the
bit timing with a precision that increases with M. For large M, the
receiver performance approaches that of a synchronized CSK receiver
despite the absence of *a priori* synchronization information.

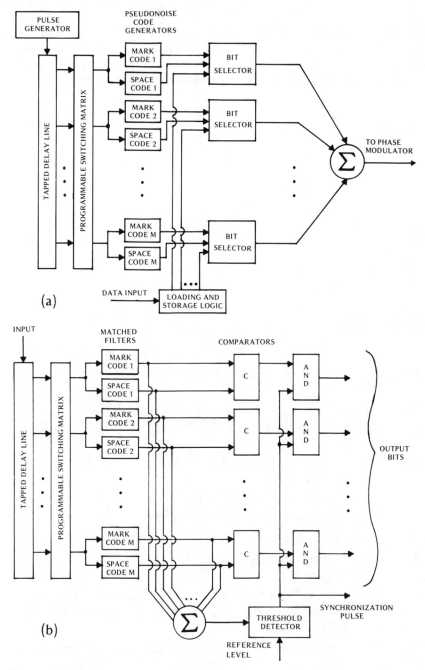

Figure 2.19/Burst-communication system: (a) transmitter and (b) receiver.

Because the switching matrices are programmable, the system of Figure 2.19 allows selective addressing and resists deceptive jamming. With the appropriate choice of the threshold detector's reference level, received bursts without the proper code order are rejected.

REFERENCES

[1]   R.C. Dixon, *Spread Spectrum Systems*. New York: Wiley, 1976.

[2]   *Spread Spectrum Communication*, NATO Advisory Group for Aerospace Research and Development AGARD-LS-58, National Technical Information Service AD-766 914, 1973.

[3]   M.G. Unkauf, in *Surface Wave Filters*, H. Mathews, ed., New York: Wiley, 1977.

[4]   *Special Issue on Spread Spectrum Communications, IEEE Trans. Comm.* COM-25 (August 1977).

[5]   S. Haykin, *Communication Systems*. New York: Wiley, 1978.

[6]   R.E. Ziemer and W.H. Tranter, *Principles of Communications*. Boston: Houghton-Mifflin, 1976.

[7]   M.K. Simon, "Pseudonoise Code Tracking Performance of Spread Spectrum Receivers," *IEEE Trans. Comm.* COM-25 (March 1977), 327.

[8]   D.V. Sarwate and M.B. Pursley, "Crosscorrelation Properties of Pseudorandom and Related Sequences," *Proc. IEEE* 68 (May 1980), 593.

3

Frequency Hopping

3.1 INTRODUCTION

Frequency hopping is the periodic changing of the frequency or frequency set associated with a transmission. Successive frequency sets are determined by a pseudonoise code. If the data modulation is multiple frequency-shift keying, two or more frequencies are in the set that changes at each hop. For other data modulations, a single center or carrier frequency is changed at each hop.

A frequency-hopping signal may be regarded as a sequence of modulated pulses with carrier frequencies that hop in a pseudorandom pattern. Hopping occurs over a frequency band that includes a number of channels. Each channel is defined as a spectral region with a center frequency that is one of the possible carrier frequencies and a bandwidth large enough to include most of the power in a pulse with the corresponding carrier frequency.

When there is only a single carrier frequency and transmission channel between hops, digital data modulation is called *single-channel modulation.* Figure 3.1 depicts the general form of a system with single-channel data modulation. Figure 3.2(a) illustrates the frequency changes with time for frequency hopping with this type of modulation. The time duration between hops, the total hopping bandwidth, and the channel bandwidth are denoted by T_h, W, and B, respectively. If the frequency pattern produced by the receiver synthesizer in Figure 3.1(b) is synchronized with the frequency pattern of the received signal, then the mixer output is a dehopped signal at a fixed difference frequency. Before demodulation, the dehopped signal is applied to a bandpass filter that excludes power that originated outside the appropriate channel. However, as long as a signal occupies a particular channel, the noise and interference in that channel are translated in frequency so that they enter the demodulator.

Frequency hopping may be classified as fast or slow. *Fast frequency hopping* occurs if there is a frequency hop for each transmitted symbol. Thus, for binary communications fast frequency hopping implies that the hopping rate equals or exceeds the data (message) bit rate. *Slow frequency hopping* occurs if two or more symbols are transmitted in the time interval between frequency hops.

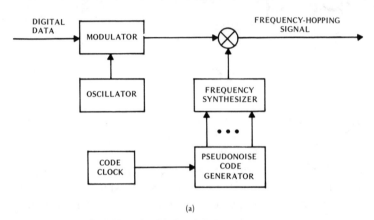

(a)

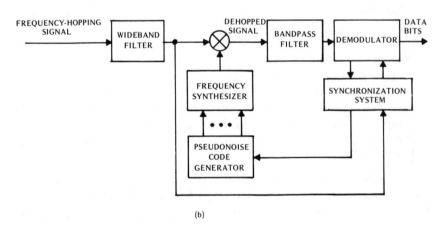

(b)

Figure 3.1/General form of frequency-hopping system with single-channel data modulation: (a) transmitter and (b) receiver. Configuration of code synchronization system is one of several possibilities.

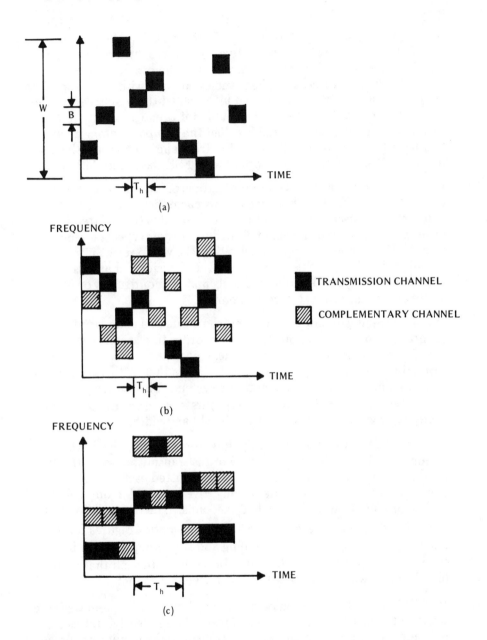

Figure 3.2/Frequency changes with time for (a) frequency hopping with single-channel data modulation, (b) fast hopping with FSK, and (c) slow hopping with FSK.

When binary frequency-shift keying (FSK) is used, each code bit (symbol) is transmitted as one of two frequencies, where one frequency represents a logical *one* (mark), and the other, a logical *zero* (space). The pair of possible frequencies changes with each hop. The channel occupied by a transmitted bit is called the *transmission channel*. The channel that would be occupied if the logical state represented by the bit were reversed is called the *complementary channel*. Figures 3.2(b) and 3.2(c) illustrate the frequency changes with time for fast and slow frequency hopping with FSK data modulation.

Frequency hopping allows communicators to hop out of jammed channels. To take full advantage of this capability, error-correcting codes must be used. If each bit of a code word is transmitted in a different channel and the channels occupy disjoint spectral regions, a code that corrects n errors enables the receiver to reject n tone jamming signals. For this reason, we assume disjoint channels in the subsequent analysis. Disjoint channels may be contiguous or have unused spectral regions between them.

In a slow frequency-hopping system, the c bits in a code word must be interleaved over c hopping periods in order to transmit each bit in a different channel. After deinterleaving in the receiver, the error-correcting capability of the block code equals that of the same block code used in a fast frequency-hopping system. Bit interleaving in fast systems permits the correction of bursts of errors due to pulsed jamming over a large fraction of the total bandwidth.

Figure 3.2(a) can represent fast or slow hopping with five-bit code words such that each bit of a code word is transmitted in a different channel. For fast hopping, one bit is transmitted each T_h seconds. For slow hopping with bit interleaving, five bits, each from a different code word, are transmitted each T_h seconds. The transmission of a five-bit code word is completed after $5T_h$ seconds. Figures 3.2(b) and 3.2(c) can represent fast hopping and slow hopping with bit interleaving, respectively, with a three-bit code word such that each bit of a code word is transmitted in a different channel.

If is difficult to maintain phase coherence between frequency synthesizers in the transmitter and the receiver. Consequently, unless the hopping rate is low compared to the transmitted symbol rate, practical frequency-hopping systems require noncoherent or differentially coherent demodulators. We initially assume FSK data modulation. Other data modulations are examined in Section 3.8.

Figure 3.3 depicts a frequency-hopping system with FSK data modulation and noncoherent demodulation. In the receiver, the two synthesizers produce frequencies that are offset from the two possible received frequencies by constant intermediate frequencies so that only two bandpass filters are needed. After the dehopping, the demodulation is the same as ordinary noncoherent FSK demodulation.

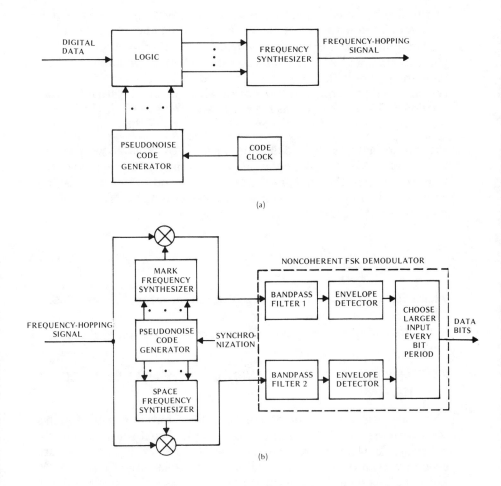

Figure 3.3/Frequency-hopping system with FSK data modulation: (a) transmitter and (b) receiver.

The use of two independent synthesizers in the receiver permits a non-constant relationship between each pair of frequency channels. As a result, the measurement of the transmitted frequency does not provide a jammer with the frequency of the complementary channel. It is shown in Section 3.4 that jamming of the complementary channel is more damaging to communications than jamming of the transmission channel.

The transmission channel, the complementary channel, or both channels associated with a bit may contain jamming energy. We denote the total number of available channels by M, and the number of jammed channels by J. By definition, $J \leqslant M$. We assume that the jamming power is the same in all jammed channels and that the received signal power is independent of which channel is used for transmission. These assumptions are reasonable for large W if the transmitters compensate for the frequency dependence of the propagation.

We assume that a (c, w) block code is produced; that is, words of w bits are encoded so that c code bits are transmitted for every word. Depending upon the code, r or more bits per code word must be in error for a word error to occur at the receiver output. Thus, the probability of a word error is

$$P_w = \sum_{m=r}^{c} P(m) \ , \qquad (3.1)$$

where P(m) is the probability of exactly m bit errors in a word of c bits.

In the following analysis, perfect code synchronization is always assumed.

3.2 FAST HOPPING AND SLOW HOPPING WITH BIT INTER-LEAVING

The analysis in this section applies to both fast systems and slow systems with ideal bit interleaving. To minimize burst errors due to jamming, 2c different transmission and complementary channels are used in transmitting a code word of c bits. We assume that $2c \leqslant M$. Let A(k, i, q) denote the event that k transmission channels and i complementary channels are jammed and q bits have both associated channels jammed. The probability of A(k, i, q) is denoted by P_5. The probability of m bit errors, given A(k, i, q), is denoted by $P(m \mid k, i, q)$. From these definitions, it follows that

$$P(m) = \sum_k \sum_i \sum_q P(m \mid k, i, q) \, P_5 \, . \tag{3.2}$$

The summation needs to be carried out only over those index values for which $P(m \mid k, i, q) \, P_5$ is nonzero. From the definitions of the probabilities, we obtain the following bounds for the index values:

$$0 \leqslant q \leqslant i \leqslant c \, , \quad 0 \leqslant q \leqslant k \leqslant c \, , \quad i + k \leqslant J \, ,$$
$$i + k - q \leqslant c \, , \quad c - k \leqslant M - J \, ,$$
$$J - k - i \leqslant M - 2c. \tag{3.3}$$

Other inequalities required for consistency are implied by those above.

P_5 can be evaluated by combinatorial analysis. Out of a total of M possible channels, c transmission channels and c complementary channels are associated with each word. We may regard the 2c different channels as fixed and the jamming as introduced into J randomly chosen channels. Alternatively, we may consider the J jammed channels as fixed and the transmission and complementary channels as randomly chosen for each word. In either case, we can derive the same formula for P_5. However, the former approach yields a simpler derivation.

There are $\binom{M}{J}$ ways to choose the J jammed channels out of the M total channels. The number of ways in which the event A(k, i, q) can occur may be determined by specifying a four-step process. There are $\binom{c}{k}$ ways to choose the k jammed transmission channels of a word. Having chosen these channels, there are $\binom{k}{q}$ ways to choose those channels that have jammed complementary channels associated with them. There are $\binom{c-k}{i-q}$ ways to choose the $i - q$ complementary channels that are jammed but are not associated with jammed transmission channels. The final step in the process is to select the $J - k - i$ jammed channels out of the $M - 2c$ channels that are not associated with the word. This selection can be accomplished in $\binom{M-2c}{J-k-i}$ ways. Thus, the probability of event A(k, i, q) is

$$P_5 = \frac{\binom{c}{k}\binom{k}{q}\binom{c-k}{i-q}\binom{M-2c}{J-k-i}}{\binom{M}{J}} \, . \tag{3.4}$$

We define $B(\alpha, \beta, \gamma)$ as the event that α errors occur in the $k - q$ bits for which only the transmission channel is jammed, β errors occur in the $i - q$ bits for which only the complementary channel is jammed, and γ errors occur in the q bits for which both associated channels are jammed. The probability of $B(\alpha, \beta, \gamma)$ given $A(k, i, q)$ is denoted by $P(\alpha, \beta, \gamma \mid k, i, q)$. The probability of m bit errors given the event $A(k, i, q) \cap B(\alpha, \beta, \gamma)$ is denoted by P_4. From these definitions, it follows that

$$P(m \mid k, i, q) = \sum_\alpha \sum_\beta \sum_\gamma P(\alpha, \beta, \gamma \mid k, i, q) \, P_4 \ . \tag{3.5}$$

The summation needs to be carried out only over those index values for which $P(\alpha, \beta, \gamma \mid k, i, q)P_4$ is nonzero. From the definitions of the probabilities, we obtain the following bounds for the index values:

$$0 \leqslant \alpha \leqslant k - q \ , \quad 0 \leqslant \beta \leqslant i - q \ ,$$
$$0 \leqslant \gamma \leqslant q \ , \quad \alpha + \beta + \gamma \leqslant m \ ,$$
$$c - (k - q) - (i - q) - q \geqslant m - (\alpha + \beta + \gamma) \ . \tag{3.6}$$

From its definition, P_4 is equal to the probability that there are $m - \alpha - \beta - \gamma$ errors among the $c - k - i + q$ bits for which there is no jamming power in either associated channel. Assuming that the bit errors are independent,

$$P_4 = \binom{c - k - i + q}{m - \alpha - \beta - \gamma} S_0^{\,m - \alpha - \beta - \gamma}$$
$$\times (1 - S_0)^{c - k - i + q - m + \alpha + \beta + \gamma} \ , \tag{3.7}$$

where S_0 is the probability of a bit error when neither associated channel is jammed. We also have

$$P(\alpha, \beta, \gamma \mid k, i, q) = P_1 P_2 P_3 \ , \tag{3.8}$$

where

$$P_1 = \binom{k - q}{\alpha} S_t^{\,\alpha} (1 - S_t)^{k - q - \alpha} \ , \tag{3.9}$$

$$P_2 = \binom{i - q}{\beta} S_c^{\,\beta} (1 - S_c)^{i - q - \beta} \ , \tag{3.10}$$

$$P_3 = \binom{q}{\gamma} S_2{}^\gamma (1 - S_2)^{q-\gamma} \ . \qquad (3.11)$$

In these equations, S_t is the probability of a bit error when only the transmission channel is jammed, S_c is the probability of a bit error when only the complementary channel is jammed, and S_2 is the probability of a bit error when both channels associated with a bit are jammed.

Combining the above definitions, equations, and inequalities, we obtain the probability of a word error,

$$P_w = \sum_{m=r}^{c} \sum_{k=k_0}^{k_1} \sum_{i=i_0}^{i_1} \sum_{q=q_0}^{q_1} \sum_{\alpha=0}^{\alpha_1} \sum_{\beta=0}^{\beta_1} \sum_{\gamma=\gamma_0}^{\gamma_1} P_1 P_2 P_3 P_4 P_5 \ ,$$

$$(3.12)$$

where

$$
\begin{aligned}
k_0 &= \max (0, c + J - M), & q_1 &= \min (i, k), \\
k_1 &= \min (c, J), & \alpha_1 &= \min (m, k - q), \\
i_0 &= \max (0, 2c + J - M - k), & \beta_1 &= \min (m - \alpha, i - q), \\
i_1 &= \min (c, J - k), & \gamma_0 &= \max (0, m - \alpha - \beta - c \\
& & & \quad + k + i - q), \\
q_0 &= \max (0, k + i - c), & \gamma_1 &= \min (m - \alpha - \beta, q) \ .
\end{aligned}
$$

The summation limits ensure that all the binomial coefficients, $\binom{a}{b}$, are well defined.

The probability of a bit error is obtained by setting $c = r = 1$ in Equation (3.12). After a considerable amount of algebra, the result is

$$P_b = \sum_{n=n_0}^{n_1} \frac{\binom{2}{n}\binom{M-2}{J-n}}{\binom{M}{J}} S_n \ , \qquad (3.13)$$

where
$$n_0 = \max(0, J + 2 - M), \quad n_1 = \min(2, J) \; ,$$
and
$$S_1 = \frac{1}{2} (S_t + S_c) \; . \tag{3.14}$$

Since it is equally likely for either of the two channels to be jammed, S_1 is the probability of a bit error given that one channel associated with a bit is jammed.

We have assumed the random selection of 2c different channels for transmitting a code word. An alternative strategy, which may be simpler to implement, is to randomly select the pair of channels associated with each transmitted bit. In this case, the independence of bit errors implies that

$$P_w = \sum_{m=r}^{c} \binom{c}{m} P_b{}^m (1 - P_b)^{c-m} \; , \tag{3.15}$$

where P_b is given by Equation (3.13). The disadvantage of this strategy is that the same channel may be used for more than one bit of a code word, resulting in a reduced receiver capability for rejecting a few interfering signals.

3.3 SLOW HOPPING WITHOUT INTERLEAVING

In slow frequency-hopping systems, a frequency hop occurs once every two or more transmitted bits. To simplify the analysis, we assume that the hops cannot occur during the transmission of a data word, but only at word boundaries. Consequently, when bit interleaving is not used, the jamming environment is the same for each bit in a single word.

Let D_0 denote the event that neither of the two frequencies associated with a word is jammed, D_1 denote the event that one frequency is jammed, and D_2 denote the event that both frequencies are jammed. We make the decomposition,

$$P(m) = \sum_{n=0}^{2} P(m \mid D_n) P(D_n) \; , \tag{3.16}$$

where $P(m \mid D_n)$ is the probability of m bit errors in a word, given that event D_n occurs, and $P(D_n)$ is the probability of event D_n. From elementary combinatorial considerations,

$$P(D_n) = \begin{cases} \dfrac{\dbinom{2}{n}\dbinom{M-2}{J-n}}{\dbinom{M}{J}}, & J-M+2 \leqslant n \leqslant J, \ 0 \leqslant n \leqslant 2, \\[1em] 0, & \text{otherwise.} \end{cases} \tag{3.17}$$

Assuming the independence of bit errors, we have

$$P(m \mid D_n) = \binom{c}{m}(1-S_n)^{c-m} S_n^m, \ n = 0, 1, 2, \tag{3.18}$$

where S_n is the probability of bit error given the occurrence of event D_n (S_0, S_1, and S_2 are defined as in the previous section). Combining Equations (3.1) and (3.16) to (3.18), we obtain

$$P_w = \sum_{m=r}^{c} \sum_{n=n_0}^{n_1} \frac{\dbinom{2}{n}\dbinom{M-2}{J-n}\dbinom{c}{m}}{\dbinom{M}{J}}(1-S_n)^{c-m} S_n^m,$$

$$\tag{3.19}$$

where

$$n_0 = \max(0, J+2-M), \ n_1 = \min(2, J).$$

The probability of a bit error, obtained by setting $c = r = 1$ in Equation (3.19), is given by Equation (3.13).

3.4 CONDITIONAL BIT ERROR PROBABILITIES

The conditional bit error probabilities, S_0, S_t, S_c, S_1, and S_2, can be evaluated from the theory of FSK demodulation. Let N_1 and N_2 represent the power levels of the Gaussian noises within the transmission and complementary channels at a receiver, respectively. In each channel, some of the noise power, denoted by N_t, is due to thermal and background noise that is uniform over the total bandwidth, while the remainder is due to noise jamming that is modeled as a Gaussian process with a flat power spectrum over the channel bandwidth. Since the jamming is statistically independent of the thermal noise,

$$N_1 = N_t + N_{j1} \, , \tag{3.20}$$

$$N_2 = N_t + N_{j2} \, , \tag{3.21}$$

where N_{j1} and N_{j2} are noise jamming powers. Let R_j represent the average power at the receiver in a narrowband, angle-modulated jamming signal having the form

$$J(t) = \sqrt{2R_j} \cos\left[\omega t + \phi(t) \right] \, . \tag{3.22}$$

The jamming, which may be a tone, is assumed to be narrowband compared with the channel bandwidth.

In the applications, we are primarily interested in two special cases. In one case, we assume that narrowband jamming may be present and that noise jamming, if present, is uniformly distributed over all M available channels so that $N_1 = N_2$. In the other case, we assume that narrowband jamming is absent, but that noise jamming is present in some of the available channels; thus, we set $R_j = 0$.

Assume $N_1 = N_2 = N_t$. Let R_s represent the average power at the receiver in the intended transmission. Suppose $J(t)$ occupies the transmission channel, but not the complementary channel. According to Equation (A.30) in Appendix A, the resulting bit error probability is

$$S_t = \frac{1}{2} \exp\left(-\frac{R_s + R_j}{2N_t} \right) I_0\left(\frac{\sqrt{R_s R_j}}{N_t} \right) \, , \tag{3.23}$$

where $I_0(x)$ is the modified Bessel function of the first kind and zero order. If the complementary channel of a bit is jammed by $J(t)$, but the transmission channel is not, then Equation (A.31) gives the bit error probability

$$S_c = Q\left(\sqrt{\frac{R_j}{N_t}} , \sqrt{\frac{R_s}{N_t}} \right) - \frac{1}{2} \exp\left(-\frac{R_s + R_j}{2N_t} \right) I_0\left(\frac{\sqrt{R_s R_j}}{N_t} \right) , \tag{3.24}$$

where the Q-function is defined by

$$Q(\alpha, \beta) = \int_{\beta}^{\infty} x \exp\left(-\frac{x^2 + \alpha^2}{2}\right) I_0(\alpha x) \, dx \ . \qquad (3.25)$$

Equations (3.14), (3.23), and (3.24) yield

$$S_1 = \frac{1}{2} Q\left(\sqrt{\frac{R_j}{N_t}} \ , \ \sqrt{\frac{R_s}{N_t}}\right) \ . \qquad (3.26)$$

If narrowband jamming signals of equal power enter both channels, Equation (A.27) yields the bit error probability

$$S_2 = \frac{1}{2\pi} \int_0^{2\pi} dx \left\{ Q\left[\sqrt{\frac{R_j}{N_t}} \ , \ \left(\frac{R_s + R_j + 2\sqrt{R_s R_j} \cos x}{N_t}\right)^{\frac{1}{2}}\right]\right.$$

$$-\frac{1}{2} \exp\left[-\frac{R_s + 2R_j + 2\sqrt{R_s R_j} \cos x}{2N_t}\right]$$

$$\times \left. I_0\left[\frac{\sqrt{R_j}\,(R_s + R_j + 2\sqrt{R_s R_j} \cos x)^{\frac{1}{2}}}{N_t}\right]\right\} \ . \qquad (3.27)$$

Assume $R_j = 0$. If the transmission channel is jammed, but the complementary channel is not, then $N_{j2} = 0$ and $N_{j1} = N_j$ in Equations (3.20), (3.21), and (A.30), which give the bit error probability

$$S_t = \frac{N_t}{2N_t + N_j} \exp\left(-\frac{R_s}{2N_t + N_j}\right), \quad R_j = 0 \ . \qquad (3.28)$$

Similarly, if the complementary channel is jammed, but the transmission channel is not, the bit error probability is

$$S_c = \frac{N_t + N_j}{2N_t + N_j} \exp\left(-\frac{R_s}{2N_t + N_j}\right), \quad R_j = 0 \ . \qquad (3.29)$$

A comparison of the last two equations shows that jamming the complementary channel causes a higher bit error probability than jamming the transmission channel with the same power. Combining Equations (3.14), (3.28), and (3.29) yields

$$S_1 = \frac{1}{2} \exp\left(-\frac{R_s}{2N_t + N_j}\right), \quad R_j = 0 . \qquad (3.30)$$

If both channels are jammed with the same power, N_j, Equation (A.32) gives the bit error probability

$$S_2 = \frac{1}{2} \exp\left(-\frac{R_s}{2N_t + 2N_j}\right), \quad R_j = 0 . \qquad (3.31)$$

Finally, if neither channel is jammed, the probability of a bit error is

$$S_0 = \frac{1}{2} \exp\left(-\frac{R_s}{2N_t}\right). \qquad (3.32)$$

3.5 EFFECT OF CODING

The use of an error-correcting code can dramatically decrease the word error probability of a frequency-hopping system in a jamming environment. If the word duration is preserved after encoding, the duration of a transmitted code bit is reduced relative to an uncoded bit and the channel bandwidths must be increased. Thus, if the total bandwidth is not changed, the number of available channels for frequency hopping, M, is reduced relative to the number of channels, M_u, that would be available in the absence of coding. The thermal noise power, N_t, is increased relative to the thermal noise power, N_{tu}, that would be present in the absence of coding. We have

$$M = \text{int}\left(\frac{M_u w}{c}\right), \qquad (3.33)$$

$$N_t = \frac{N_{tu} c}{w}, \qquad (3.34)$$

where int(x) is the largest integer contained in x. The coding is effective when its error-correcting capability is sufficient to overcome the degradation implied by these equations.

As an example, we consider the case in which M_u = 200 and four-bit words are transmitted in the presence of noise jamming signals. The results are similar for narrowband or tone jamming signals. Each jammed channel is assumed to have jamming power N_j = R_s. Figure 3.4 shows P_w calculated from Equation (3.12) as a function of the signal-to-noise ratio per word, w R_s/N_{tu}, for fast hopping or slow hopping with bit interleaving, assuming that the words are uncoded. Figure 3.5 shows the greatly improved performance when a (7, 4) single-error-correcting code is used and we still have N_j = R_s in each jammed channel. Figure 3.6 shows P_w calculated from Equation (3.15) for fast hopping or slow hopping with bit interleaving. A comparison of Figures 3.5 and 3.6 illustrates the advantage of selecting 2c different channels for transmitting a code word instead of randomly selecting each pair of channels. Figure 3.7 shows P_w for code words and slow hopping without bit interleaving. A comparison of Figures 3.5 to 3.7 illustrates that the bit interleaving is highly desirable, if not vital, for a slow frequency-hopping system in a jamming environment.

The use of a *repetition code* in a fast system or a slow system with bit interleaving is often very effective in reducing the error rates. Repetition coding consists of transmitting an odd number of code bits for each data bit. The receiver decides the logical state of the data bit according to the logical states of the majority of the received bits. To determine the probability of a data bit error, we set r = (c + 1)/2 in Equation (3.12) and w = 1 in Equations (3.33) and (3.34). As an example, we consider the case in which M_u = 1000 and there are three narrowband or tone jamming signals, each having power R_j = R_s in a separate hopping channel. Figure 3.8 shows the probability of a data bit error as a function of the signal-to-noise ratio per data bit, R_s/N_{tu}, for c = 1, 3, 5, and 7. Each code bit is transmitted at a different frequency or *chip*. Increasing the amount of repetition is helpful only if the received signal power is sufficiently great relative to the thermal noise.

3.6 PARTIAL-BAND JAMMING

If the jammer's available power is less than the product of the number of hopping channels and the signal power, then it is usually advantageous for the jammer to concentrate the power in part of the total hopping band. Let N_{jt} denote the total jamming power produced for use in the M channels. As the number of jammed channels, J, is

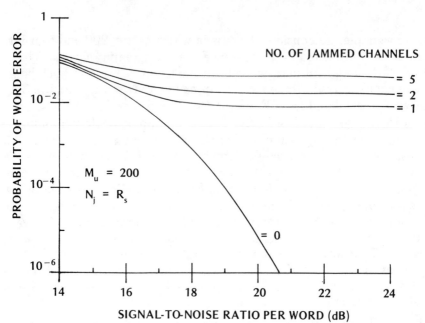

Figure 3.4/Word error probability for fast hopping or slow hopping with bit interleaving, four-bit uncoded word, randomly selected channel set, and FSK modulation.

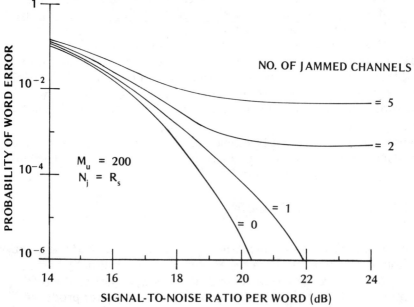

Figure 3.5/Word error probability for fast hopping or slow hopping with bit interleaving, (7,4) block code, randomly selected channel set, and FSK modulation.

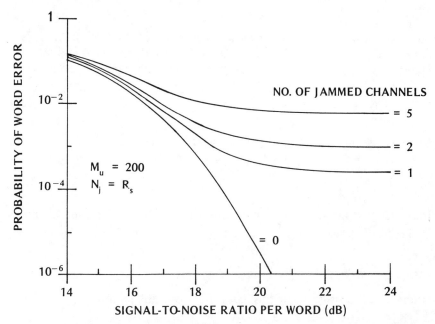

Figure 3.6/Word error probability for fast hopping or slow hopping with bit interleaving, (7,4) block code, randomly selected channel pairs, and FSK modulation.

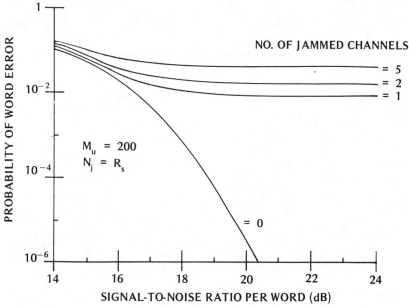

Figure 3.7/Word error probability for slow hopping without bit interleaving, (7,4) block code, and FSK modulation.

increased, the jamming power available for each of these channels is decreased. If the jamming power is uniformly distributed and the channels are disjoint, the jamming power in each jammed channel is

$$R_j = \frac{N_{jt}}{J} \qquad (3.35)$$

for narrowband jamming signals in separate channels or

$$N_j = \frac{N_{jt}}{J} \qquad (3.36)$$

for noise jamming. In the latter case, the number of jammed channels is approximately

$$J = \text{int}(\mu M) = \text{int}\left(\frac{\mu M_u w}{c}\right) \quad , \qquad (3.37)$$

where μ is the fraction of the band that contains jamming.

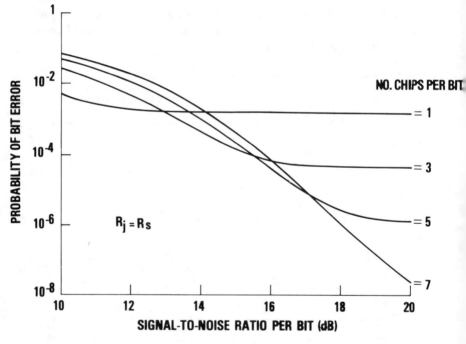

Figure 3.8/Bit error probability for repetition code, randomly selected channel set, FSK modulation, and three tone jamming signals.

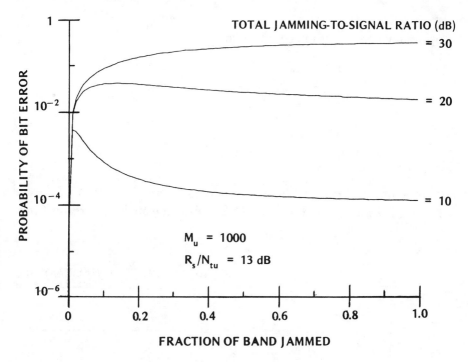

Figure 3.9/Bit error probability for FSK modulation and partial-band jamming.

To illustrate the implications, we assume that M_u = 1000 and R_s/N_{tu} = 13 dB and calculate the error probabilities as functions of μ, using Equations (3.12) and (3.13). Nearly identical results for P_w are obtained from Equation (3.15). We assume that noise jamming is present, but the results are similar for narrowband jamming. Figures 3.9 and 3.10 show P_b and P_w versus μ for total jamming-to-signal ratios of N_{jt}/R_s = 10, 20, and 30 dB. In Figure 3.10, we assume a (7,4) block code. In both figures, the optimal band occupancy for the jammer gradually increases as the available jamming power increases. However, the word error probability exhibits a smaller peak than the bit error probability because of the error-correcting capability of the block code.

It is intuitively reasonable that the highest bit error rate occurs when the jamming power in the jammed channels is approximately equal to the signal power, since increasing the jamming power beyond this level does not significantly increase the probability of a bit error when the communicators hop into a jammed channel. Consequently, the optimal value of μ is expected to be

$$
\mu_0 \approx
\begin{cases}
\dfrac{N_{jt}}{R_s M}, & N_{jt} < R_s M, \\[2em]
1, & N_{jt} \geq R_s M.
\end{cases}
\tag{3.38}
$$

This equation is reasonably accurate for the cases illustrated in Figures 3.9 and 3.10. Equation (1.36) gives the analogous result for pulsed jamming.

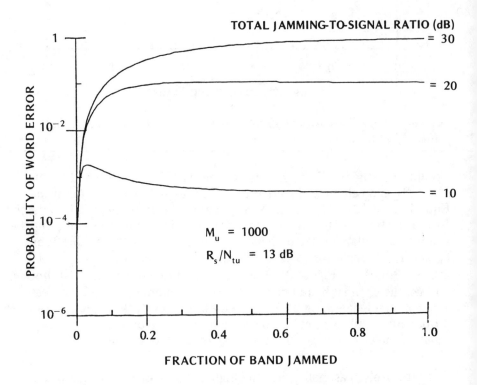

Figure 3.10/Word error probability for fast hopping or slow hopping with bit interleaving, (7,4) block code, randomly selected channel set, FSK modulation, and partial-band jamming.

3.7 REPEATER JAMMING

A *repeater jammer*, also known as a *follower* or *transponder jammer*, is a device that intercepts a signal, processes it, and then transmits jamming at the same center frequency. To be effective against a frequency-hopping system, the jamming energy must reach the victim receiver before it hops to a new set of frequency channels. Thus, the greater the hopping rate is, the more protected the frequency-hopping system is against a repeater jammer.

Figure 3.11 depicts the geometrical configuration of communicators and a jammer. For the repeater jamming to effective, we must have

$$\frac{d_2 + d_3}{v} + T_p \leqslant \frac{d_1}{v} + \eta T_h \, , \tag{3.39}$$

where v is the velocity of an electromagnetic wave, T_p is the processing time required by the repeater, T_h is the hopping period, and η is a fraction. This equation states that the time delay of the jamming relative to the intended signal must not exceed a certain fraction of the hopping period if the jamming is to be effective.

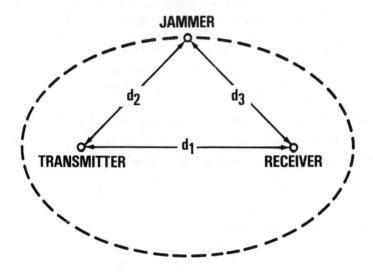

Figure 3.11/Geometrical configuration of communicators and jammer.

The value of η is determined by the details of the receiver design. Consider fast frequency hopping for which the hopping period is equal to the duration of a transmitted bit. For the receiver of Figure 3.3, the outputs of the envelope detectors are sampled every bit period. If the sampling occurs in the middle of a bit period, then $\eta = 1/2$. Since it is advantageous to the communicators to force as low a value of the parameter η as possible, the receiver can be designed so that the sampling occurs close to the leading edge of each bit. However, such a strategy increases the degradation due to intersymbol interference and requires greater synchronization accuracy.

Rearranging Equation (3.39), we may write

$$d_2 + d_3 \leqslant (\eta T_h - T_p)v + d_1 \ . \tag{3.40}$$

If the right-hand side of this inequality is regarded as a constant, then equating the two sides defines an ellipse with the transmitter and the receiver at the two foci. If the repeater jammer is located outside this ellipse, the jamming cannot be effective. Figure 3.11 shows a jammer located on the boundary of the ellipse.

Assuming that the jammer is located inside the ellipse, we can derive equations for the bit and word error probabilities under various conditions. We first consider jamming by a repeater that responds rapidly enough to interfere with the reception of the same bit that is intercepted, so that the jamming enters the transmission channel. If the jamming has the form specified by Equation (3.22), then the bit error probability is given by Equation (3.23); thus,

$$P_b = \frac{1}{2} \exp\left(-\frac{R_s + R_j}{2N_t}\right) I_0\left(\frac{\sqrt{R_s R_j}}{N_t}\right) \ . \tag{3.41}$$

From this equation, we can determine the value of R_j that maximizes P_b for each choice of R_s and N_t. If we assume $\sqrt{R_s R_j} \gg N_t$, we can use the asymptotic expression for the Bessel function,

$$I_0(x) \cong \frac{e^x}{\sqrt{2\pi x}} \ , \qquad x \gg 1 \ , \tag{3.42}$$

in Equation (3.41) to obtain

$$P_b \cong \left(\frac{N_t}{8\pi\sqrt{R_s R_j}}\right)^{1/2} \exp\left[-\frac{(\sqrt{R_s} - \sqrt{R_j})^2}{2N_t}\right] \ ,$$

$$\sqrt{R_s R_j} \gg N_t \ . \tag{3.43}$$

It is now easy to verify with elementary calculus that the optimal value of R_j is $R_j \cong R_s$. Substituting into Equation (3.43), we obtain a simple expression for the bit error probability when the jamming power is optimal,

$$P_b \cong \sqrt{\frac{N_t}{8\pi R_s}} \quad , \quad R_j = R_s \gg N_t \ . \tag{3.44}$$

Thus, the repeater jamming is potentially effective. However, if the jamming power at the receiver deviates significantly from the optimal value, the effectiveness rapidly decreases, as indicated by Equation (3.43).

Suppose that a repeater jammer produces a facsimile of white Gaussian noise over the bandwidth of the victim receiver. In this idealized case, the probability of a bit error is given by Equation (3.28) so that

$$P_b = \frac{N_t}{2N_t + N_j} \exp\left(-\frac{R_s}{2N_t + N_j}\right) . \tag{3.45}$$

Calculus indicates that the optimal jamming power is $N_j = R_s - 2N_t$ if $R_s \geqslant 2N_t$. The corresponding bit error probability is

$$P_b = \frac{N_t}{eR_s} \quad , \quad N_j = R_s - 2N_t \geqslant 0 \ . \tag{3.46}$$

The effectiveness of the jamming decreases more slowly than in the preceding case as the jamming power deviates from its optimal value.

As an example, Figure 3.12 plots Equations (3.41) and (3.45) when the signal-to-noise ratio is $R_s/N_t = 13$ dB. The ordinate is the probability of bit error, P_b, and the abscissa is the jamming-to-signal ratio, N_j/R_s or R_j/R_s. The figure demonstrates that excessive narrowband jamming power can actually be helpful to the communicators. The reason is that the receiver responds to the strong jamming, which has the same form and enters the same channel as the desired signal. Figure 3.13 illustrates how P_b decreases with the signal-to-noise ratio for various fixed values of the narrowband jamming-to-signal ratio.

If the bit errors due to repeater jamming are independent, the probability of a word error is

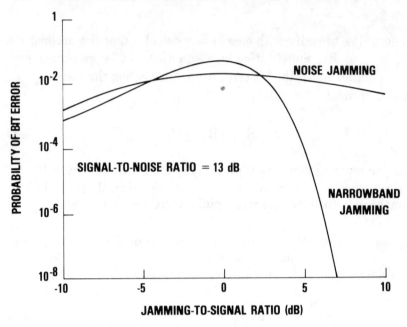

Figure 3.12/Bit error probability for FSK modulation and repeater jamming.

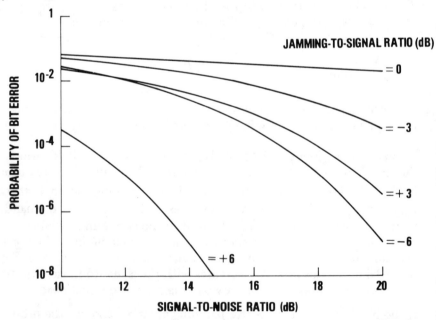

Figure 3.13/Bit error probability for FSK modulation and narrowband jamming by repeater.

$$P_w = \sum_{m=r}^{c} \binom{c}{m} (1 - P_b)^{c-m} P_b{}^m \ . \tag{3.47}$$

Repeater jamming is potentially effective against slow frequency hopping even if the repeater cannot respond rapidly enough to interfere with the reception of the same bit that is intercepted. Suppose there are n code bits during the dwell time between hops. If the jamming energy reaches the receiver too late to affect the first m bits, then the bit error probability for one of these bits is $P_b = S_0$. If $n > m$, the jamming energy may enter either the transmission or the complementary channels of each of the final n-m bits. Thus, the bit error probability for one of these bits is $P_b = S_1$. Assuming ideal bit interleaving, the error probability for a word consisting of bits always located at the same relative position during dwell times is given by Equation (3.47), where either $P_b = S_0$ or $P_b = S_1$.

In addition to possible geometric and power restrictions, there are sometimes other problems entailed in using a repeater jammer. For example, to be effective in the presence of many communicators, the repeater must be capable of isolating the signal to be repeated.

If it is not feasible to hop at a fast enough rate to eliminate the repeater jamming threat, then a hybrid system combining frequency hopping and pseudonoise spread spectrum may solve the problem (Section 3.10). If the chip rate of the pseudonoise code is sufficiently high, repeater jamming effectiveness is greatly impaired even if the hopping is easily followed.

3.8 OTHER DATA MODULATIONS

It has been assumed that the data modulation is impressed on each transmitted pulse by binary FSK. Noncoherent demodulation gives the practical advantages of minimal hardware and synchronization requirements.

In a white Gaussian noise environment, frequency hopping with multiple frequency-shift keying (MFSK) is sometimes advantageous. As the number of different frequencies, n, increases, the symbol error probability for a fixed signal-to-noise ratio per bit decreases as long as the latter exceeds a threshold. However, MFSK with $n > 2$ requires more hardware and occupies more bandwidth per symbol than binary FSK. As the bandwidth occupancy increases, so does the susceptibility to partial-band jamming. Thus, an elaborate error-correcting code may be necessary [2].

Both fast and slow frequency-hopping systems can use FSK or MFSK data modulation. For slow frequency-hopping systems, single-channel modulations such as binary phase-shift keying (PSK), quadriphase-shift keying (QPSK), continuous-phase frequency-shift keying (CPFSK), and minimum-shift keying (MSK) [1] are alternatives. Although the frequency of a CPFSK or MSK signal varies, its compact spectrum allows it to be considered a single-channel modulation.

Because of the difficulty in maintaining phase coherence between frequency synthesizers in the transmitter and the receiver, nearly all frequency-hopping systems must use *differential* (differentially coherent) or *noncoherent* data demodulation. If differential demodulation is used, an extra phase reference symbol may have to be transmitted every hopping period. The resulting loss of signal energy per data symbol causes a degradation from the ideal performance, which may be negligible if the hopping rate is much less than the information rate.

The data symbol error probability for slow frequency hopping with a single-channel data modulation can be obtained in a straightforward manner, since there is no complementary channel. If J channels out of M are jammed, the probability that the transmission channel is jammed is J/M. If each jammed channel receives the same jamming power, the probability of a data symbol error is

$$P_s = \frac{J}{M} S_1 + \left(1 - \frac{J}{M}\right) S_0 \ , \tag{3.48}$$

where S_1 is the probability of a symbol error given that the transmission channel is jammed, and S_0 is the probability of a symbol error given that the channel is not jammed.

If the only type of jamming present is noise jamming, we often can write equations for S_0 and S_1. For example, *ideal differential demodulation* of binary MSK results in (from Equation (3.59) with $\xi = 1$),

$$S_0 = \frac{1}{2} \exp\left(-\frac{R_s}{N_t}\right) \ , \tag{3.49}$$

$$S_1 = \frac{1}{2} \exp\left(-\frac{R_s}{N_t + N_j}\right) , \tag{3.50}$$

where R_s is the signal power, N_t is the sum of the thermal and background noise powers in a channel, and N_j is the jamming power in a jammed channel.

The word error probability for binary single-channel slow hopping with bit interleaving is derived analogously to the derivation of Equation (3.12). If a set of c different channels is randomly selected for transmitting a code word, the word error probability is

$$
P_w = \sum_{m=r}^{c} \sum_{k=k_0}^{k_1} \sum_{\alpha=\alpha_0}^{\alpha_1} \frac{\binom{J}{k}\binom{M-J}{c-k}\binom{c-k}{m-\alpha}\binom{k}{\alpha}}{\binom{M}{c}}
$$

$$
\times [S_0^{\,m-\alpha} S_1^{\,\alpha} (1 - S_0)^{c-k-m+\alpha} (1 - S_1)^{k-\alpha}] ,
$$

(3.51)

where

$$
k_0 = \max(0, c + J - M), \qquad \alpha_0 = \max(0, m - c + k),
$$
$$
k_1 = \min(c, J), \qquad\qquad \alpha_1 = \min(m, k) .
$$

A crucial assumption in the derivation of Equation (3.51) is the independence of bit errors. This assumption is reasonable even for differential demodulation because the interleaving process ensures that each bit of a data word is transmitted over a different frequency channel.

If a channel is randomly selected for each transmitted bit of a code word, the word error probability is

$$
P_w = \sum_{m=r}^{c} \binom{c}{m} \left[\frac{J}{M} S_1 + \left(1 - \frac{J}{M}\right) S_0 \right]^m
$$

$$
\times \left[1 - \frac{J}{M} S_1 - \left(1 - \frac{J}{M}\right) S_0 \right]^{c-m} .
$$

(3.52)

Although it may be simpler to implement than the random selection of a set of c different channels, the random selection of each channel results in a reduced receiver capability for rejecting a few interfering signals.

In Figures 3.14 to 3.16, examples of P_w are depicted for noise jamming and slow hopping with bit interleaving, (7,4) block coding, and ideal differential MSK demodulation. Comparison of these figures with Figures 3.5, 3.6, and 3.10 illustrates the potential improved performance of slow frequency-hopping systems with MSK relative to

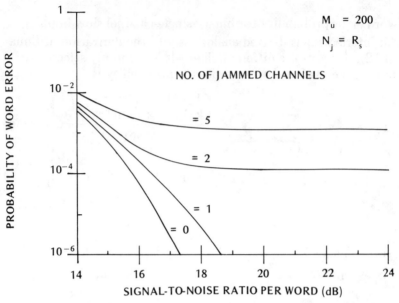

Figure 3.14/Word error probability for slow hopping with bit inter-leaving, (7,4) block code, randomly selected channel set, MSK modulation, and noise jamming signals.

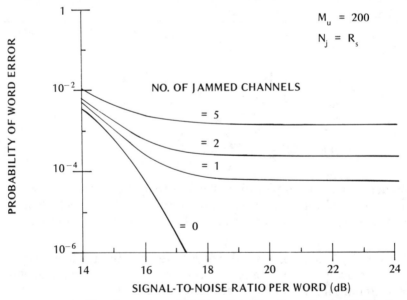

Figure 3.15/Word error probability for slow hopping with bit inter-leaving, (7,4) block code, randomly selected channels, MSK modulation, and noise jamming signals.

systems with noncoherent FSK. Figure 3.16 illustrates the considerable jamming advantage that is sometimes gained by ensuring a nearly
optimal value of μ. Equation (3.38) can be verified for the bit error
probability by using Equations (3.36) and (3.48) to (3.50) and the
method of Section 1.4.

For slow frequency hopping without bit interleaving, the word error
probability is determined by reasoning similar to that used in Section
3.3. The result is

$$
P_w = \sum_{m=r}^{c} \binom{c}{m}\left[\frac{J}{M} \, S_1^{\,m} \, (1 - S_1)^{c-m} + \left(1 - \frac{J}{M}\right)S_0^{\,m}\right.
$$
$$
\left. \times (1 - S_0)^{c-m}\right]. \tag{3.53}
$$

The assumption of independent bit errors, which is necessary to derive
this equation, is reasonable for noncoherent demodulation, but not
necessarily for differential demodulation. Thus, in the latter case,
Equation (3.53) must be regarded as a rough approximation. Because

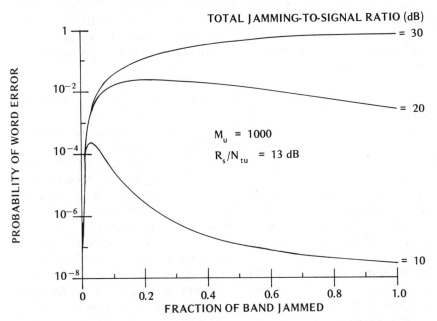

*Figure 3.16/Word error probability for slow hopping with bit inter-
leaving, (7,4) block code, randomly selected channel set, MSK modulation, and partial-band jamming.*

it is susceptible to jamming, slow hopping without bit interleaving is rarely acceptable for military communications.

In the presence of repeater jamming, the symbol error probability for frequency hopping with single-channel data modulation is $P_s = S_1$. The word error probability for binary modulation is determined by setting $J = M$ in Equation (3.51), (3.52), or (3.53), which yields

$$P_w = \sum_{m=r}^{c} \binom{c}{m} S_1^m (1 - S_1)^{c-m} \ . \tag{3.54}$$

3.9 CODE SYNCHRONIZATION

The basic issues of synchronization for military spread-spectrum communications are presented in Chapter 2. The implementation of code synchronization for a frequency-hopping system is similar to the implementation for a pseudonoise system. A serial acquisition system can be implemented as in Figure 2.15, except that the pseudonoise code generator feeds a frequency synthesizer, which produces an output that is applied to the mixer.

A frequency-hopping acquisition system based on the matched-filter concept can provide substantial protection against interference [2]. A functional block diagram of this acquisition system is illustrated in Figure 3.17. The hopping pattern for code synchronization is varied by changing the frequency synthesizer outputs. Each threshold detector output is a logical *one* if a specific frequency is received, and a logical *zero* otherwise. The use of digital outputs prevents the system from being overwhelmed by a few strong narrowband interference signals. One input of the comparator is the number of the frequencies in the hopping pattern that are received. The other input is the number of frequencies simultaneously received, which is an indication of the amount of interference. Thus, the comparator usually does not give a false indication of synchronization even if most of the frequency channels contain interference. Of course, if all of the frequency channels of the hopping pattern are jammed, synchronization may be prevented.

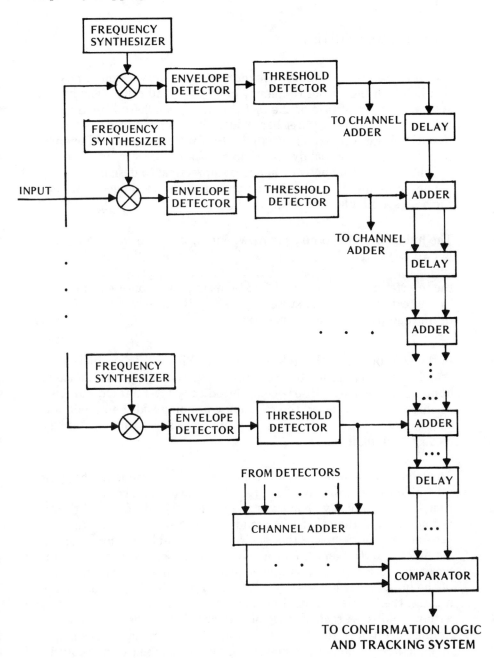

Figure 3.17/Matched-filter acquisition system with protection against interference.

3.10 HYBRID SYSTEM

A *hybrid frequency-hopping pseudonoise system* is a pseudonoise system in which the carrier frequency changes periodically. The hybrid system takes advantage of the fact that it is possible to hop in frequency over a much greater bandwidth than the bandwidth of a pseudonoise waveform. Thus, the hybrid system can spread energy over a much greater bandwidth than a pseudonoise system. The hybrid system is attractive when it is impractical to design a frequency-hopping system with the number of channels needed to use the entire available bandwidth.

The hybrid system combats narrowband or partial-band interference in two ways. The hopping allows the avoidance of the interference spectrum part of the time. When the system hops into the interference, the interference is spread and filtered as in a pseudonoise system. These features of hybrid systems also help them reduce the effects of mutual interference in a network.

In the transmitter of the hybrid system of Figure 3.18, a single pseudonoise code generator controls the spreading and the choice of hopping frequencies. Hops occur periodically after a fixed number of chips. In the receiver, the frequency hopping and the pseudonoise code are removed in succession to produce a carrier with the biphase message modulation.

The frequency synthesizers allow generation of a frequency-hopping preamble for acquisition. The preamble consists of a code-controlled tone that periodically changes in frequency. The duration of the tone is much greater than that of a pseudonoise chip. Therefore, the timing accuracy requirements at the receiver for preamble synchronization are much less stringent than for the pseudonoise code used for communication. As a result, the initial acquisition, which provides alignment of the hopping frequencies, is relatively rapid. If a hop occurs every n chips, then initial acquisition aligns the receiver's pseudonoise code within n chips. A second stage of acquisition over the remaining code timing uncertainty finishes acquisition relatively rapidly since n is much less than the code sequence length. Thus, the overall acquisition time for practical hybrid systems is less than the acquisition time for a pseudonoise system with the same code generator.

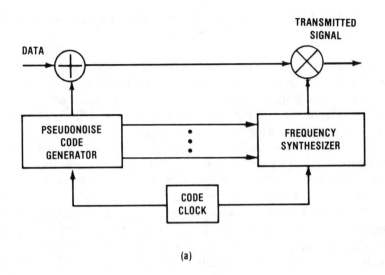

(a)

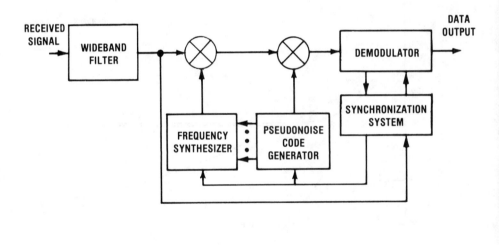

(b)

Figure 3.18/Hybrid frequency-hopping pseudonoise system: (a) transmitter and (b) receiver.

3.11 COMPARISON OF FREQUENCY-HOPPING SYSTEMS AND PSEUDONOISE SYSTEMS

Aside from hybrid systems, the two major candidates for communications that resist jamming and interception are pseudonoise systems and frequency-hopping systems. Using the equations of this chapter and Chapter 2, we compare the word error probabilities of a pseudonoise system and a slow frequency-hopping system that has bit interleaving, ideal differential MSK demodulation, and randomly selected channel sets. We assume that the information rate and the total available bandwidth are the same for both systems, so that the processing gain of the pseudonoise system is equal to the number of channels of the frequency-hopping system. We set $G_u = M_u = 1000$. We assume the presence of a single tone jamming signal at the center frequency of the available bandwidth. We assume that the channel bandwidth is equal to the reciprocal of the bit duration so that $R_s/N_{tu} = E_{bu}/N_0$.

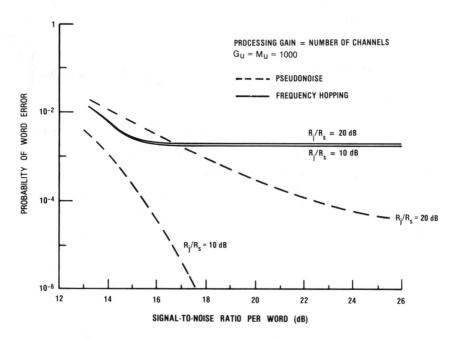

Figure 3.19/Word error probabilities for pseudonoise and frequency-hopping systems, four-bit uncoded word, and tone jamming at center frequency.

Figures 3.19 and 3.20 show P_w as a function of the signal-to-noise ratio per word, $wR_s/N_{tu} = wE_b/N_0$. In Figure 3.19, the four-bit word is un-coded; in Figure 3.20, (7,4) block coding is assumed. As the jamming-to-signal ratio, R_j/R_s, is increased, the frequency-hopping P_w is essentially unchanged, while the pseudonoise P_w increases rapidly. Since errors in frequency-hopping systems occur primarily when the system hops into a jammed channel, an increase in the jamming energy in a channel beyond a certain level has little effect. In contrast, pseudonoise systems spread jamming energy over the total bandwidth. An increase in the jamming energy has a direct effect on the probability of an error. A comparison of Figures 3.19 and 3.20 illustrates that error-correcting codes are usually much more helpful in frequency-hopping systems than in pseudonoise systems.

Although the figures illustrate important differences in error rate performance between frequency-hopping systems and pseudonoise systems, we cannot draw general conclusions for at least two reasons. First, we

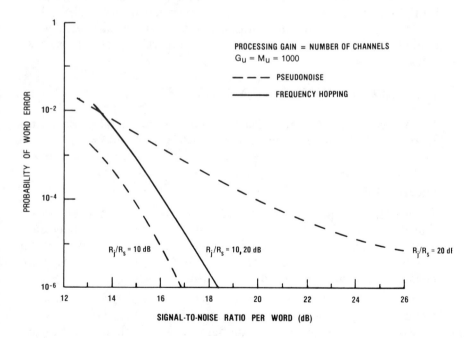

Figure 3.20/Word error probabilities for pseudonoise and frequency-hopping systems, (7,4) block code, and tone jamming at center frequency.

have considered optimal jamming against the pseudonoise system. For the parameter values chosen, partial-band jamming over a number of channels is far more effective against a frequency-hopping system than tone jamming in a single channel. Second, by equating the total bandwidths of the two systems, we have not allowed for the fact that it is possible to hop in frequency over a much greater bandwidth than the bandwidth of a pseudonoise waveform. Thus, the nature of the jamming threat and constraints upon the potential total bandwidth are crucial considerations in deciding the relative merits of the two systems with respect to error rates.

An advantage of frequency hopping is that acquisition of frequency-hopping synchronization is generally much more rapid and inherently more jam-resistant than the acquisition of pseudonoise synchronization.

The relative performances of a pseudonoise network and a frequency-hopping network depend upon the deployment of the network elements and the degree of network coordination. When there are potentially large power differentials at the receivers between desired and interfering signals, frequency-hopping systems are usually less degraded by mutual interference than are comparable pseudonoise systems.

3.12 FREQUENCY-HOPPING NETWORKS

Frequency-hopping communicators do not often operate in isolation. Instead, they are usually elements of a network of frequency-hopping systems that cause mutual interference. The impact of simultaneous mutual interference and jamming is analyzed in this section.

Spectral Splatter

Spectral splatter is the spectral overlap in extraneous channels produced by a time-limited transmitted pulse. Whether or not spectral splatter is significant in causing bit errors in a network depends upon the deployment, the hopping rate, the frequency separation between channels, and the spectrum of the transmitted signals.

Since the transmitted symbol rate equals the hopping rate in fast frequency-hopping systems, the hopping rate strongly influences the transmitted spectrum and the number of available channels. In slow frequency-hopping systems, the hopping rate influences the spectrum through the *switching time*, which is defined as the part of the time interval between hops during which the frequency synthesizer is not operating, plus any rise time or fall time not directly due to the data modulation. The nonzero switching time decreases the transmitted symbol duration, which in turn affects the transmitted spectrum.

If the total bandwidth over which hopping occurs is fixed, increasing the frequency separation between channels may reduce the effects of splatter, but it also decreases the number of available channels. As a result, the rate at which network systems hop into the same channel increases, which may cancel the improvement due to reduced splatter.

The spectral sidelobes of FSK pulses can be reduced if approximately Gaussian or raised cosine pulses are generated instead of rectangular pulses. However, nonlinearities in the final transmitter power amplifier and the propagation channel can considerably increase the spectral sidelobes so that the net benefit from the pulse shaping is significantly reduced.

If an approximately constant-envelope signal is generated, the spectral effect of the nonlinearities is usually negligible. A number of digital frequency-modulation methods such as binary CPFSK provide constant-envelope signals having sharp spectral roll-offs [3]. The general form of binary CPFSK signals is

$$s(t) = A \cos [2\pi f_0 t + \phi(t, \boldsymbol{\alpha}_n)] , \qquad (3.55)$$

where A is the amplitude, f_0 is the carrier frequency, and $\phi(t, \boldsymbol{\alpha}_n)$ is the phase function, which carries the message. The phase function usually has the form

$$\phi(t, \boldsymbol{\alpha}_n) = 2\pi h \sum_{i=-\infty}^{n} \alpha_i \int_{-\infty}^{t} g(x - iT_b) \, dx , \qquad (3.56)$$

where h is a constant called the *deviation ratio*, $g(t)$ represents a pulse, T_b is the bit duration, $\boldsymbol{\alpha}_n$ is the data bit sequence, and $\alpha_i = \pm 1$. Binary CPFSK signals can often be demodulated with a relatively inexpensive frequency discriminator, as diagrammed in Figure 3.21.

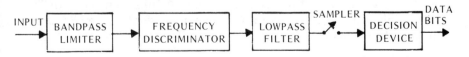

Figure 3.21/Demodulator for CPFSK signals.

If g(t) is a rectangular pulse such that

$$g(t) = \begin{cases} \dfrac{1}{2T_b} & , \quad 0 \leqslant t \leqslant T_b , \\ \\ 0 & , \quad \text{otherwise} , \end{cases} \qquad (3.57)$$

a binary CPFSK signal shifts between two frequencies separated by h/T_b. MSK is defined as CPFSK with

$$\int_0^{T_b} g(x)\, dx = 1/2 , \quad h = 1/2 . \qquad (3.58)$$

If g(t) is a rectangular pulse, then binary MSK is called *ordinary* MSK; otherwise, we refer to it as *generalized* MSK. The class of generalized MSK signals includes signals with much faster spectral roll-offs than ordinary MSK signals [4, 5, 6].

With binary MSK, both discriminator demodulation and differential demodulation without an extra phase reference bit are possible. Theoretical and experimental results indicate that the bit error probability for differential demodulation of MSK is approximately given by [7]

$$P(E) = \frac{1}{2} \exp\left(-\frac{\xi R_s}{N_1}\right), \qquad (3.59)$$

where R_s is the power of the desired signal at the receiver, N_1 is the total white Gaussian noise power, and ξ has a value on the order of unity. The exact value of ξ depends upon the details of the differential demodulation and the bandpass filter bandwidth. Comparison with experimental results [8] indicates that Equation (3.59) provides an approximation of the bit error probability for discriminator demodulation of MSK or CPFSK; however, ξ is then less than unity. Slightly better but more complicated approximations, inspired by theoretical results, are possible but appear to be usually unnecessary. For a rectangular g(t), the deviation ratio that gives the minimum value of P(E) for CPFSK is h = 0.7. According to the data of reference [8], the corresponding value of ξ is approximately 0.75.

Bit Error Probability

Assuming single-channel data modulation, we derive equations for the bit error probability when the splatter is significant only in the two channels adjacent to the transmission channel. The generalization of the derivation to the case in which many channels are affected is straightforward but notationally complicated; the resulting equations are expensive to evaluate with a computer. Thus, a rough approximation of the bit error probability for multiple-channel splatter is given subsequently.

We consider a network of independent frequency-hopping systems that have omnidirectional antennas, generate the same output power, share the same M frequency channels, are nearly stationary in location over a bit duration, and use similar waveforms.

Consider the transmission of a bit from a hopper at A to a receiver at B, as depicted in Figure 3.22. The distance between the two is D. The numbered light dots in the figure represent some of the N potentially interfering hoppers in the network of N + 2 total hoppers. We assume that each interferer uses at most one channel during the bit reception, which is true if the switching time of the hoppers exceeds a bit duration.

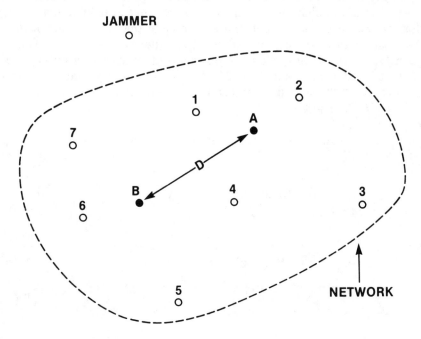

Figure 3.22/Frequency-hopping network and jammer.

The event B_{jk} is defined to be the event that j of the interferers use the transmission channel and each of k interferers uses one of the two channels adjacent to the transmission channel. We denote the probability of B_{jk} by $P(B_{jk})$. The probability of a bit error given B_{jk} is denoted by $P_s(j,k)$. Thus, the bit error probability is

$$P_b = \sum_{j=0}^{N} \sum_{k=0}^{N-j} P(B_{jk}) \, P_s(j,k) \ . \tag{3.60}$$

Let d represent the *duty factor*, which is defined as the probability that an interferer is emitting power during a bit interval. Thus, d is the product of the probability that an interferer is transmitting and the probability that a significant portion of the interferer's transmitted waveform occurs during the bit interval. If the hoppers transmit their waveforms independently and the switching time exceeds a bit duration, the latter probability is proportional to the hopper *duty cycle*, which is the fraction of a hopping period that is occupied by the generated waveform. Since an interferer may transmit in any hopping channel with equal probability, the probability that power from an interferer enters the transmission channel is d/M. We assume that M is sufficiently large that we may neglect the fact that a channel at one of the ends of the total bandwidth has only one adjacent channel instead of two. Consequently, the probability that the power from an interferer enters one of the two adjacent channels is 2d/M. The probability that the power enters neither the transmission channel nor the adjacent channels is $(1 - 3d/M)$. There are

$$\binom{N}{j}\binom{N-j}{k}$$ ways to select one set of j interferers and another set of k interferers when $j + k \leqslant N$. Thus,

$$P(B_{jk}) = \left(\frac{d}{M}\right)^j \left(\frac{2d}{M}\right)^k \left(1 - \frac{3d}{M}\right)^{N-j-k} \binom{N}{j}\binom{N-j}{k} \ . \tag{3.61}$$

Substituting into Equation (3.60) yields

$$P_b = \sum_{j=0}^{N} \sum_{k=0}^{N-j} 2^k \left(1 - \frac{3d}{M}\right)^{N-j-k} \left(\frac{d}{M}\right)^{j+k} \binom{N}{j}\binom{N-j}{k} P_s(j,k) \ . \tag{3.62}$$

In general, approximations of this expression are necessary to obtain an estimate of the bit error probability that is computationally reasonable. To avoid evaluating multiple integrals of order greater than L, we can set $P_s(j,k) = 0$ for $j + k > L$ in Equation (3.62). This truncation gives a lower bound for P_b if $N > L$. Denoting this lower bound by P_L, we have

$$P_L = \sum_{\substack{j = 0 \\ j+k \leq L}}^{N} \sum_{k = 0}^{N-j} 2^k \left(1 - \frac{3d}{M}\right)^{N-j-k} \left(\frac{d}{M}\right)^{j+k} \binom{N}{j}\binom{N-j}{k} P_s(j,k) .$$

$$(3.63)$$

If $N > L$, an upper bound for P_b results if we set $P_s(j,k) = 1/2$ for $j + k > L$. The difference between the two bounds is one-half the probability that more than L interferers produce power in the transmission channel or the adjacent channels. Denoting the upper bound for P_b by P_U, we have

$$P_U = P_L + \frac{1}{2} P(j + k > L) , \qquad (3.64)$$

$$P(j + k > L) = \sum_{\substack{j = 0 \\ j+k > L}}^{N} \sum_{k = 0}^{N-j} 2^k \left(1 - \frac{3d}{M}\right)^{N-j-k} \left(\frac{d}{M}\right)^{j+k}\binom{N}{j}\binom{N-j}{k}.$$

$$(3.65)$$

As dN/M decreases, $P(j + k > L)$ decreases, and the upper and lower bounds become tighter.

If interferer i is using the transmission channel, the ratio of the power from interferer i to the power of the desired signal at the demodulator is denoted by x_i. If interferer i is using an adjacent channel, the ratio of the power from interferer i to the power of the desired signal at the demodulator is denoted by z_i. Let $P_1(x_1, \ldots, x_j, z_1, \ldots, z_k)$ denote the probability of a bit error given that $x_1, x_2, \ldots, x_j, z_1, z_2, \ldots, z_k$ are the interference-to-signal ratios caused by j interferers using the transmission channel and k interferers using an adjacent channel. If the interfering signals are modeled as independent zero-mean processes, this probability is a function of the sum of the interference-to-signal ratios. Thus, we may write

$$P_1(x_1, \ldots, x_j, z_1, \ldots, z_k) = P\left(\sum_{i=1}^{j} x_i + \sum_{i=1}^{k} z_i\right). \quad (3.66)$$

Let $f(u)$ denote the probability density function for an interference-to-signal ratio given that the interference enters the transmission channel. Let $f_1(u)$ denote the probability density function for an interference-to-signal ratio given that the interference enters an adjacent channel. We denote by K the ratio of the power due to an adjacent-channel interferer to the corresponding power that would exist if the interferer were using the transmission channel. Because each hopper in the network is assumed to produce an identical spectrum, K is a constant independent of the index i. Thus, $z_i = Kx_i'$, where x_i' has the density $f(u)$. Since $f_1(u)$ is the density for z_i, elementary probability theory gives

$$f_1(u) = \frac{1}{K} f\left(\frac{u}{K}\right). \quad (3.67)$$

Since each interferer is located and hops independently of the other interferers, Equations (3.66) and (3.67) and the definition of $P_s(j,k)$ imply that

$$P_s(j,k) = \left(\frac{1}{K}\right)^k \int_0^\infty \ldots \int_0^\infty P\left(\sum_{i=1}^{j} x_i + \sum_{i=1}^{k} z_i\right)$$

$$\times \prod_{i=1}^{j} f(x_i) \prod_{i=1}^{K} f\left(\frac{z_i}{K}\right) dx_1 \ldots dx_j \, dz_1 \ldots dz_k.$$

$$(3.68)$$

An alternative form of this equation results if we change variables to $y_i = z_i/K$. We get

$$P_s(j,k) = \int_0^\infty \ldots \int_0^\infty P\left(\sum_{i=1}^{j} x_i + K \sum_{i=1}^{k} y_i\right) \prod_{i=1}^{j} f(x_i)$$

$$\times \prod_{i=1}^{k} f(y_i) \, dx_1 \ldots dx_j \, dy_1 \ldots dy_k. \quad (3.69)$$

To evaluate $P_s(j,k)$, we need expressions for $P(x)$ and $f(x)$. The former function depends upon the data modulation and the latter upon the deployment statistics.

To determine $P(x)$, we assume the validity of Equation (3.59). If we assume that both the interference and the jamming that enter a frequency-hopping receiver can be approximated by independent Gaussian processes with flat spectra over each affected channel, then

$$N_1 = N_t + N_j + R_s x , \qquad (3.70)$$

where N_t is the thermal and background noise power, N_j is the jamming power, and $R_s x$ is the sum of the interference powers due to the other network hoppers. When jamming is absent, we set $N_j = 0$ in Equation (3.70) and substitute it into Equation (3.59) to get

$$P(x) = \frac{1}{2} \exp \left(- \frac{\xi R_s}{N_t + R_s x} \right) . \qquad (3.71)$$

For a repeater that is sufficiently close, we obtain

$$P(x) = \frac{1}{2} \exp \left(- \frac{\xi R_s}{N_t + N_j + R_s x} \right) , \qquad (3.72)$$

where N_j is the jamming power that passes the receiver bandpass filter. The same formula holds for noise jamming over the total hopping band.

For partial-band jamming, let D_0 denote the event that the transmission channel is not jammed and D_1 denote the event that it is jammed. If J out of the M channels are jammed,

$$P(x) = \left(1 - \frac{J}{M} \right) S_0(x) + \frac{J}{M} S_1(x) , \qquad (3.73)$$

where $S_n(x)$ is the probability of a bit error given x and D_n. From the definition of $S_0(x)$, we obtain

$$S_0(x) = \frac{1}{2} \exp \left(- \frac{\xi R_s}{N_t + R_s x} \right) . \qquad (3.74)$$

Assuming that a jammed channel always receives jamming power N_j, Equations (3.70) and (3.59) imply

$$S_1(x) = \frac{1}{2} \exp \left(- \frac{\xi R_s}{N_t + N_j + R_s x} \right) . \qquad (3.75)$$

Equations (3.73) to (3.75) determine $P(x)$ for partial-band jamming.

Deployment Statistics

Let R represent the distance between an interferer and the receiver at B in Figure 3.22., and let U represent the potential interference-to-signal ratio at the receiver. If g(r), the radial density function for R, and a propagation model are specified, then f(u), the density function for U, can be determined. We assume that the received power varies inversely as the nth power of the distance to the source. Thus, if the hoppers have identical system parameters, the interference-to-signal ratio at a receiver is

$$U = \left(\frac{D}{R}\right)^n ,$$
(3.76)

where D is the distance between the receiver and the intended transmitter.

A plausible statistical deployment model is illustrated in Figure 3.23. The receiver is at B, which is the center of two circles with radii R_0 and R_1, such that $R_1 > R_0 > 0$. The intended transmitter is located at A, a distance D from the receiver. Each significant interferer is assumed to have a uniform location probability in the annular ring between R_0 and R_1. Radius R_0 is the minimum possible separation between an interferer and the receiver. Radius R_1 is the maximum possible separation between the receiver and a significant interferer. In other words, if an interferer is at a distance greater than R_1 from the receiver, the interferer contributes negligibly to the bit error rate. The radial density corresponding to a uniform location probability is

$$g(r) = \begin{cases} \left(\dfrac{2}{R_1{}^2 - R_0{}^2}\right) r , & R_0 \leqslant r \leqslant R_1 , \\ \\ 0 , & \text{otherwise} , \end{cases}$$
(3.77)

which is depicted in Figure 3.24. If for each interferer R has the radial density of Equation (3.77), the deployment of the interferers is called a uniform deployment. Elementary probability theory and Equations (3.76) and (3.77) give

$$f(u) = \begin{cases} \left[\dfrac{2D^2}{n(R_1{}^2 - R_0{}^2)} \right] u^{-(n+2)/n} \,, & \left(\dfrac{D}{R_1}\right)^n \le u \le \left(\dfrac{D}{R_0}\right)^n \,, \\[2em] 0 \,, & \text{otherwise.} \end{cases} \tag{3.78}$$

In all the subsequent examples, we assume $n = 4$.

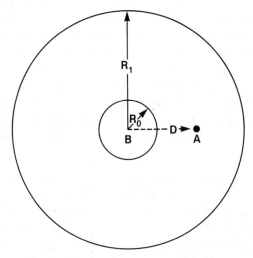

Figure 3.23/Geometry of uniform deployment.

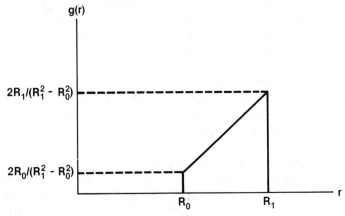

Figure 3.24/Radial density for interferer in uniform deployment of interferers.

Examples

Figures 3.25 to 3.30 plot the upper and lower bounds of the bit error probability as a function of the number of interferers, assuming that $L = 2$, $R_0/D = 0.2$, and $R_1/D = 2$. The values of P_U and P_L are usually so close that only one curve appears on the graph. Thus, this single curve can be considered a plot of P_b.

Figures 3.25 to 3.28 illustrate the effects of mutual interference alone, assuming that jamming is absent. When jamming is absent or repeater jamming is present, it is convenient to use the parameter $M_1 = M/d$, which can be interpreted as the equivalent number of available channels. In Figure 3.25, $\xi = 1$, $K^{\cdot} = 0$, $M_1 = 2000$, and the signal-to-noise ratio, R_s/N_t, is a parameter. If this ratio exceeds approximately 15 dB, the exact thermal noise level is irrelevant and the effect of the mutual interference predominates. Figure 3.26 shows the performance improvement that results when the number of equivalent channels is increased.

Figure 3.27 illustrates the effect of adjacent-channel spectral splatter when the parameter K, called the *adjacent splatter ratio*, equals 0.05. The result of the splatter is to raise the curves by a small amount relative to the corresponding curves for no splatter. The value of the adjacent splatter ratio might arise in the following way. If the channels are designed to capture 90 percent of the intended signal's power, then less than five percent, or 0.05, of the power can fall into one of the adjacent channels. If the data modulation is ordinary MSK, the channel bandwidth required is approximately $0.8\, T_b$. With this bandwidth value, the effect of splatter on a received bit from channels farther in frequency than the adjacent channels is usually negligible if $R_0/D \geqslant 0.2$ in a uniform deployment.

Figure 3.28 illustrates the small effect of the parameter ξ when no jamming is present and the signal-to-noise ratio is 15 dB. If this ratio is reduced or if jamming is present, the sensitivity of the bit error probability to ξ is often magnified.

Figures 3.29 and 3.30 provide examples of the impact of combined jamming and mutual interference. In Figure 3.29, the jamming-to-signal ratio per jammed channel, N_j/R_s, and the fraction of the band that contains jamming, μ, are parameters. Figure 3.30 illustrates the strong effect of the jamming-to-signal ratio for repeater jamming.

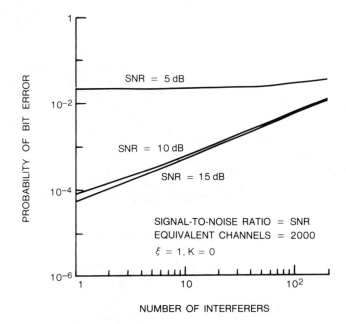

Figure 3.25/Bit error probability for various signal-to-noise ratios.

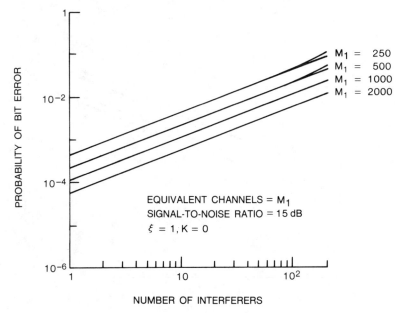

Figure 3.26/Bit error probability for various numbers of equivalent channels.

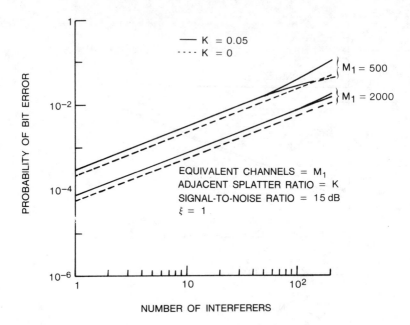

Figure 3.27/Bit error probability for different adjacent splatter ratios.

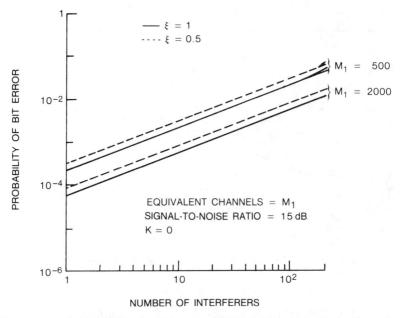

Figure 3.28/Bit error probability for different values of ξ.

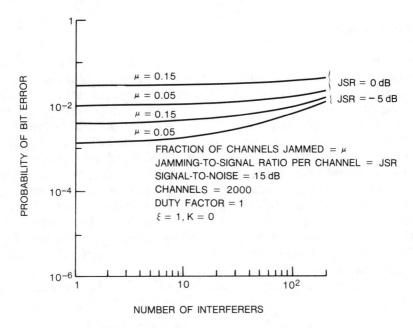

Figure 3.29/Bit error probability for partial-band jamming.

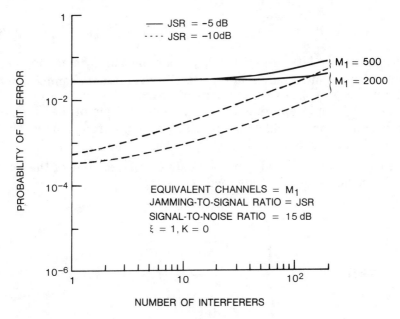

Figure 3.30/Bit error probability for repeater jamming.

Close Interferers

In most practical deployments, only a few interferers are close enough to a receiver to cause significant spectral splatter when hopping in channels beyond the adjacent channels. Suppose that there are ν of these *close interferers* and also N other interferers uniformly deployed beyond a minimum radius R_0. To make a rough estimate of the bit error probability, we estimate the maximum number of nearby channels that can be significantly affected by splatter from one of the close interferers and denote this even number by 2q. We assume that if one or more of the ν interferers hops into a transmission channel or the 2q channels closest to it, then a bit error probability of 1/2 is produced. If no close interferer hops into these (2q + 1) channels, then the bit error probability is determined by the interferers beyond R_0. We ignore the effects of a close interferer and an interferer beyond R_0 simultaneously hopping into the transmission channel or the adjacent channels. Thus, the bit error probability, $P_b{}'$, is roughly approximated by

$$P_b{}' \cong P_b + \frac{1}{2}\left\{ 1 - \left[1 - \frac{(2q + 1)d}{M} \right]^{\nu} \right\}$$

$$\cong P_b + \frac{\nu(2q + 1)d}{2M} \quad , \quad \nu(2q + 1)d \ll M \ , (3.79)$$

where P_b is the bit error probability assuming a uniform deployment beyond a minimum radius and splatter from adjacent channels only. Alternatively, if the exact deployment of the ν close interferers is known, $P_b{}'$ can be approximated by P_b plus the sum of the bit error probabilities that would be produced by each interferer alone. This approximation is reasonable if $\nu(2q + 1)d \ll M$.

The calculation of K and q are facilitated if we use plots of the *fractional out-of-band power* [4,5], defined as

$$G(f) = 1 - \frac{\displaystyle\int_{-f}^{f} S(f')\,df'}{\displaystyle\int_{-\infty}^{\infty} S(f')\,df'} \quad , \quad f \geqslant 0 \ , \quad (3.80)$$

where $S(f)$ is the two-sided power spectral density of the equivalent lowpass generalized MSK waveform and f is the frequency variable. Figure 3.31 depicts smoothed plots of $G(f)$ for QPSK, ordinary MSK, and *sinusoidal frequency-shift keying* (SFSK), which is one type of generalized MSK. The plots show $G(f)$ in decibels as a function of f in units of $1/T_b$. The fractional power within a transmission channel of one-sided bandwidth B is given by

$$K_0 = 1 - G\left(\frac{B}{2}\right) . \tag{3.81}$$

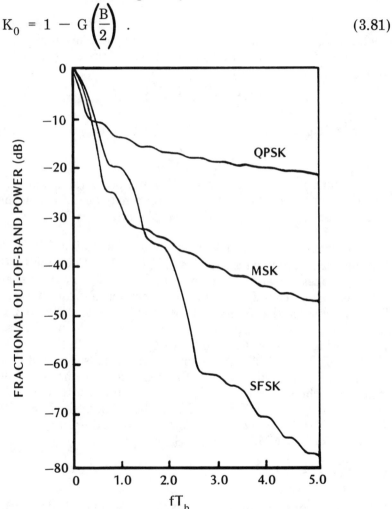

Figure 3.31/Fractional out-of-band power for equivalent lowpass waveforms.

Let the index i denote a channel that is i channels removed from the transmission channel. If the bandwidth of each channel is B, the fractional power intercepted by channel i due to spectral splatter from the transmission channel is given by

$$K_i = \frac{1}{2} \left[G\left(iB - \frac{B}{2}\right) - G\left(iB + \frac{B}{2}\right) \right], \quad i = 1, 2, \ldots$$

(3.82)

The factor 1/2 is due to the fact that there are two channels, one on each side, that are i channels removed from the transmission channel. From Equations (3.81) and (3.82), we obtain the adjacent splatter ratio,

$$K = \frac{K_1}{K_0} = \frac{G\left(\frac{B}{2}\right) - G\left(\frac{3B}{2}\right)}{2\left[1 - G\left(\frac{B}{2}\right)\right]}$$

(3.83)

The maximum interference-to-signal ratio due to a single interferer is called the *near-far ratio*. The parameter q may be defined as the largest index i for which K_0/K_i is less than the near-far ratio.

As an example, suppose that the channel bandwidth is $1.2/T_b$ and interferers can be located as close as 0.01 D. Then Equation (3.76) with n = 4 implies a near-far ratio equal to 80 dB. Such a large near-far ratio causes significant splatter in many channels if ordinary MSK is used. Thus, we assume that SFSK is the data modulation. Figure 3.31 indicates that q = 4 is appropriate and K $\cong$ 0.02. Figure 3.32 shows the resulting bit error probability for ξ = 1, L = 2, R_0/D = 0.2, R_1/D = 2, M_1 = 2000, no jamming, and various values of ν. If ordinary MSK is used instead of SFSK and $\nu \geqslant 1$, the large value of q increases the bit error probability despite the fact that the adjacent splatter ratio, K $\approx$ 0.005, is much smaller than in the SFSK case. However, if there are no close interferers, the bit error probability is lower for ordinary MSK than for SFSK.

Word Error Probability

The word error probability for binary, single-channel, slow frequency-hopping systems with bit interleaving and randomly selected channel sets is given by Equation (3.51). To allow for mutual interference, it

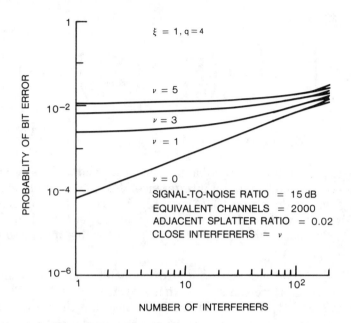

Figure 3.32/Bit error probability for close interferers.

is convenient to change the notation. Let P_{bn} denote the bit error probability given event D_n, for n = 0,1. Then

$$P_w = \sum_{m=r}^{c} \sum_{n=n_0}^{n_1} \sum_{i=i_0}^{i_1} \frac{\binom{J}{n}\binom{M-J}{c-n}\binom{c-n}{m-i}\binom{n}{i}}{\binom{M}{c}}$$

$$\times P_{b0}^{m-i} P_{b1}^{i} (1 - P_{b0})^{c-n-m+i} (1 - P_{b1})^{n-i} ,$$

$$(3.84)$$

where

$$n_0 = \max (0, c + J - M) , \quad i_0 = \max (0, m - c + n) ,$$
$$n_1 = \min (c, J) , \quad\quad\quad i_1 = \min (m, n) .$$

We can evaluate P_{bn} for n = 0, 1 by using Equations (3.62) to (3.65) and (3.79) with $P_s(j,k)$ replaced by $P_{sn}(j,k)$, where $P_{sn}(j,k)$ is the probability of a bit error given $B_{jk} \cap D_n$. A derivation similar to that of

Equation (3.69) yields

$$P_{sn}(j,k) = \int_0^\infty \cdots \int_0^\infty S_n\left(\sum_{i=1}^j x_i + K \sum_{i=1}^k y_i\right) \prod_{i=1}^j f(x_i) \prod_{i=1}^k f(y_i)$$

$$\times \, dx_1 \ldots dx_j dy_1 \ldots dy_k , \qquad\qquad (3.85)$$

where $S_n(x)$ is the bit error probability given D_n and an interference-to-signal ratio x due to mutual interference. For MSK data modulation, $S_n(x)$ is given by Equations (3.74) and (3.75). For a uniform deployment of interferers, we calculate the upper and lower bounds of Equation (3.84) by using the appropriate equations for the upper and lower bounds of P_{b0} and P_{b1} .

Figures 3.33 to 3.36 plot the word error probability as a function of the number of interferers, assuming that $\xi = 1, K = 0, L = 2$, $R_0/D = 0.2$, and $R_1/D = 2$. Figure 3.33 illustrates the improvement due to coding when jamming is absent and the word duration is preserved after coding. The uncoded word length is w = 4, and the signal-to-noise ratio per uncoded bit is $R_s/N_{tu} = 15$ dB. We denote the number of equivalent channels before coding by the symbol $M_{u1} = M_u/d$.

Figure 3.34 illustrates the degradation in the word error probability caused by partial-band jamming for a (7,4) block code and two values of the jamming-to-signal ratio in each jammed channel of the encoded transmission.

Figures 3.35 and 3.36 depict the probability of a data bit error for a repetition code as a function of the signal-to-noise ratio per data bit, R_s/N_{tu}, assuming that the data bit duration is preserved. In Figure 3.35, the number of interferers is N = 10; in Figure 3.36, N = 50.

The preceding analysis assumes no coordination in the frequency-hopping network. If the hoppers synchronize their choices of channels, the mutual interference can be greatly reduced. In general, network coordination becomes more difficult as the hopping rate increases.

Other aspects of the mutual interference problem are analyzed in References [9] and [10], notably, the effects of FSK data modulation. FSK is potentially useful in networks without a spectral splatter problem

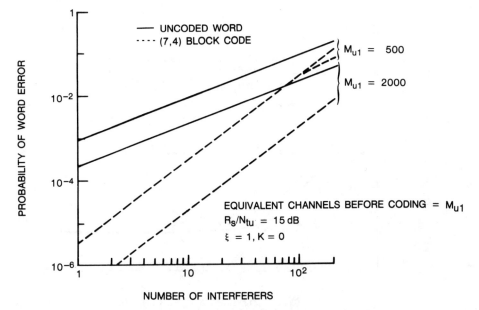

Figure 3.33/Word error probability for four-bit word.

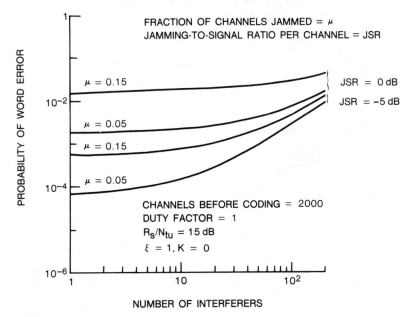

Figure 3.34/Word error probability for (7,4) block code and partial-band jamming.

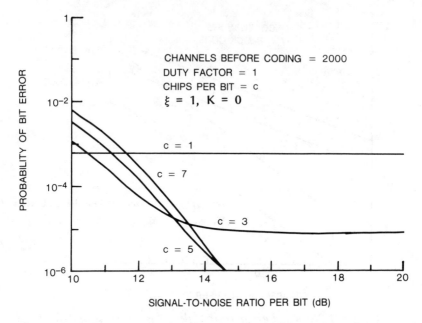

Figure 3.35/Bit error probability for repetition code and 10 interferers.

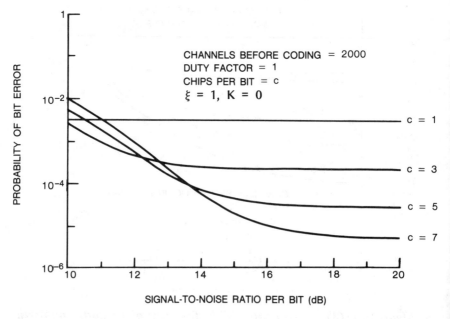

Figure 3.36/Bit error probability for repetition code and 50 interferers.

Although the performance of a frequency-hopping network depends upon a host of factors, a few general conclusions can be drawn. The impact of mutual interference on the network is a sensitive function of the number of interferers and the proximity of close interferers that contribute spectral splatter. If there are no close interferers and $R_0 \geqslant 0.2D$, spectral splatter is not an important effect in practical networks with $K_0 \geqslant 0.9$ and MSK data modulation. To reduce the susceptibility of a frequency-hopping network to wideband jamming, it is desirable to have as large a total bandwidth as possible. To reduce the effects of mutual interference, the total bandwidth may be divided into a large number of available hopping channels. However, if the total bandwidth and message characteristics are fixed, increases in the number of channels eventually lead to sufficient spectral splatter to offset any potential performance improvement.

REFERENCES

[1]   S. Haykin, *Communication Systems*. New York: Wiley, 1978.

[2]   *Spread Spectrum Communications*, NATO Advisory Group for Aerospace Research and Development AGARD-LS-58, National Technical Information Service AD-766 914, 1973.

[3]   N. Rydbeck and C. Sundberg, "Recent Results on Spectrally Efficient Constant Envelope Digital Modulation Methods," *IEEE Int. Conf. Comm. Record* (June 1979), 42.1.

[4]   M.K. Simon, "A Generalization of Minimum-Shift-Keying (MSK) — Type Signaling Based upon Input Data Symbol Pulse Shaping," *IEEE Trans. Comm.* COM-24 (August 1976), 845.

[5]   M. Rabzel and S. Pasupathy, "Spectral Shaping in Minimum Shift Keying (MSK) — Type Signals," *IEEE Trans. Comm.* COM-26 (January 1978), 189.

[6]   F. Amoroso, "The Use of Quasi-Bandlimited Pulses in MSK Transmission," *IEEE Trans. Comm.* COM-27 (October 1979), 912.

[7]   T. Masamura *et al.*, "Differential Detection of MSK with Non-redundant Error Correction," *IEEE Trans. Comm.* COM-27 (June 1979), 912.

[8]   C.H. Chen, "Discriminator Detection of Wide-Band PCM/FM," *IEEE Trans. Aerosp. Electron. Syst.* AES-5 (January 1969), 126.

[9]   D.J. Torrieri, "Simultaneous Mutual Interference and Jamming in a Frequency-Hopping Network," US Army Materiel Development and Readiness Command CM/CCM-80-3, National Technical Information Service AD-A087 598, 1980.

[10]   S.A. Musa and W. Wasylkiwskyj, Co-Channel Interference of Spread Spectrum Systems in a Multiple User Environment, *IEEE Trans. Comm. COM-26* (October 1978), 1405.

4

Interception

4.1 INTRODUCTION

Interception of hostile communications is attempted for many diverse reasons, such as reconnaissance, surveillance, position fixing, identification, or a prelude to jamming. Different purposes require different systems, but whatever the purpose, an interception system nearly always must achieve the three basic functions of *detection, frequency estimation,* and *direction finding.* Although these three elements of interception are usually integrated in a practical system, they are discussed separately in this chapter for clarity of presentation. The basic concepts and issues of the three elements are presented at the systems level, assuming that little is known about the signals to be intercepted. Primarily because of the rapidly changing technological base, the implementation and the engineering details of the interception systems are not addressed. Although this chapter is concerned with the interception of communications, only slight modifications of the results are required to apply them to the interception of radar.

The potential interceptor has at least one major advantage over the communicators. The accuracies of detection, frequency estimation, and direction finding are determined by the energy of the entire message transmitted, which may include many symbols. In contrast, the intended receiver makes decisions with accuracies determined by the energy of each transmitted symbol. From another point of view, the intended receiver generally must make many separate decisions, whereas the interception receiver must make only a few decisions.

4.2 DETECTION

If the form and the parameters of the signal to be intercepted, s(t), were known, optimum *detection* in white Gaussian noise, n(t), could be accomplished by a matched filter or an ideal *correlator*. Figure 4.1 depicts a correlator for the received signal, r(t) = s(t) + n(t), and an observation interval of duration T. The comparator input is compared

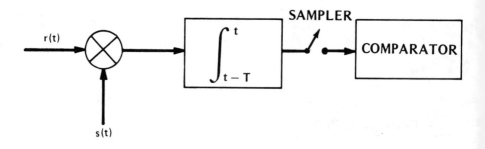

Figure 4.1/Correlator.

with a fixed threshold level, V_T, to determine the presence of an intercepted signal. It is a standard result that the probability of false alarm, P_F, and the probability of detection, P_D, are given by [1]

$$P_F = \frac{1}{2} \, \text{erfc} \left[\frac{V_T}{(N_0 E)^{\frac{1}{2}}} \right] , \tag{4.1}$$

$$P_D = \frac{1}{2} \, \text{erfc} \left[\frac{V_T}{(N_0 E)^{\frac{1}{2}}} - \left(\frac{E}{N_0} \right)^{\frac{1}{2}} \right] , \tag{4.2}$$

where E is the signal energy, $N_0/2$ is the two-sided noise power spectral density, and the complementary error function is defined as

$$\text{erfc}(x) = \frac{2}{\sqrt{\pi}} \int_x^\infty \exp(-y^2) \, dy . \tag{4.3}$$

Denoting the inverse complementary error function by erfc^{-1}, we define

$$\beta = \text{erfc}^{-1}(2P_F) , \tag{4.4}$$

$$\xi = \text{erfc}^{-1}(2P_D) . \tag{4.5}$$

From Equations (4.1) and (4.2), we can calculate the value of E/N_0 necessary to ensure specified values of P_F and P_D. The result is

$$\frac{E}{N_0} = (\beta - \xi)^2 . \tag{4.6}$$

Although the ideal correlator cannot be used when s(t) is unknown, Equation (4.6) provides a basis of comparison for more realistic interception receivers.

To detect the presence of an unknown signal, we assume that the intercepted signal has random phase and frequency and an unknown constant amplitude. The signal frequency is assumed to be one of M possible values; that is, the band to be searched is divided into M channels with center frequencies ω_1, ω_2, etc. To each discrete frequency, ω_i, we assign a hypothesis, H_i. Thus, the multiple alternative hypotheses over an observation interval are

$$H_0 : r(t) = n(t), \ 0 \leqslant t \leqslant T ,$$

$$H_1 : r(t) = A \sin(\omega_1 t + \theta_1) + n(t), \ \ 0 \leqslant t \leqslant T ,$$

.

.

.

$$H_M : r(t) = A \sin(\omega_M t + \theta_M) + n(t), \ \ 0 \leqslant t \leqslant T ,$$

where the θ_i are phase angles. We assume that the phase angles are uniformly distributed and that each frequency is equally likely to occur. Detection theory [1] yields the receiver depicted in Figure 4.2. The decision rule is the following: choose H_i, i = 1, . . ., M, if x_i is the largest detector output and x_i exceeds the threshold, and choose H_0 otherwise. If a signal is detected, this receiver automatically identifies the frequency as the center frequency of the filter with the largest output.

The matched filters of Figure 4.2 are matched to intercepted signals that are pulsed sinusoids. To accommodate more general, unknown signals, the matched filters could be replaced by bandpass filters. However, such a replacement would give a detector that is not necessarily optimum.

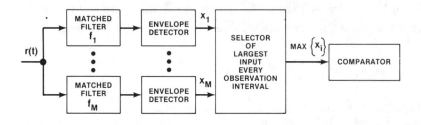

Figure 4.2/Optimum detector for pulsed sinusoid of unknown frequency.

There remain other problems with this receiver. It is doubtful that the envelope detectors can function efficiently against some signal forms. Furthermore, the receiver is designed to operate on a narrowband signal. The detection of spread-spectrum communications usually requires additional hardware.

Radiometer

Another approach is to model the signal as a stationary Gaussian process with a flat power spectral density. Assuming that the noise present is white and Gaussian, detection theory yields the optimum receiver depicted in Figure 4.3, which is called an *energy detector* or a *radiometer* [2]. This receiver has the major advantages that it requires relatively little hardware, and no additional hardware is needed for the detection of spread-spectrum communications.

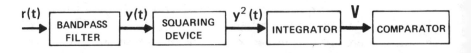

Figure 4.3/Radiometer.

In addition to being optimum if we model the signal as a stationary Gaussian process, the radiometer is a reasonable configuration for determining the presence of unknown deterministic signals. We give a performance analysis of the radiometer, assuming a deterministic signal. The original analysis was done by Urkowitz [3].

The output of the bandpass filter in Figure 4.3 is $y(t) = s(t) + n(t)$, where $s(t)$ is a deterministic signal and $n(t)$ is Gaussian noise. If the bandpass filter has center frequency f_c and bandwidth W, the deterministic signal can be represented as [2]

$$s(t) = s_c(t) \cos \omega_c t - s_s(t) \sin \omega_c t , \qquad (4.7)$$

where $\omega_c = 2\pi f_c$. Since the spectrum of $s(t)$ is confined within the filter passband, $s_c(t)$ and $s_s(t)$ have frequency components confined to the band $|f| \leqslant W/2$. The Gaussian noise emerging from the bandpass filter can be represented in terms of quadrature components as [4]

$$n(t) = n_c(t) \cos \omega_c t - n_s(t) \sin \omega_c t . \qquad (4.8)$$

If $n(t)$ is bandlimited white noise of spectral density $N_0/2$, then $n_c(t)$ and $n_s(t)$ have flat power spectral densities, each equal to N_0 over $|f| \leqslant W/2$.

As shown in Figure 4.3, the input to the comparator is

$$V(t) = \int_{t-T}^{t} y^2(\tau) \, d\tau , \qquad (4.9)$$

where the integration interval is equal to the observation interval. The comparator output may be sampled or continuously fed to a processor.

We determine the probabilities of false alarm and detection associated with $V(t)$ at a fixed time. For convenience, we normalize the test statistic to

$$V = \frac{2}{N_0} \int_{0}^{T} y^2(t) \, dt . \qquad (4.10)$$

Substituting Equations (4.7) and (4.8) and assuming that $f_c T \gg 1$ and $f_c \gg W$, we obtain the approximation

$$V = \frac{1}{N_0} \int_0^T [s_c(t) + n_c(t)]^2 dt$$

$$+ \frac{1}{N_0} \int_0^T [s_s(t) + n_s(t)]^2 dt. \tag{4.11}$$

From the sampling theorems for deterministic and stochastic processes [5], respectively, we obtain expressions that facilitate a statistical performance analysis. After an appropriate choice of time origin, we may write

$$s_c(t) = \sum_{i=-\infty}^{\infty} s_c\left(\frac{i}{W}\right) \text{sinc}(Wt - i), \tag{4.12}$$

$$s_s(t) = \sum_{i=-\infty}^{\infty} s_s\left(\frac{i}{W}\right) \text{sinc}(Wt - i), \tag{4.13}$$

$$n_c(t) = \sum_{i=-\infty}^{\infty} n_c\left(\frac{i}{W}\right) \text{sinc}(Wt - i), \tag{4.14}$$

$$n_s(t) = \sum_{i=-\infty}^{\infty} n_s\left(\frac{i}{W}\right) \text{sinc}(Wt - i), \tag{4.15}$$

where $\text{sinc } x = (\sin \pi x) / \pi x$. We make the following approximations, based upon the known properties of the sinc function:

$$\int_0^T \text{sinc}(Wt - i) \text{ sinc}(Wt - j) dt \cong 0, \quad i \neq j, \tag{4.16}$$

$$\int_0^T \text{sinc}^2(Wt - i) dt \cong \int_{-\infty}^{\infty} \text{sinc}^2(Wt - i) dt = \frac{1}{W},$$

$$0 < i \leqslant TW, \tag{4.17}$$

$$\int_0^T \text{sinc}^2(Wt - i) dt \cong 0, \quad i \leqslant 0 \text{ or } i > TW. \tag{4.18}$$

Assuming that TW $\geqslant$ 1, the error introduced by Equation (4.18) at
i = 0 is nearly 1/2W. For other values of i, except possibly i = TW,
the errors caused by the approximations are much less than 1/2W and
decrease as TW increases. Substituting Equations (4.12) to (4.18)
into Equation (4.11), we obtain

$$V = \frac{1}{N_0 W} \sum_{i=1}^{\gamma} \left[s_c\left(\frac{i}{W}\right) + n_c\left(\frac{i}{W}\right) \right]^2$$

$$+ \frac{1}{N_0 W} \sum_{i=1}^{\gamma} \left[s_s\left(\frac{i}{W}\right) + n_s\left(\frac{i}{W}\right) \right]^2 , \qquad (4.19)$$

where γ is the largest integer less than or equal to TW. In view of the
approximations made, this equation becomes an increasingly accurate
approximation of Equation (4.11) as γ increases. It is always assumed
that $\gamma \geqslant 1$.

We assume that the bandpass filter has a transfer function that is rectangular about f_c. Since n(t) has a power spectral density that is symmetrical about f_c, $n_c(t)$ and $n_s(t)$ are independent Gaussian processes
[4]. Thus, $n_c(i/W)$ and $n_s(j/W)$ are independent Gaussian random variables. The power spectral densities of both $n_c(t)$ and $n_s(t)$ are S(f)
= N_0 for $|f| \leqslant W/2$ and S(f) = 0 otherwise. The associated autocor-
relation function is

$$R(\tau) = N_0 W \text{ sinc } W\tau . \qquad (4.20)$$

This expression indicates that $n_c(i/W)$ is statistically independent of
$n_c(j/W)$, i $\neq$ j, and similarly for $n_s(i/W)$ and $n_s(j/W)$. If n(t) is assumed
to be zero mean, so are $n_c(i/W)$ and $n_s(i/W)$. Using these facts, we re-
write Equation (4.19) as

$$V = \sum_{i=1}^{\gamma} A_i^2 + \sum_{i=1}^{\gamma} B_i^2 , \qquad (4.21)$$

where the A_i's and the B_i's are statistically independent Gaussian random variables with unit variances and means

$$m_{1i} = E[A_i] = \frac{1}{(N_0 W)^{1/2}} s_c \left(\frac{i}{W}\right) , \qquad (4.22)$$

$$m_{2i} = E[B_i] = \frac{1}{(N_0 W)^{1/2}} s_s \left(\frac{i}{W}\right) . \qquad (4.23)$$

The first sum in Equation (4.21) has a noncentral χ^2 distribution (Appendix B) with γ degrees of freedom and a noncentral paraneter $\lambda_1 = \Sigma\, m_{1i}^2$. Similarly, the second sum has a noncentral χ^2 distribution with γ degrees of freedom and a noncentral parameter $\lambda_2 = \Sigma\, m_{2i}^2$. Since the two χ^2 variables are independent, V has a noncentral χ^2 distribution with 2γ degrees of freedom and noncentral parameter $\lambda = \lambda_1 + \lambda_2$. Thus,

$$\lambda = \frac{1}{N_0 W} \sum_{i=1}^{\gamma} s_c^2 \left(\frac{i}{W}\right) + \frac{1}{N_0 W} \sum_{i=1}^{\gamma} s_s^2 \left(\frac{i}{W}\right)$$

$$\cong \frac{1}{N_0} \int_0^T \left[s_c^2(t) + s_s^2(t)\right] dt$$

$$\cong \frac{2}{N_0} \int_0^T s^2(t)\, dt . \qquad (4.24)$$

In terms of the signal energy, E, we have the approximation

$$\lambda = \frac{2E}{N_0} . \qquad (4.25)$$

By straightforward calculations using the statistics of Gaussian variables, the mean and the variance of V are determined to be

$$E[V] = \lambda + 2\gamma , \qquad (4.26)$$

$$VAR(V) = 4\lambda + 4\gamma. \qquad (4.27)$$

By using the known probability density functions for a noncentral χ^2 random variable, the false alarm and detection probabilities can be expressed as integrals. In the absence of a signal, the χ^2 probability density function for V is

$$p_0(v) = \frac{1}{2^\gamma \Gamma(\gamma)} \, v^{\gamma-1} \, e^{-v/2} \, , \qquad\qquad v \geqslant 0 \, ,$$

$$p_0(v) = 0 \, , \qquad\qquad\qquad\qquad v < 0 \, , \qquad (4.28)$$

where $\Gamma(x)$ is the gamma function and $\Gamma(\gamma) = (\gamma - 1)!$. The false alarm probability is

$$P_F = \int_{V_T}^{\infty} p_0(v) \, dv \, . \qquad\qquad\qquad\qquad (4.29)$$

If the signal is present, the χ^2 probability density function for V is

$$p_1(v) = \frac{1}{2} \left(\frac{v}{\lambda} \right)^{(\gamma-1)/2} \exp\left(-\frac{v+\lambda}{2} \right) I_{\gamma-1}(\sqrt{v\lambda})$$

$$v \geqslant 0 \, ,$$

$$p_1(v) = 0 \, , \qquad\qquad\qquad\qquad v < 0 \, , \qquad (4.30)$$

where $I_n(x)$ is the modified Bessel function of the first kind and order n. The probability of detection is

$$P_D = \int_{V_T}^{\infty} p_1(v) \, dv \, . \qquad\qquad\qquad\qquad (4.31)$$

The integrals in Equations (4.29) and (4.31) belong to the class of integrals called *generalized Q-functions*. Many algorithms for evaluating these functions can be found in the literature.

We are particularly interested in the case in which TW is large, since this case includes the interception of spread-spectrum communications. When TW is large, $\gamma \cong$ TW, and the central limit theorem indicates that V is approximated by a Gaussian variable. Using Equations (4.26) and

(4.27) with $\lambda = 0$ and Equation (4.29) with a Gaussian density for $p_0(v)$, we obtain

$$P_F = \frac{1}{(8\pi TW)^{\frac{1}{2}}} \int_{V_T}^{\infty} \exp\left[-\frac{(v - 2TW)^2}{8TW}\right] dv$$

$$= \frac{1}{2} \operatorname{erfc}\left[\frac{V_T - 2TW}{(8TW)^{\frac{1}{2}}}\right]. \tag{4.32}$$

Similarly, we obtain

$$P_D = \frac{1}{2} \operatorname{erfc}\left[\frac{V_T - 2TW - \lambda}{(8TW + 8\lambda)^{\frac{1}{2}}}\right]. \tag{4.33}$$

Combining Equations (4.4), (4.5), (4.32), and (4.33) gives

$$(8TW + 8\lambda)^{\frac{1}{2}}\xi = (8TW)^{\frac{1}{2}}\beta - \lambda. \tag{4.34}$$

We can solve this equation to determine the value of E/N_0 necessary to achieve specified values of P_F and P_D. Solving for λ and using Equation (4.25), we obtain

$$\frac{E}{N_0} = 2\xi^2 + \beta(2TW)^{\frac{1}{2}} - \xi\left[2TW + 4\xi^2 + 2\beta(8TW)^{\frac{1}{2}}\right]^{\frac{1}{2}}. \tag{4.35}$$

We expand this equation as a Taylor series in $\beta/\sqrt{TW}$ and $\xi/\sqrt{TW}$ and retain only the lowest order terms. The result is

$$\frac{E}{N_0} = (2TW)^{\frac{1}{2}}(\beta - \xi), \qquad TW \gg \max(\beta^2, \xi^2). \tag{4.36}$$

Comparing Equations (4.36) and (4.6), we see that the disparity in performance between the radiometer and the matched filter increases with TW. Equation (4.36) indicates that detection difficulties increase as spectrum spreading forces a larger value of W.

Denoting the intercepted signal power by R_s and the signal duration by T_1, the intercepted power necessary to achieve specified values of

P_F and P_D is

$$R_s = N_0 \frac{(2TW)^{\frac{1}{2}}}{T_1} (\beta - \xi) , \quad T_1 < T , \quad TW \gg \max(\beta^2 , \xi^2) ,$$

$$R_s = N_0 \left(\frac{2W}{T}\right)^{\frac{1}{2}} (\beta - \xi) , \quad T_1 \geqslant T , \quad TW \gg \max(\beta^2 , \xi^2) .$$

$$(4.37)$$

As long as $T_1 \geqslant T$, this equation indicates that increasing the observation interval decreases the required power. However, if $T_1 < T$, an increase in the observation interval increases the required power.

If the outputs of ν independent radiometers are averaged, a straightforward calculation shows that the required R_s can be reduced by a factor of $\nu^{-\frac{1}{2}}$.

Channelized Radiometer

A *channelized radiometer* forms when M radiometers are inserted in the branches of Figure 4.2, as depicted in Figure 4.4(a). Each block labeled radiometer contains a bandpass filter of bandwidth W/M, a squaring device, and an integrator, but no comparator. Let T_s denote the duration of the sampling interval, which is the observation interval of the constituent radiometers. To avoid processing extraneous noise, the arrival time of the signal to be intercepted may be estimated by additional hardware. The sampling interval may equal or be somewhat less than the minimum expected signal duration in a channel. To increase effectiveness against frequency hopping or multiple frequency-shift keying (MFSK), the processor examines N consecutive comparator outputs and determines that a signal is present if r of these outputs correspond to comparator inputs that exceed the threshold. For example, if N is odd, a majority decision rule requires r = (N + 1)/2. The effective observation time of the channelized radiometer, given by $T = NT_s$, should usually be less than the minimum expected message duration. If it is known that the intercepted signal is narrowband, we can set N = 1. If the presence of more than one signal is to be verified, it is desirable to employ an array of radiometers of the form of Figure 4.3 with the comparator outputs feeding into a processor that analyzes the activity of individual channels, as shown in Figure 4.4(b).

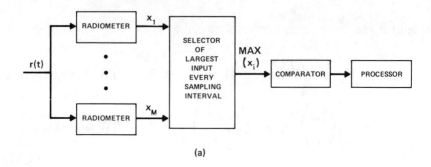

(a)

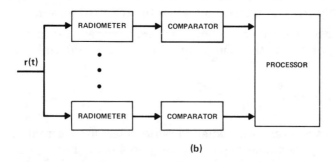

(b)

Figure 4.4/Channelized radiometers (a) for detection of presence of hostile communications and (b) for simultaneous detection of multiple signals.

To simplify the analysis of the interception of a single signal, we assume that the N sets of radiometer outputs are statistically independent. If P_F' is the probability that a particular radiometer output exceeds the threshold when no signal is present, then the probability that none of the radiometer outputs exceeds the threshold is $(1 - P_F')^M$, assuming that the channel noises are statistically independent. The probability that exactly i out of N comparator inputs exceeds the threshold is

$$P(i, N) = \binom{N}{i}\left[1 - (1 - P_F')^M\right]^i (1 - P_F')^{M(N-i)} ,$$

$$i \leqslant N ,$$

$$P(i, N) = 0 \qquad\qquad i > N . \quad (4.38)$$

It follows that the probability of false alarm associated with the observation interval is

$$P_F = \sum_{i=r}^{N} P(i, N) .$$

(4.39)

If the intercepted signal duration, T_1, is less than the observation time, T, we assume for simplicity that $N_1 = T_1/T_s$, the number of sampling intervals during which the signal is present, is an integer. Furthermore, we assume that a single radiometer contains the intercepted signal during each sampling interval. Let $P_D{''}$ denote the probability that the threshold is exceeded at the end of a sampling interval when a signal is present. Let $P_D{'}$ denote the probability that a particular radiometer output exceeds the threshold when a signal is present in that radiometer. From these definitions, it follows that

$$P_D{''} = 1 - (1 - P_D{'})(1 - P_F{'})^{M-1} .$$

(4.40)

The probability of detection associated with the observation interval is determined by reasoning similar to that which led to Equations (4.38) and (4.39). The result is

$$P_D = \sum_{i=r}^{N} \sum_{j=0}^{i} \binom{N_1}{j} (P_D{''})^j (1 - P_D{''})^{N_1 - j} P(i - j, N - N_1) .$$

(4.41)

To compare the channelized radiometer with a single wideband radiometer, we assume that the energy of the intercepted signal is equally divided among N_1 sampling intervals. Since the total receiver bandwidth is W, the bandwidth of each constituent radiometer is $W_s = W/M$. Thus, for large values of $T_s W_s$, $P_F{'}$ and $P_D{'}$ are given by Equations (4.32) and (4.33) with $W_s = W/M$ substituted for W, $T_s = T_1/N_1$ substituted for T, and $\lambda_s = \lambda/N_1$ substituted for λ. We have

$$P_F{'} = \frac{1}{2} \operatorname{erfc} \left[\frac{MN_1 V_T - 2T_1 W}{(8T_1 WMN_1)^{1/2}} \right] ,$$

(4.42)

$$P_D{'} = \frac{1}{2} \operatorname{erfc} \left[\frac{MN_1 V_T - 2T_1 W - \lambda M}{(8T_1 WMN_1 + 8\lambda M^2 N_1)^{1/2}} \right] .$$

(4.43)

We define

$$\beta_1 = \text{erfc}^{-1} (2P_F') , \qquad\qquad (4.44)$$

$$\xi_1 = \text{erfc}^{-1} (2P_D') . \qquad\qquad (4.45)$$

If P_F and P_D are specified, we solve Equations (4.38) to (4.41) for P_F' and P_D'. Using Equations (4.42) to (4.45), we perform a calculation analogous to that used in deriving Equation (4.37). Using $T_1/N_1 = T/N$, we obtain the required R_s for detection with specified values of P_F and P_D,

$$R_s = N_0 \left(\frac{2WN}{MT}\right)^{\frac{1}{2}} (\beta_1 - \xi_1) , \qquad TW \gg MN \; \max(\beta_1^2, \xi_1^2) .$$
$$(4.46)$$

A rough comparison of Equations (4.46) and (4.37) indicates that, if $M > N$, the channelized receiver usually requires approximately the same power as or less power than a wideband radiometer with the same values of T and W.

To process frequency-hopping signals efficiently, the sampling interval duration, $T_s = T/N$, should be proportional to the hopping period. The minimum channel bandwidth, $W_s = W/M$, increases with the hopping rate. Thus, Equation (4.46) indicates that the minimum required power increases with the hopping rate.

Suppose that the energy is concentrated in a narrow band during the observation interval and enters a single radiometer. Then we have $N = 1$ and

$$P_F = 1 - (1 - P_F')^M , \qquad\qquad (4.47)$$

$$P_D = 1 - (1 - P_D')(1 - P_F')^{M-1} \qquad\qquad (4.48)$$

The required value of R_s for detection is determined by the usual method to be

$$R_s = N_0 \left(\frac{2\,TW}{MT_1^2}\right)^{\frac{1}{2}} (\beta_1 - \xi_1) , \quad T_1 < T , \; TW \gg M \max(\beta_1^2, \xi_1^2) ,$$

$$R_s = N_0 \left(\frac{2W}{MT}\right)^{\frac{1}{2}} (\beta_1 - \xi_1) , \quad T_1 \geq T , \; TW \gg M \max(\beta_1^2, \xi_1^2) ,$$
$$(4.49)$$

where

$$\beta_1 = \text{erfc}^{-1} [2 - 2(1 - P_F)^{1/M}] , \qquad (4.50)$$

$$\xi_1 = \text{erfc}^{-1} \left[2 - \frac{2(1 - P_D)}{(1 - P_F)^{1 - 1/M}} \right]. \qquad (4.51)$$

Thus, the required power falls approximately as the inverse of the square root of the number of channels.

To determine P_F' and P_D' when the intercepted signal energy is equally divided among N_1 sampling intervals, but the Gaussian approximation is not valid, we use Equations (4.28) to (4.31) with $\lambda_s = \lambda/N_1$ substituted for λ and η, the largest integer less than or equal to $T_s W_s$, substituted for γ. The results are

$$P_F' = \frac{1}{2^\eta \Gamma(\eta)} \int_{V_T}^{\infty} v^{\eta - 1} \exp\left(- \frac{v}{2}\right) dv , \qquad (4.52)$$

$$P_D' = \frac{1}{2} \int_{V_T}^{\infty} \left(\frac{v}{\lambda_s}\right)^{(\eta - 1)/2} \exp\left(- \frac{v + \lambda_s}{2}\right) I_{\eta - 1}(\sqrt{v \lambda_s}) \, dv . \qquad (4.53)$$

By numerical methods, this pair of equations can be solved simultaneously to eliminate V_T and express $\lambda = N_1 \lambda_s$ as a function of P_F' and P_D'. If we solve Equations (4.38) to (4.41) for P_F' and P_D' in terms of P_F and P_D, then we can obtain an equation for λ in terms of P_F and P_D. From this equation, we finally obtain the required value of R_s necessary to achieve specified values of P_F and P_D.

The required power for radiometers has been expressed in terms of a fixed observation interval of duration T. Successive observation intervals may be related to each other in a variety of ways. If the successive observation intervals do not overlap, except possibly at end points, then the false alarm rate, defined as

$$F = \frac{P_F}{T} , \qquad (4.54)$$

is usually a more appropriate design parameter than P_F.

Another possibility is an observation interval that is constructed by dropping the first sampling interval of the preceding observation interval and adding a new sampling interval. Let P_r denote the probability of the event that an observation interval results in a false alarm, and that the preceding observation interval did not. This event occurs only if the comparator input for the added sampling interval exceeds the threshold, but the comparator input for the discarded sampling interval did not. It follows that

$$P_r = P(0,1)P(r - 1, N - 1)P(1,1). \tag{4.55}$$

The false alarm rate is defined by $F = P_r/T_s$. Thus,

$$F = \frac{N}{T} P(0,1) P(r - 1, N - 1) P(1,1) . \tag{4.56}$$

Examples of the performance of a channelized radiometer of this type have been computed numerically [6].

The channelized radiometer has been shown to be potentially effective against conventional and frequency-hopping communications. It is useful against pseudonoise spread-spectrum communications if preliminary processing is used to produce a signal with a narrow bandwidth (Section 4.3).

Cross Correlator

The ideal correlator of Figure 4.1 can be approximated if the signal is intercepted at two spatially separated antennas. The cross correlation of the two antenna outputs is computed for various relative arrival times, and the peak value of this function is applied to a comparator. Figure 4.5 shows an analytically tractable, but not necessarily practical, realization using the discrete Fourier transform (DFT). One way to implement the DFT is to use a digital filter and the fast Fourier transform algorithm. An alternative implementation is to use the chirp Z-transform algorithm and charge-coupled devices. An analog realization of the cross correlation that is similar to the configuration of Figure 4.5 can be implemented with chirp filters providing Fourier transforms (Section 4.3). Elegant realizations are possible with acousto-optical devices [7].

Figure 4.5(a) depicts the initial processing of each antenna output. After passage through the bandpass filter of bandwidth W, the intercepted waveform, $r(t) = s(t) + n(t)$, can be represented as

$$r(t) = r_c(t) \cos \omega_c t - r_s(t) \sin \omega_c t , \tag{4.57}$$

where the quadrature components, $r_c(t)$ and $r_s(t)$, are confined to the band $|f| \leq W/2$. If the two lowpass filters have bandwidths $W/2$ and $f_c = \omega_c/2\pi > W/2$, then $r_c(t)$ and $r_s(t)$ are extracted by the operations shown in Figure 4.5(a). Analog-to-digital converters produce the discrete sequences $r_c(i/W_1)$ and $r_s(i/W_1)$, where W_1 is the sampling rate.

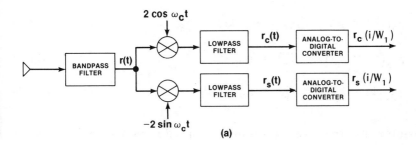

(a)

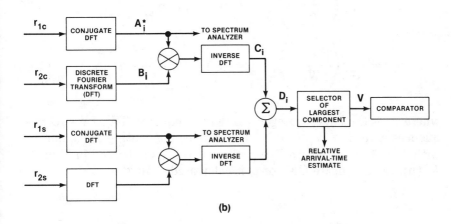

(b)

Figure 4.5/Cross correlator: (a) initial processing of each antenna output and (b) final processing.

We regard one of the antennas as a reference and denote its output by the subscript 1. In terms of the signal and the noise, Equations (4.7) and (4.8) imply that

$$r_1(t) = s(t) + n_1(t) , \qquad (4.58)$$

$$r_{1c}(t) = s_c(t) + n_{1c}(t) , \qquad (4.59)$$

$$r_{1s}(t) = s_s(t) + n_{1s}(t) . \qquad (4.60)$$

Let T_r denote the arrival time of the intercepted signal at the second antenna output relative to the arrival time at the reference antenna output. By inserting a sufficiently long delay, we ensure that $T_r \geqslant 0$. We assume that the separation of the antennas is small enough that $\omega_c T_r \ll 1$. Denoting the output of the second antenna by the subscript 2, we have approximately

$$r_2(t) \; = \; s(t - T_r) + n_2'(t) \; , \qquad\qquad (4.61)$$

$$r_{2c}(t) \; = \; s_c(t - T_r) + n_{2c}'(t) \; , \qquad\qquad (4.62)$$

$$r_{2s}(t) \; = \; s_s(t - T_r) + n_{2s}'(t) \; , \qquad\qquad (4.63)$$

We assume that the observation interval has duration $T \gg T_r$. Let

$$a_i \; = \; r_{1c} \left(\frac{i + 1}{W_1} \right) , \quad i = 0, 1, \ldots, \gamma_1 - 1 \; , \qquad (4.64)$$

$$b_i \; = \; r_{2c} \left(\frac{i + 1}{W_1} \right) , \quad i = 0, 1, \ldots, \gamma_1 - 1 \; , \qquad (4.65)$$

where γ_1 is the largest integer less than or equal to TW_1. We form sequences with $K = \gamma_1 + \nu - 1$ points by augmenting the a_i and b_i with $\nu - 1$ zeros, where $T_r W_1 < \nu \ll \gamma_1$. As indicated in Figure 4.5(b), the conjugate DFT of a_i is calculated, giving

$$A_i^* \; = \; \sum_{n = 0}^{K - 1} a_n \, \Omega_K^{-in} \; , \quad i = 0, 1, \ldots, K - 1 \; , \qquad (4.66)$$

where $\Omega_K = \exp(-j\, 2\pi/K)$ and $j = \sqrt{-1}$. Similarly, the DFT of b_i is

$$B_i \; = \; \sum_{n = 0}^{K - 1} b_n \, \Omega_K^{in} \; , \quad i = 0, 1, \ldots, K - 1 \; . \qquad (4.67)$$

The inverse DFT of the product $A_i^* B_i$ for $0 \leqslant i \leqslant \nu - 1$ is

$$
\begin{aligned}
C_i &= \frac{1}{K} \sum_{n=0}^{K-1} A_n^* B_n \, \Omega_K^{-in} \\
&= \frac{1}{K} \sum_{m=0}^{K-1} \sum_{k=0}^{K-1} a_m b_k \sum_{n=0}^{K-1} \Omega_K^{n(-m+k-i)} \\
&= \sum_{k=0}^{\gamma_1-1} \sum_{m=0}^{\gamma_1-1} a_m b_k \delta_{m,k-i} \\
&= \sum_{k=i}^{\gamma_1-1} a_{k-i} b_k \,,
\end{aligned}
\tag{4.68}
$$

where $\delta_{ik} = 0$, $i \neq k$, and $\delta_{ik} = 1$, $i = k$. From the original definitions, and equations similar to Equations (4.12) to (4.18), we obtain

$$
\begin{aligned}
C_i &= \sum_{k=i}^{\gamma_1-1} r_{1c}\!\left(\frac{k+1-i}{W_1}\right) r_{2c}\!\left(\frac{k+1}{W_1}\right) \\
&\cong W_1 \int_{i/W_1}^{T} r_{1c}\!\left(t - \frac{i}{W_1}\right) r_{2c}(t)\, dt \,.
\end{aligned}
\tag{4.69}
$$

This sequence is the output of one of the inverse DFT operations shown in Figure 4.5(b). An analogous expression can be written for the output of the other inverse DFT operation. The addition of the two sequences produces a sequence

$$
D_i = W_1 \int_{i/W_1}^{T} \left[r_{1c}\!\left(t - \frac{i}{W_1}\right) r_{2c}(t) + r_{1s}\!\left(t - \frac{i}{W_1}\right) r_{2s}(t) \right] dt \,.
\tag{4.70}
$$

If $W \ll f_c \ll W_1/\nu$ and $f_c T \gg 1$, then expansions similar to Equation (4.57) lead to the approximation

$$D_i = 2W_1 \int_{i/W_1}^{T} r_1\left(t - \frac{i}{W_1}\right) r_2(t)\, dt \ , \ i = 0, 1, \ldots, \nu - 1 \ .$$

(4.71)

To interpret the next operation in Figure 4.5(b), we initially assume that no noise is present. In this case, Equations (4.58) and (4.61) yield

$$D_i = 2W_1 \int_{i/W_1}^{T} s\left(t - \frac{i}{W_1}\right) s(t - T_r)\, dt \ , \ i = 0, 1, \ldots, \nu - 1 \ .$$

(4.72)

Thus, the D_i provide sample values proportional to an approximation of the autocorrelation of $s(t)$. Let i_0 denote the index that corresponds to the largest D_i. Assuming that the approximation is adequate and that the autocorrelation has a sharp peak, i_0 is the index closest to the value $T_r W_1$. When noise is present, this statement may not be true; however, to proceed with the analysis, we assume that it is. Note that T_r can be estimated as i_0/W_1. This estimate can be used for direction finding (Section 4.4).

Assuming that the largest D_i has index $i_0 = T_r W_1 \leqslant \nu - 1$ and normalizing, the input to the comparator in Figure 4.5(b) is the test statistic

$$V = \frac{2}{N_0} \int_{T_r}^{T} r_1(t - T_r)\, r_2(t)\, dt$$

$$= \frac{2}{N_0} \int_{0}^{T - T_r} r_1(t)\, r_2(t + T_r)\, dt \ .$$

(4.73)

Substituting Equations (4.58) and (4.61) and defining $n_2(t) = n_2'(t + T_r)$ and $T_a = T - T_r$, we get

$$V = \frac{2}{N_0} \int_0^{T_a} [s(t) + n_1(t)][s(t) + n_2(t)] \, dt \; . \qquad (4.74)$$

In the usual manner, we obtain the series expansion

$$V = \frac{1}{N_0 W} \sum_{i=1}^{\gamma_a} \left[s_c\left(\frac{i}{W}\right) + n_{1c}\left(\frac{i}{W}\right) \right]\left[s_c\left(\frac{i}{W}\right) + n_{2c}\left(\frac{i}{W}\right) \right]$$

$$+ \frac{1}{N_0 W} \sum_{i=1}^{\gamma_a} \left[s_s\left(\frac{i}{W}\right) + n_{1s}\left(\frac{i}{W}\right) \right]\left[s_s\left(\frac{i}{W}\right) + n_{2s}\left(\frac{i}{W}\right) \right] ,$$

$$(4.75)$$

where γ_a is the largest integer less than or equal to $T_a W$. Assuming that $n_1(t)$ and $n_2(t)$ are statistically independent, zero-mean, Gaussian processes, a straightforward calculation yields

$$E[V] = \lambda_a , \qquad (4.76)$$

$$VAR(V) = 2\lambda_a + 2\gamma_a , \qquad (4.77)$$

where $\lambda_a = 2E_a/N_0$ and E_a is the energy in interval T_a.
For large values of $T_a W$, the test statistic is approximately normally distributed. It follows that

$$P_D = \frac{1}{2} \text{erfc}\left[\frac{V_T - \lambda_a}{(4T_a W + 4\lambda_a)^{\frac{1}{2}}} \right] . \qquad (4.78)$$

The maximum possible value of T_r may be such that only a few sample values of D_i need to be computed to obtain an appropriate test statistic. When no signal is present, a false alarm occurs if any of the ν estimated autocorrelation values exceeds the threshold. If ν is sufficiently small, it is reasonable to assume that each estimated value has approximately the same probability, denoted by $P_F{}'$, of exceeding the threshold. This assumption implies the approximation

$$P_F = 1 - (1 - P_F{}')^\nu , \qquad (4.79)$$

where $P_F{}'$ is the probability that

$$V = \int_0^{T_a} n_1(t)\, n_2(t)\; dt \tag{4.80}$$

exceeds the threshold. The mean and the variance of Equation (4.80). are given by Equations (4.76) and (4.77) with $\lambda_a = 0$. For large values of $T_a W$, we obtain

$$P_F' = \frac{1}{2}\, \mathrm{erfc}\left[\frac{V_T}{(4T_a W)^{\frac{1}{2}}}\right]. \tag{4.81}$$

Equations (4.44) and (4.79) yield

$$\beta_1 = \mathrm{erfc}^{-1}\,[2 - 2(1 - P_F)^{1/\nu}]. \tag{4.82}$$

We obtain in the usual manner the required R_s to detect a signal with specified values of P_F and P_D. The result is

$$R_s = N_0\, \frac{(T_a W)^{\frac{1}{2}}}{T_1}\, (\beta_1 - \xi)\,,\quad T_1 < T_a,\ T_a W \gg \max(\beta_1^2, \xi^2)$$

$$R_s = N_0 \left(\frac{W}{T_a}\right)^{\frac{1}{2}} (\beta_1 - \xi)\,,\quad T_1 \geq T_a\,,\ T_a W \gg \max(\beta_1^2, \xi^2)\,, \tag{4.83}$$

where T_1 is the signal duration, and ξ is given by Equation (4.5).

Comparison with Equation (4.37) indicates that the cross correlator can give a theoretical improvement of approximately 1.5 dB over a single wideband radiometer. Taking into account the approximations made to derive Equation (4.83), it is possible that in practice the cross correlator provides no improvement at all. A comparison of Figures 4.3 and 4.5 indicates that the implementation of the cross correlator entails considerably more hardware than the implementation of a wideband radiometer. However, as discussed in subsequent sections, the cross correlator requires little additional hardware to provide frequency estimation and direction finding. Furthermore, interference or jamming can often be reduced by inserting filters between the DFT blocks and the multipliers in Figure 4.5.

The *channelized cross correlator* is an array of M cross correlators, each of which has a bandwidth of W/M. The outputs of the array are applied to a processor. Analogously to the channelized radiometer, the channelized cross correlator may be preferable to a single wideband cross correlator when the hostile communications are narrowband or when two or more simultaneous signals are to be intercepted.

Equations (4.37) and (4.83) indicate that increasing the bandwidth of a frequency-hopping system degrades the performance against a single signal of both the wideband cross correlator and the wideband radiometer. However, neither of these receivers is sensitive to the hopping rate. Increasing the hopping rate makes the practical design of a channelized receiver more difficult and degrades its performance. If the rate is sufficiently high, the channelized receiver may have to be abandoned in favor of a wideband receiver.

4.3 FREQUENCY ESTIMATION

The immediate purpose of a *frequency-estimation system* is to determine the center frequency and possibly the spectral shape of an intercepted signal. If a frequency-hopping signal is intercepted, the purpose is to determine each hopping frequency or at least the frequency range over which the hopping occurs.

Although not desirable for some purposes, such as message analysis, preliminary processing of pseudonoise spread-spectrum communications is desirable before estimation of the center frequency is attempted. An intercepted binary pseudonoise signal has the form

$$s(t) = Am(t)p(t) \cos \omega_0 t , \qquad (4.84)$$

where A is the amplitude, ω_0 is the center frequency, $m(t)$ is the binary message sequence, and $p(t)$ is a binary pseudorandom sequence. Both $m(t)$ and $p(t)$ take the values $+1$ or -1. Suppose $s(t)$ enters a wideband receiver and is squared. Since $m^2 = p^2 = 1$, the output of the squaring device is proportional to

$$s^2(t) = A^2 \cos^2 \omega_0 t = \frac{A^2}{2} + \frac{A^2}{2} \cos 2\omega_0 t . \qquad (4.85)$$

The double-frequency term is now a pure pulsed sinusoid. Its frequency and, thus, the center frequency of $s(t)$ can be estimated by the systems described in this section. The same preliminary processing is useful against phase-shift keying communications.

Channelized Receiver

Estimation theory leads to the receiver of Figure 4.2 for frequency estimation, assuming that the arrival time and the signal waveform, except for a uniformly distributed phase angle, are known [1]. After the largest output is selected, the unknown frequency is estimated as the center frequency of the filter producing the largest output. The channelized radiometers of Figure 4.4 are practical approximations to the ideal frequency estimator.

Suppose we desire a *frequency resolution* of Δ, where Δ is not less than the Cramer-Rao bound [1]. If the entire range of reconnoitered frequencies is W, then each filter must have bandwidth 2Δ, and M = $W/2\Delta$ is the number of required filters to attain the desired accuracy. If the intercepted signal has duration T, then each filter must have bandwidth $2/T$ for most of the signal energy to pass through it. Thus, we have $\Delta \cong 1/T$.

If M $\geqslant$ 6, the number of required filters can be reduced by arranging the filters in successive stages, as shown in Figure 4.6 for the case in which each stage has the same number of filters. After an intercepted signal passes through the first filter bank, its frequency is theoretically known within an accuracy of Δ_1 = $W/2m$, where m is the number of filters in each stage and $2\Delta_1$ is the bandwidth of the first stage filters. A bank of mixers ensures that the filter outputs are shifted in frequency so that the input to the second stage has a frequency between f_{11} — f_{c1} — Δ_1 and f_{11} — f_{c1} + Δ_1, where f_{11} is the center frequency of the top filter in the first bank and f_{c1} is the frequency of a local oscillator. After the input passes through the second filter bank, the frequency is known within an accuracy of Δ_2 = Δ_1/m. If n stages of m filters each are used, then an accuracy of Δ is attained if

$$m^n = \frac{W}{2\Delta} . \tag{4.86}$$

The total number of filters required is mn. Disadvantages of the channelized receiver of Figure 4.6, relative to that of Figure 4.4, are the increased processing time required for frequency estimation, the reduced amount of noise and interference filtering, and the ambiguities that arise when more than one signal is intercepted.

It is not necessary that each stage have the same number of filters. However, if n, W, and Δ are fixed, it can easily be shown, by using Lagrange multipliers, that the total number of filters is minimized if each stage has approximately the same number of filters (exactly the

same number if an integer m exists that satisfies Equation (4.86)).
If each stage has the same number of filters and W and $\triangle$ are fixed, it
can be shown that the total number of filters is minimized if each
stage has three filters. (Lagrange multipliers yield m = e, but m must
be an integer.)

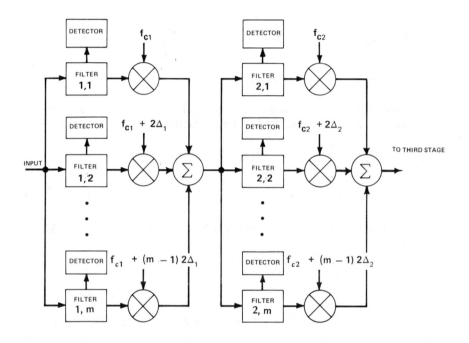

*Figure 4.6/Channelized receiver with filters arranged in successive
stages.*

Even when minimized, the number of filters and detectors required in
a channelized receiver may make this method of frequency estimation
expensive. The detectors of a stage can be eliminated by replacing the
summer with a commutator and detector, but then a signal may be
missed. Alternatively, a limited number of filters can be used to reduce the total bandwidth examined by other frequency estimation
devices.

Spectrum Analysis with the Discrete Fourier Transform

The outputs of the two conjugate DFT blocks in Figure 4.5(b) can be
used to estimate the intercepted spectrum over the receiver bandwidth.

To see how the spectrum is estimated, we first define the truncated waveforms:

$$s'(t) \ = \ s(t)q(t) \ ,$$
$$s_c'(t) \ = \ s_c(t)q(t) \ ,$$
$$s_s'(t) \ = \ s_s(t)q(t) \ , \tag{4.87}$$

where

$$q(t) \ = \ 1, \ 0 < t \leqslant T \ ,$$
$$q(t) \ = \ 0, \ \text{otherwise} \ . \tag{4.88}$$

We denote the Fourier transforms of $s'(t)$, $s_c'(t)$, and $s_s'(t)$ by $S(\omega)$, $S_c(\omega)$, and $S_s(\omega)$, respectively. From Equation (4.7),

$$S(\omega) \ = \ \frac{1}{2} \, S_c(\omega - \omega_c) + \frac{1}{2} \, S_c(\omega + \omega_c)$$

$$- \frac{1}{2j} \, S_s(\omega - \omega_c) + \frac{1}{2j} \, S_s(\omega + \omega_c) \ . \tag{4.89}$$

We are interested in determining $S(\omega)$ for $\omega \geqslant 0$. If $\omega_c \geqslant \pi W$, then

$$S(\omega) \ = \ \frac{1}{2} \, S_c(\omega - \omega_c) - \frac{1}{2j} \, S_s(\omega - \omega_c) \ ,$$

$$\omega \geqslant 0 \ , \ \omega_c \geqslant \pi W \ . \tag{4.90}$$

Thus, we can estimate $S(\omega)$ if we first estimate $S_c(\omega)$ and $S_s(\omega)$.

We give the details of the estimation of $S_c(\omega)$; the estimation of $S_s(\omega)$ is similar. For spectrum analysis, it is not necessary for the sampling rate to exceed the bandwidth. Thus, we set $W_1 = W$. The sample values of $S_c(\omega)$ are related to those of $s_c(t)$ through the fundamental relation (Appendix C)

$$\bar{S}_c\left(\frac{i2\pi W}{K}\right) \ = \ \frac{1}{W} \sum_{n=0}^{K-1} \bar{s}_c\left(\frac{n}{W}\right) \Omega_K^{in}$$

$$= \ \frac{1}{W} \sum_{n=1}^{K} \bar{s}_c\left(\frac{n}{W}\right) \Omega_K^{in} \ , \quad i = 0, 1, \dots, K - 1$$

$$\tag{4.91}$$

where

$$\bar{s}_c\left(\frac{n}{W}\right) = \sum_{m=-\infty}^{\infty} s_c'\left(\frac{n}{W} + m\frac{K}{W}\right) , \qquad (4.92)$$

$$\bar{S}_c\left(\frac{i2\pi W}{K}\right) = \sum_{m=-\infty}^{\infty} S_c\left(\frac{i2\pi W}{K} + m2\pi W\right) . \qquad (4.93)$$

Since $s_c'(t) = 0$ unless $0 < t \leqslant T$, and $K \geqslant TW$, Equation (4.92) implies that

$$\bar{s}_c\left(\frac{n}{W}\right) = s_c'\left(\frac{n}{W}\right) , \qquad 1 \leqslant n \leqslant K . \qquad (4.94)$$

We assume that $S(\omega) \cong 0$, unless $|\omega - \omega_c| < \pi W$ or $|\omega + \omega_c| < \pi W$. Consequently, $S_c(\omega) \cong 0$ for $|\omega| \geqslant \pi W$, and Equation (4.93) yields the approximate result

$$\bar{S}_c\left(\frac{i2\pi W}{K}\right) = S_c\left(\frac{i2\pi W}{K}\right) , \qquad 0 \leqslant i \leqslant K/2 ,$$

$$\bar{S}_c\left(\frac{i2\pi W}{K}\right) = S_c\left(\frac{i2\pi W}{K} - 2\pi W\right), \quad K/2 \leqslant i \leqslant K . \quad (4.95)$$

Equations (4.91), (4.94), and (4.95) imply that

$$S_c\left(\frac{i2\pi W}{K}\right) = \frac{1}{W} \sum_{n=1}^{K} s_c'\left(\frac{n}{W}\right) \Omega_K^{in} , \quad |i| \leqslant K/2 . \quad (4.96)$$

We conclude that, in the presence of noise, a reasonable estimate of the sample values of $S_c(\omega)$ is given by the right side of Equation (4.96) with s_c' replaced by r_{1c}. Using Equations (4.64) and (4.66), we obtain

$$\hat{S}_c\left(\frac{i2\pi W}{K}\right) = \frac{1}{W} A_i \Omega_K^i , \qquad 0 \leqslant i \leqslant K/2 ,$$

$$\hat{S}_c\left(\frac{i2\pi W}{K}\right) = \frac{1}{W} A_{i+K} \Omega_K^i , \quad -K/2 \leqslant i < 0 . \qquad (4.97)$$

Thus, simple operations on the DFT give the estimate. If no noise is present, then $\hat{S}_c(\omega) = S_c(\omega)$ at the sample values.

If the frequencies of frequency-hopping or MFSK communications are to be successfully estimated, the observation time, T, must be less than the period between frequency changes.

It has been shown that, by sampling the input every 1/W seconds and using a DFT of size $K \geq TW$, accurate sampled values of the Fourier transform can be obtained. However, as W increases, the attainable speed of the logic circuitry becomes a limiting factor. Faster rates are possible if many parallel devices are used, but then the power dissipation and system size become problems. Thus, for a large bandwidth, analog processing may be necessary.

If the bandwidth is not too large, digital processing with the DFT has major advantages. For example, an almost arbitrary linear dynamic range is obtainable by increasing the number of bits per sample and the system complexity.

Acousto-optical Spectrum Analyzer

Spectrum analysis using acousto-optical diffraction has the potential capability for real-time, wideband frequency estimation of many simultaneous signals. The principal components of an *acousto-optical spectrum analyzer* are shown in Figure 4.7. The diffraction geometry associated with the *Bragg cell* is illustrated in Figure 4.8. The Bragg cell converts an electronic input at frequency f_0 into a traveling acoustic wave with velocity v and wavelength $\Lambda_a = v/f_0$. The laser light has wavelength Λ_0 in free space. Under certain conditions, the acoustic wave interacts with the light beam to produce a principal diffracted beam that is offset from the incident beam by an angle

$$\theta = 2 \sin^{-1}\left(\frac{\Lambda_0 f_0}{2v}\right) \tag{4.98}$$

outside the cell [8]. This equation is valid provided that the acoustic wave has a single wavelength across the cell. For small values of the argument, Equation (4.98) becomes

$$\theta \cong \frac{\Lambda_0 f_0}{v} \quad , \quad \Lambda_0 f_0 \ll 2v \ . \tag{4.99}$$

The lens produces a Fourier transform on its focal plane at the photodetector array. The center of the diffracted beam converges to a position a distance

$$F\theta = \frac{F\Lambda_0 f_0}{v} \qquad (4.100)$$

from the center of the corresponding undiffracted beam, where F is the focal length of the lens. Thus, the frequency f_0 can be estimated by measuring the relative intensities at the photodetector array elements.

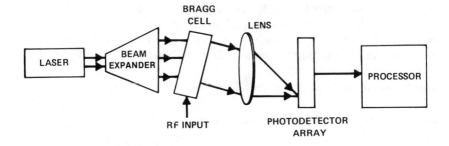

Figure 4.7/Acousto-optical spectrum analyzer.

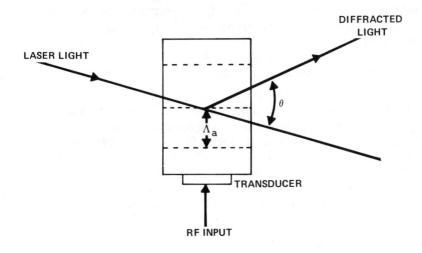

Figure 4.8/Acousto-optical diffraction geometry for input at single frequency.

The diffracted beam has an angular width on the order of Λ_0/D, where D is the effective aperture of the Bragg cell. Consequently, the diffracted beam spreads over a length $F\Lambda_0/D$ in the focal plane. The frequency resolution is defined to be the difference in frequency between two intercepted signals such that the corresponding positions in the focal plane differ by the spread of the diffracted beam in the focal plane. From this definition and Equation (4.100), the resolution is

$$\Delta \cong \frac{v}{D} = \frac{1}{T_c} \; , \tag{4.101}$$

where T_c is the time that it takes an acoustic wave to cross the cell aperture. This equation applies when an acoustic wave of fixed wavelength occupies the aperture. A necessary condition for its validity most of the time is that T_c be less than the period between frequency changes of a frequency-hopping signal or an MFSK signal. Thus, the resolution is no better than the hopping rate.

Instantaneous Frequency Measurement

The *instantaneous frequency measurement* (IFM) receiver, illustrated in Figure 4.9, is often used to estimate radar frequencies. It is useful also as a supplementary frequency estimator for communications. Its operation is based on the relationship among carrier frequency, path length, and phase shift of a signal. Suppose that, after passage through the bandpass filter of bandwidth W, an intercepted signal has the form

$$s(t) = A(t) \cos [\omega_0 t + \phi(t)] \; , \tag{4.102}$$

where $A(t)$ is the amplitude modulation and $\phi(t)$ is the angle modulation. As shown in Figure 4.9, this signal is delayed by time δ in one branch relative to the other branch. If δ is sufficiently small, then $A(t - \delta) \cong A(t)$ and $\phi(t - \delta) \cong \phi(t)$ for most of the time. It follows that

$$s_1(t) \cong A(t) \cos [\omega_0 t + \phi(t) - \omega_0 \delta] \; , \tag{4.103}$$

$$A(t - \delta) \cong A(t), \quad \phi(t - \delta) \cong \phi(t) \; .$$

By trigonometric identities, the outputs of the sum and difference operations in the figure are found to be

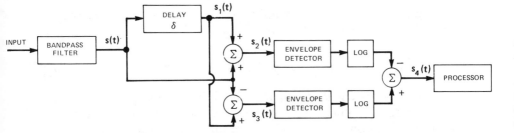

Figure 4.9/Instantaneous frequency measurement receiver.

$$s_2(t) = 2A(t) \cos\left(\frac{\omega_0 \delta}{2}\right) \cos\left[\omega_0 t + \phi(t) - \frac{\omega_0 \delta}{2}\right] , \quad (4.104)$$

$$s_3(t) = 2A(t) \sin\left(\frac{\omega_0 \delta}{2}\right) \sin\left[\omega_0 t + \phi(t) - \frac{\omega_0 \delta}{2}\right] , \quad (4.105)$$

for most of the time. The envelope detectors produce the magnitudes of the first factors in these equations. The detector outputs pass through logarithmic amplifiers, and the difference is taken. The processor input is

$$s_4(t) = \log \left| \tan\left(\frac{\omega_0 \delta}{2}\right) \right| . \quad (4.106)$$

Since the modulation effects have been removed and δ is known, the processor can calculate an estimate of $f_0 = \omega_0/2\pi$. The function on the right-hand side of Equation (4.106) has an unambiguous inverse only over a range of $\pi/2$ radians. Thus, for unambiguous operation over the frequency range of W hertz, we must have $\delta \leqslant 1/2W$. A major problem with the IFM receiver is that the estimation accuracy is inversely proportional to δ. Since δ must be sufficiently small that Equation (4.103) is valid for most of the time, the accuracy may be inadequate. Another problem is that the IFM receiver cannot handle two or more simultaneously intercepted signals of comparable magnitudes. Against a single narrowband signal, unambiguous and accurate frequency estimation can sometimes be achieved by using several different values of δ [9].

Scanning Superheterodyne Receiver

Figure 4.10 shows a block diagram of a realization of a *scanning superheterodyne receiver* for frequency estimation. To explain the operation, we consider the system response to one scan of the generator and an input that has constant amplitude and frequency over the scan period, T. The input is represented by

$$s(t) = A \cos(\omega_0 t + \theta_0) , \quad 0 \leqslant t \leqslant T , \qquad (4.107)$$

where ω_0 is the carrier frequency and θ_0 is the phase angle at $t = 0$, which defines the beginning of the scan. The scanning waveform is a periodic function. Over one scan period, it is represented by

$$y(t) = \cos(\omega_s t + \pi\mu t^2 + \theta_s) , \quad 0 \leqslant t \leqslant T , \qquad (4.108)$$

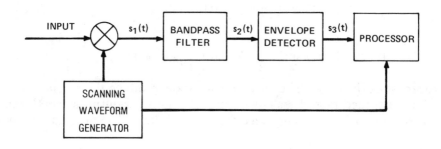

Figure 4.10/Scanning superheterodyne receiver.

where ω_s is the frequency at $t = 0$, μ is the scan rate, and θ_s is the phase angle at $t = 0$. The output of the mixer, $s_1(t) = s(t)y(t)$, passes through a bandpass filter with impulse response $h(t)$ and bandwidth 2B. Ignoring a high-frequency term that is suppressed by the bandpass filter, we have

$$s_1(t) = \frac{1}{2} A \cos(\omega_1 t + \pi\mu t^2 + \theta) , \quad 0 \leqslant t \leqslant T , \quad (4.109)$$

where $\omega_1 = \omega_s - \omega_0$ and $\theta = \theta_s - \theta_0$. The symmetrical bandpass filter has transfer function $H(\omega)$ that can be written as

$$H(\omega) = H_1(\omega - \omega_c) + H_1(\omega + \omega_c) , \qquad (4.110)$$

where $H_1(\omega)$ is the transfer function of a lowpass filter and ω_c is the center frequency of the bandpass filter. The first term on the right-hand side has significant values only for positive frequencies, and the second term has significant values only for negative frequencies. If $h_1(t)$ is the impulse response of the lowpass filter, then

$$h(t) = 2h_1(t) \cos \omega_c t . \tag{4.111}$$

The output of the bandpass filter is

$$s_2(t) = \int_{-\infty}^{\infty} s_1(\tau) h(t - \tau) d\tau . \tag{4.112}$$

By using Equations (4.109) and (4.111) and the pertinent trigonometric relations, Equation (4.112) becomes

$$s_2(t) = \frac{A}{2} \int_0^T h_1(t - \tau) \cos [(\omega_1 - \omega_c)\tau + \pi\mu\tau^2 + \theta + \omega_c t] d\tau$$

$$+ \frac{A}{2} \int_0^T h_1(t - \tau) \cos [(\omega_1 + \omega_c)\tau + \pi\mu\tau^2 + \theta - \omega_c t] d\tau$$

$$\tag{4.113}$$

It is assumed that $H_1(\omega)$ has a sufficiently narrow bandwidth relative to $\omega_1 + \omega_c$ that the second integral on the right-hand side of this equation is negligible. The time-frequency diagram of Figure 4.11, in which $f = \omega/2\pi$, illustrates the effect of the filter. The filter output, $s_2(t)$, is significant only over a portion of the scan period. Thus, we can extend the limits of the first integral to $\pm \infty$ with negligible error if $f_1 + \mu T > f_c + B/2$ and $f_1 < f_c - B/2$. Under these assumptions,

$$s_2(t) = \frac{A}{2} \int_{-\infty}^{\infty} h_1(t - \tau) \cos (\omega_2\tau + \pi\mu\tau^2 + \theta_1) d\tau , \tag{4.114}$$

where $\omega_2 = \omega_s - \omega_0 - \omega_c$ and $\theta_1 = \theta + \omega_c t$. To further simplify Equation (4.114), we assume a Gaussian bandpass filter; that is,

$$H_1(\omega) = \exp\left(-\frac{\omega^2}{4a^2} - j\omega\delta\right), \tag{4.115}$$

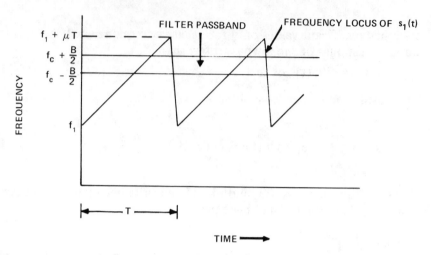

Figure 4.11/Time-frequency diagram for scanning superheterodyne receiver.

where parameter a is proportional to the bandwidth and δ is the filter delay. If δ is sufficiently large, Equation (4.115) approximates a realizable filter. The corresponding impulse response is

$$h_1(t) = \frac{1}{2\pi} \int_{-\infty}^{\infty} H_1(\omega)\, e^{i\omega t}\, d\omega = \frac{a}{\sqrt{\pi}}\, \exp\left[-a^2(t-\delta)^2\right].$$

(4.116)

Substituting Equation (4.116) into Equation (4.114), expressing the cosine in terms of complex exponentials, and simplifying the result, we obtain

$$s_2(t) = \mathrm{Re}\left\{ \frac{Aa}{2\sqrt{\pi}}\, \exp\left[-a^2(t-\delta)^2 + j\theta_1 + sc^2\right] \right.$$

$$\left. \times \int_{-\infty}^{\infty} \exp\left[-s(\tau+c)^2\right] d\tau \right\},$$

(4.117)

where Re(x) denotes the real part of x and

$$s = a^2 - j\pi\mu,$$

$$c = \frac{-2a^2(t-\delta) - j\omega_2}{2s}.$$

(4.118)

The integral in Equation (4.117) has been evaluated as [5]

$$\int_{-\infty}^{\infty} \exp\left[-s(\tau + c)^2\right] d\tau = \left(\frac{\pi}{s}\right)^{1/2} , \quad \mathrm{Re}(s) > 0,$$

$$\mathrm{Re}(\sqrt{s}) > 0 . \quad (4.119)$$

Thus, we have

$$s_2(t) = \mathrm{Re}\left\{ \exp\left[-a^2(t - \delta)^2 + j\theta_1 + sc^2\right] \frac{Aa}{2\sqrt{s}} \right\}$$

$$= s_3(t) \cos\left[\phi(t)\right] , \quad (4.120)$$

where

$$\phi(t) = \frac{4\pi a^4 \mu(t - \delta)^2 + 4a^4 \omega_2(t - \delta) - \pi\mu \omega_2{}^2}{4(a^4 + \pi^2\mu^2)}$$

$$+ \theta_1 + \frac{1}{2} \tan^{-1}\left(\frac{\pi\mu}{a^2}\right) ,$$

$$s_3(t) = \frac{A}{2}\left(1 + \frac{\pi^2\mu^2}{a^4}\right)^{-1/4} \exp\left[-\frac{a^2(2\pi\mu t - 2\pi\mu\delta + \omega_2)^2}{4(a^4 + \pi^2\mu^2)}\right].$$

$$(4.121)$$

As indicated in Figure 4.10, $s_2(t)$ is applied to an envelope detector that extracts the envelope, $s_3(t)$, from the input. The peak value of $s_3(t)$ is attained when $t = \delta - (\omega_2/2\pi\mu) = \delta + (f_0 - f_s + f_c)/\mu$. Thus, the input frequency f_0 can easily be estimated from the time location of the peak value. The normalized peak value, α, which is defined as the peak value relative to $A/2$, the peak value for small μ, is

$$\alpha = \left(1 + \frac{\pi^2\mu^2}{a^4}\right)^{-1/4} . \quad (4.122)$$

The half-power points of $s_3(t)$ are determined by setting the exponential factor in Equation (4.121) equal to $1/\sqrt{2}$. The pulse duration of $s_3(t)$ between half-power points is found to be

$$T_p = \frac{a(2 \ln 2)^{1/2}}{\pi\mu}\left(1 + \frac{\pi^2\mu^2}{a^4}\right)^{1/2} . \quad (4.123)$$

The frequency resolution in hertz, Δ, is approximately equal to μT_p, the frequency range scanned during pulse duration T_p. Thus, the resolution is

$$\Delta = \frac{a(2 \ln 2)^{\frac{1}{2}}}{\pi} \left(1 + \frac{\pi^2 \mu^2}{a^4}\right)^{\frac{1}{2}}. \qquad (4.124)$$

From Equation (4.115), the 3-dB power spectrum bandwidth in hertz is related to parameter a by

$$B = \frac{(2 \ln 2)^{\frac{1}{2}}}{\pi} \, a \,. \qquad (4.125)$$

In terms of B, we can write

$$\alpha = \left(1 + 0.195 \frac{\mu^2}{B^4}\right)^{-\frac{1}{4}}, \qquad (4.126)$$

$$\Delta = B\left(1 + 0.195 \frac{\mu^2}{B^4}\right)^{\frac{1}{2}}. \qquad (4.127)$$

These equations have long been used to explain the operational characteristics of spectrum analyzers.

If the scan rate, μ, is high,

$$\alpha \cong 1.5 \frac{B}{\sqrt{\mu}}, \qquad \Delta \cong 0.44 \frac{\mu}{B}, \qquad \mu \gg B^2, \qquad (4.128)$$

which clearly show the effects of increasing μ.

Using elementary calculus, we determine the optimal filter bandwidth, B_0, to minimize Δ. Substituting this value of B_0 into Equation (4.127), we obtain Δ_0, the minimum resolution as a function of μ. The results are

$$B_0 = 0.66\sqrt{\mu},$$

$$\Delta_0 = \sqrt{2}\, B_0 = 0.94\sqrt{\mu}. \qquad (4.129)$$

The corresponding normalized peak value is

$$\alpha_0 = 0.84, \qquad (4.130)$$

which is no longer a function of μ. If the optimal bandwidth is used, these equations indicate that the achievable resolution becomes worse as μ increases, but the peak value does not change.

Microscan Receiver

Improved resolution at a high scan rate is provided by the *microscan receiver*. The version of this receiver shown in Figure 4.12(a) is similar to the scanning superheterodyne receiver, except that a *chirp filter* is used instead of a bandpass filter. The chirp filter can be realized by a surface acoustic wave device.

For carrier frequency estimation, the chirp filter has an impulse response,

$$h(t) = \cos(\omega_c t - \pi\mu t^2) , \quad 0 \leqslant t \leqslant T , \qquad (4.131)$$

where the amplitude has been normalized to unity and the duration is equal to the scan period. Substituting Equation (4.131) and (4.109) into Equation (4.112) yields the chirp filter response to the receiver input over one scan period. Using $2 \cos u \cos v = \cos(u - v) + \cos(u + v)$, we may write the result as the sum of the two integrals.

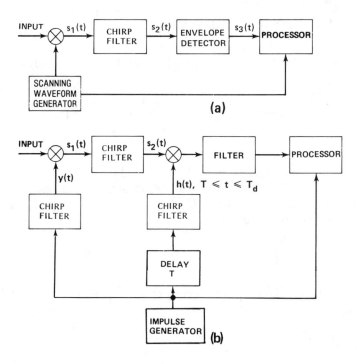

Figure 4.12/Microscan receivers for estimating (a) carrier frequency or magnitude of Fourier transform and (b) real part of Fourier transform.

We assume that $|\omega_s - \omega_0 - \omega_c + 4\pi\mu T| \ll |\omega_s - \omega_0 + \omega_c - 4\pi\mu T|$ so that we may neglect one of the integrals. We are left with the approximation

$$s_2(t) = \frac{A}{4} \int_{T_1}^{T_2} \cos(\omega_3\tau + \theta_2) \, d\tau , \quad 0 \leqslant t \leqslant 2T ,$$

$$s_2(t) = 0 , \quad t < 0 \text{ or } t > 2T , \tag{4.132}$$

where

$$\begin{aligned}
\omega_3 &= \omega_s - \omega_0 - \omega_c + 2\pi\mu t , \\
\theta_2 &= \theta + \omega_c t - \pi\mu t^2 , \\
T_1 &= \max(t - T, 0) , \\
T_2 &= \min(t, T) .
\end{aligned} \tag{4.133}$$

If $\omega_3 \neq 0$, Equation (4.132) yields

$$\begin{aligned}
s_2(t) &= \frac{A}{4\omega_3} [\sin(\omega_3 T_2 + \theta_2) - \sin(\omega_3 T_1 + \theta_2)] \\
&= \frac{A}{2\omega_3} \sin\left[\frac{\omega_3}{2}(T_2 - T_1)\right]\cos\left[\frac{\omega_3}{2}(T_1 + T_2) + \theta_2\right].
\end{aligned} \tag{4.134}$$

The final form of Equation (4.134) is valid even if $\omega_3 = 0$. For practical values of the parameters, the cosine factor varies much more rapidly with time than other factors. Consequently, after using Equations (4.133) the output of the envelope detector is

$$s_3(t) = \frac{At}{4} \operatorname{sinc} [(f_s - f_0 - f_c) t + \mu t^2] , \quad 0 \leqslant t \leqslant T ,$$

$$s_3(t) = \frac{A(2T - t)}{4} \operatorname{sinc} [(f_s - f_0 - f_c + \mu t)(2T - t)] ,$$

$$T \leqslant t \leqslant 2T , \tag{4.135}$$

where we have set $\omega = 2\pi f$.

The peak value of $s_3(t)$ is $AT/4$. We define parameter ϵ as

$$\epsilon = f_0 + f_c - f_s - \mu T . \tag{4.136}$$

If the frequency of the intercepted signal is such that $\epsilon = 0$, then the peak value of $s_3(t)$ occurs at $t = T$; that is,

$$s_3(T) = \frac{AT}{4} \, , \qquad \epsilon = 0 \, . \tag{4.137}$$

We also have

$$s_3\left(T \pm \frac{1}{2\mu T}\right) \cong \frac{AT}{4} \, (0.64) \, , \qquad \epsilon = 0 \, , \quad T \gg \frac{1}{\mu T} \, ,$$

$$s_3\left(T \pm \frac{1}{\mu T}\right) \cong 0 \, , \qquad \epsilon = 0, \quad T \gg \frac{1}{\mu T} \, . \tag{4.138}$$

These equations indicate that $1/\mu T$ is an approximate measure of the width of the compressed output pulse. Satisfying the inequality ensures that the response of the microscan receiver due to one scan does not interact significantly with the response due to the next scan.

If the frequency of the intercepted signal shifts slightly, then $\epsilon \neq 0$. A small shift yields

$$s_3\left(T + \frac{\epsilon}{\mu}\right) \cong \frac{AT}{4} \, , \qquad \left|\frac{\epsilon}{\mu}\right| \ll T \, , \tag{4.139}$$

where the right-hand side of the equation is the peak value of $s_3(t)$. Thus, the peak value occurs at time $t = T + \epsilon/\mu$. Using Equation (4.136), we can estimate the input frequency, $f_0 = \omega_0/2\pi$, from the time location of the peak value.

We define the resolution of the microscan receiver, Δ, as the value of the frequency shift in hertz, ϵ, that produces a shift in the time of the peak output equal to the width of the output when $\epsilon = 0$. Thus,

$$\Delta = \frac{1}{T} = \frac{\mu}{W} \, , \tag{4.140}$$

where $W = \mu T$ is the total bandwidth scanned.

The ratio of the input pulse width to the compressed output pulse width is TW, which is called the *compression ratio* of the microscan receiver. When this ratio is large, a comparison of Equations (4.140) and (4.129) indicates that there is a substantial improvement in resolution of the microscan receiver over the scanning superheterodyne receiver. A comparison of the receiver outputs for typical inputs of the form of Equation (4.107) is depicted in Figure 4.13.

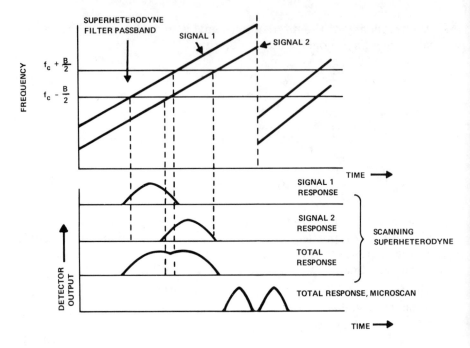

Figure 4.13/Response of scanning superheterodyne and microscan receivers to simultaneous signals.

Equation (4.135) exhibits sidelobes in addition to the main peak. The sidelobes generated by a strong signal may mask main peaks due to weaker signals or may be mistaken for main peaks. To alleviate this problem, we may multiply the received waveform by a weighting function, use a scanning waveform with amplitude modulation, follow the chirp filter with a shaping filter, or modify the impulse response of the chirp filter [10].

For a large compression ratio, the transfer function associated with Equation (4.131) has a flat, nearly rectangular amplitude response and a quadratic phase response [5].

The preceding analysis is valid if the modulation period of the input is large compared with the scan period. If a more rapidly modulated input is present, the microscan receiver can be designed to produce an output that is an approximation of the Fourier transform of the modulation. In this case, the system is often called a *chirp transform processor*. During the interval $0 \leqslant t \leqslant T$, the input is assumed to have the form

$$s(t) = s_0(t) \cos(\omega_0 t + \theta_0) , \quad 0 \leqslant t \leqslant T . \qquad (4.141)$$

This input is mixed with the scanning waveform

$$y(t) = \cos(\omega_s t - \pi \mu t^2 + \theta_s), \quad 0 \leqslant t \leqslant T, \quad (4.142)$$

to produce

$$s_1(t) = \frac{1}{2} s_0(t) \cos(\omega_1 t - \pi \mu t^2 + \theta), \quad 0 \leqslant t \leqslant T, \quad (4.143)$$

where $\omega_1 = \omega_s - \omega_0$ and $\theta = \theta_s - \theta_0$. The impulse response of the chirp filter is

$$h(t) = \cos(\omega_c t + \pi \mu t^2), \quad 0 \leqslant t \leqslant T_d, \quad (4.144)$$

where we assume that $T_d \geqslant T$. We calculate the system output in the time interval $T \leqslant t \leqslant T_d$. Substituting Equations (4.143) and (4.144) into Equation (4.112), using trigonometry, dropping a negligible integral, and substituting a complex exponential, we obtain

$$s_2(t) = \text{Re}\left\{ \frac{1}{4} \exp[j(\omega_c t + \pi\mu t^2 + \theta)] \right.$$

$$\left. \times \int_{-\infty}^{\infty} s_0(\tau)q(\tau) \exp[-j\tau(\omega_c - \omega_1 + 2\pi\mu t)] \, d\tau \right\}$$

$$= \text{Re}\left\{ \frac{1}{4} \exp[j(\omega_c t + \pi\mu t^2 + \theta)] S_0(\omega_c - \omega_1 + 2\pi\mu t) \right\}$$

$$= \frac{1}{4} |S_0(\omega_c - \omega_1 + 2\pi\mu t)| \cos[\omega_c t + \pi\mu t^2 + \theta$$

$$+ \phi(\omega_c - \omega_1 + 2\pi\mu t)], \quad T \leqslant t \leqslant T_d, \quad (4.145)$$

where $q(t)$ is defined in Equation (4.88), $S_0(\omega)$ is the Fourier transform of $s_0(\tau)q(\tau)$, and $\phi(\omega)$ is the phase angle of the Fourier transform. The output of the envelope detector is proportional to

$$s_3(t) = |S_0(\omega_0 + \omega_c - \omega_s + 2\pi\mu t)|, \quad T \leqslant t \leqslant T_d. \quad (4.146)$$

Thus, the magnitude of the Fourier transform of the input modulation has been produced as a time signal.

If $s_2(t)$ is multiplied by $h(t)$, then, after elimination of a double frequency term by filtering, the phase-shifted real part of $S_0(\omega)$ is produced as a time signal. As shown in Figure 4.12(b), the waveform $h(t)$, $T \leqslant t \leqslant T_d$, can be produced by applying an impulse at time T to a dispersive filter with impulse response $h_1(t) = h(t + T)$, $0 \leqslant t \leqslant T_d - T$. The phase-shifted imaginary part of $S_0(\omega)$ can be produced as a time signal by multiplying $s_2(t)$ by $\sin(\omega_c t + \pi \mu t^2)$.

Let ω_b denote the maximum value of ω for which $|S_0(\omega)|$ has a significant value, and let ω_a denote the minimum value. If

$$T - \frac{\omega_a}{2\pi\mu} \leqslant \frac{\omega_s - \omega_c - \omega_0}{2\pi\mu} \leqslant T_d - \frac{\omega_b}{2\pi\mu} \quad , \quad (4.147)$$

then, during the time interval $T \leqslant t \leqslant T_d$, $s_3(t)$ exhibits all the values of $|S_0(\omega)|$ for $\omega_a \leqslant \omega \leqslant \omega_b$. The range of possible values of $f_0 = \omega_0/2\pi$ for which Equation (4.147) can be satisfied is

$$W_R = \mu T_d - \mu T - f_m \quad , \quad \mu T_d \geqslant \mu T + f_m \quad , \quad (4.148)$$

where $f_m = (\omega_b - \omega_a)/2\pi$. The scanning waveform is a periodic sequence of signals of the form of Equation (4.142). If the scan period is T_d and $y(t) = 0$, $T \leqslant t \leqslant T_d$, then the output due to a scan does not interfere with the Fourier transform generated by the next scan. If T_d is specified, a large value of T/T_d limits the fraction of the receiver input signal that cannot be processed. However, the total bandwidth that can be processed, $W_R + f_m$, decreases as T increases. As a compromise, we may choose T to maximize the product $(W_R + f_m)T$. Equation (4.148) and calculus yield $T = T_d/2$ and a maximum product

$$(W_R + f_m)T = \frac{T_d W_d}{4} \quad , \quad T_d = 2T \quad , \quad (4.149)$$

where $W_d = \mu T_d$ is approximately equal to the bandwidth of the chirp filter.

The chirp transform processor can be used as the basic building block of an analog version of the cross correlator of Figure 4.5. The output of the processor can be time gated or amplitude limited to provide notch filtering of narrowband interference.

If the scanning period is less than the period between frequency changes of the intercepted signal, the microscan and scanning superheterodyne receivers can estimate each frequency of a frequency-hopping or MFSK signal. If not, some frequencies may be missed.

4.4 DIRECTION FINDING

A signal must be detected, and sometimes its frequency must be estimated, if the direction to its source is to be found. Conversely, *direction finding* enhances signal sorting, which restricts the number of signals that the detection and frequency-estimation systems must process simultaneously.

For simplicity, the estimation of a single *bearing angle* is considered. In a ground-based interception system, an azimuth angle may be all that is needed. However, airborne systems may require estimates of both the azimuth and the elevation angles to the intercepted transmitter.

The attainable direction-finding accuracy of an antenna system is limited by physical and electrical design imperfections. Receiver noise generated internally or externally causes an additional loss of accuracy. Here, we assess the effect of white Gaussian noise, keeping in mind that a residual angle-estimation error remains even in the absence of noise.

Energy Comparison Systems

Amplitude comparison systems are often used in radar [11-13]. However, when communications with unknown characteristics are to be intercepted, it is logical to base comparisons upon the energy. Thus, we analyze *energy comparison systems* rather than the analogous amplitude comparison systems, which are sometimes equally viable.

Throughout this section, we assume Gaussian antenna radiation patterns for mathematical convenience. However, the analytical methods can be used to obtain analogous results for non-Gaussian patterns.

We denote the true bearing angle to a transmitter by ϕ and an estimate of this angle by $\hat{\phi}$. As a measure of system performance, we use the *root-mean-square error* of $\hat{\phi}$, which we denote by ζ. By definition and a straightforward expansion,

$$\zeta^2 = E[(\hat{\phi} - \phi)^2] = VAR(\hat{\phi}) + B_\phi^2 , \qquad (4.150)$$

where $VAR(\hat{\phi})$ is the variance of ϕ and B_ϕ is the *bias*,

$$B_\phi = E[\hat{\phi}] - \phi . \qquad (4.151)$$

The *stationary multibeam system* for direction finding is illustrated in Figure 4.14. First, the largest of the receiver outputs is selected. Next, the larger of the two receiver outputs corresponding to beams adjacent to the beam that produced the largest output is selected. The two selected outputs are denoted by L_1 and L_2. The processor compares the outputs to a threshold for detection. The signal direction is estimated from the logarithm of the ratio of L_1 to L_2. The radiation patterns of the adjacent beams are illustrated in Figure 4.15, where ϕ represents the angle of arrival of an intercepted signal, and beam pattern $F_i(\theta)$ produces L_i. The origin of the coordinate system is defined so that $+\psi$ and $-\psi$ indicate the peak responses of the two beams, respectively. Suppose that the beam patterns are approximately Gaussian; that is, they are described by

$$F_1(\theta) = G \exp\left[-\frac{2(\theta - \psi)^2}{b^2}\right],$$
(4.152)

$$F_2(\theta) = G \exp\left[-\frac{2(\theta + \psi)^2}{b^2}\right],$$
(4.153)

where G is the maximum gain of the patterns and b is a measure of the beam width. If the receivers contain radiometers, then the L_i are proportional to the F_i. Thus, in the absence of noise, the processor input is

$$Z = \ln \frac{L_1(\phi)}{L_2(\phi)} = \frac{8\psi\phi}{b^2} \ .$$
(4.154)

The bearing angle can be determined by inverting this equation. In the presence of noise, the same inverse provides an estimate, $\hat{\phi}$, of the true angle ϕ. We have

$$\hat{\phi} = \frac{b^2}{8\psi} Z \ ,$$
(4.155)

where Z is now a random variable. We give an error analysis neglecting the effect of the selection process for L_1 and L_2.

We assume that the white Gaussian noises in the receivers are statistically independent and have equal powers. Because L_1 and L_2 are the outputs of radiometers, they are statistically independent, noncentral χ^2 random variables with γ degrees of freedom and noncentral parameters λ_1 and λ_2, respectively. From elementary probability theory, the probability density function of $Y = L_1/L_2$, the quotient of two nonnegative random variables, is

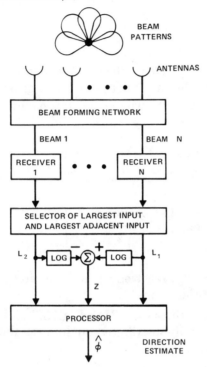

Figure 4.14/Stationary multibeam system.

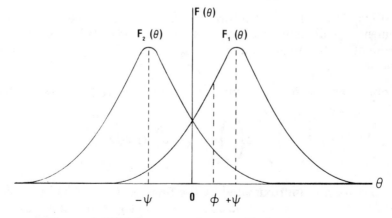

Figure 4.15/Adjacent antenna radiation patterns.

$$p_2(y) = \int_0^\infty x p_{11}(yx) p_{12}(x)\, dx , \qquad y \geqslant 0 ,$$

$$p_2(y) = 0 , \qquad\qquad\qquad\qquad\qquad y < 0 , \qquad (4.156)$$

where $p_{11}(\ )$ and $p_{12}(\ )$ are the density functions for L_1 and L_2, respectively. The density function $p_{1i}(\ )$ is given by Equation (4.30) with λ_i substituted for λ. The noncentral parameters are given by

$$\lambda_1 = \frac{2E}{N_0} \exp\left[-\frac{2(\phi - \psi)^2}{b^2} \right] , \qquad (4.157)$$

$$\lambda_2 = \frac{2E}{N_0} \exp\left[-\frac{2(\phi + \psi)^2}{b^2} \right] , \qquad (4.158)$$

where E is the energy received when the intercepted signal enters the center of one of the beams.

When $\phi = 0$, Equations (4.157) and (4.158) give $\lambda_1 = \lambda_2$ so that L_1 and L_2 are identically distributed random variables. Since $Z = \ln L_1 - \ln L_2$, it follows that

$$E[Z] = 0 , \qquad \phi = 0 . \qquad (4.159)$$

At other values of ϕ, closed-form expressions for the mean and other moments are difficult to obtain. In general, the distribution of L_1 at ϕ is identical to the distribution of L_2 at $-\phi$. Thus, ζ is symmetric about $\phi = 0$.

To obtain an approximate expression for $E[Z]$, we first observe that

$$E[Z] = \int_0^\infty \int_0^\infty \ln\left(\frac{y}{x}\right) p_{11}(y)\, p_{12}(x)\, dx\, dy . \qquad (4.160)$$

The logarithm is approximated by the first six terms of its two-dimensional Taylor-series expansion about the point $y = m_1$, $x = m_2$, where m_1 and m_2 are the mean values of L_1 and L_2, respectively. Thus,

$$\ln\left(\frac{y}{x}\right) = \ln\left(\frac{m_1}{m_2}\right) + \frac{y - m_1}{m_1} - \frac{x - m_2}{m_2} - \frac{(y - m_1)^2}{2m_1{}^2}$$

$$+ \frac{(x - m_2)^2}{2m_2{}^2} - \frac{(y - m_1)(x - m_2)}{2m_1 m_2} \qquad . \quad (4.161)$$

This approximation is accurate over some range of y and x about y = m_1, x = m_2. If $p_{11}(y)$ and $p_{12}(x)$ are negligible outside this range, then the substitution of Equation (4.161) into Equation (4.160) yields an accurate approximation of $E[Z]$. The ranges of significant values of $p_{11}(y)$ and $p_{12}(x)$ are approximately limited by $|y - m_1| < 3\sigma_1$ and $|x - m_2| < 3\sigma_2$, where σ_1 and σ_2 are the standard deviations of L_1 and L_2, respectively. Consequently, the remainder of the Taylor series indicates that sufficient conditions for the validity of Equation (4.161) are $\sigma_1 \ll m_1$ and $\sigma_2 \ll m_2$.

Making the substitution and using the properties of density functions, we obtain

$$E[Z] \cong \ln\left(\frac{m_1}{m_2}\right) - \frac{\sigma_1{}^2}{2m_1{}^2} + \frac{\sigma_2{}^2}{2m_2{}^2} \quad , \qquad \sigma_1 \ll m_1 \; , \quad \sigma_2 \ll m_2 \; .$$

$$(4.162)$$

From Equations (4.26) and (4.27), we have

$$m_i = \lambda_i + 2\gamma \; , \quad i = 1, 2 \; , \tag{4.163}$$

$$\sigma_i{}^2 = 4\lambda_i + 4\gamma \; , \quad i = 1, 2 \; . \tag{4.164}$$

An approximate expression for $E[Z^2]$ is obtained in an analogous manner. Combining this expression with Equation (4.162) and dropping terms higher than second order in σ_1/m_1 and σ_2/m_2, we obtain

$$VAR(Z) \cong \frac{\sigma_1{}^2}{m_1{}^2} + \frac{\sigma_2{}^2}{m_2{}^2} \quad , \qquad \sigma_1 \ll m_1 \; , \quad \sigma_2 \ll m_2 \; . \quad (4.165)$$

By using Equations (4.150), (4.155), (4.162), and (4.165), an equation for ζ can be derived. Dropping terms higher than second order gives

$$\zeta = \frac{b^2}{8\psi}\left\{\left[\ln\left(\frac{m_1}{m_2}\right) - \frac{8\psi\phi}{b^2}\right]^2 - \left[\ln\left(\frac{m_1}{m_2}\right) - \frac{8\psi\phi}{b^2}\right]\left(\frac{\sigma_1^{\,2}}{m_1^{\,2}}\right)\right.$$

$$\left. - \frac{\sigma_2^{\,2}}{m_2^{\,2}}\right) + \frac{\sigma_1^{\,2}}{m_1^{\,2}} + \frac{\sigma_2^{\,2}}{m_2^{\,2}}\right\}^{\frac{1}{2}} , \quad \sigma_1 \ll m_1 , \quad \sigma_2 \ll m_2$$

$$(4.166)$$

At $\phi = 0$, we have $m_1 = m_2 = m$ and $\sigma_1 = \sigma_2 = \sigma$ so that

$$\zeta = \frac{\sqrt{2}\,b^2\sigma}{8\psi m} , \quad \phi = 0 , \quad \sigma \ll m . \qquad (4.167)$$

To assess the implications of Equations (4.166) and (4.167), it is convenient to define the parameter

$$\rho = \frac{E}{N_0\gamma} , \qquad (4.168)$$

which is approximately equal to the signal-to-noise ratio in a receiver when the bearing angle is aligned with the center of the corresponding beam. For large values of ρ, Equation (4.167) becomes

$$\zeta = \frac{b^2}{4\psi}\,(\rho\gamma)^{-\frac{1}{2}}\exp\left(\frac{\psi^2}{b^2}\right) , \quad \phi = 0 , \quad \rho \gg \frac{1}{2}\exp\left(\frac{2\psi^2}{b^2}\right).$$

$$(4.169)$$

This equation indicates that we can achieve $\zeta \ll b$ if ρ is sufficiently large. Thus, the potential direction-finding accuracy is much better than a beam width.

The beam width $b = \psi$ minimizes ζ in Equation (4.169). However, this choice of beam width is not optimal for all values of ϕ. Figure 4.16 illustrates the effect of the normalized beam width, b/ψ, on ζ. For $\rho = 10, \gamma = 100$, and $\phi = \psi$, the normalized beam width that minimizes ζ is approximately 3.6.

Figure 4.17 illustrates the effect of increasing the duration of the observation interval, T. Assuming an increase in T causes proportionate increases in E and γ, we set $\rho = 10$ for each value of γ. A nearly optimal normalized beam width for each value of γ and $\phi = \psi$ is chosen. The curves show a steady decrease in ζ as γ increases.

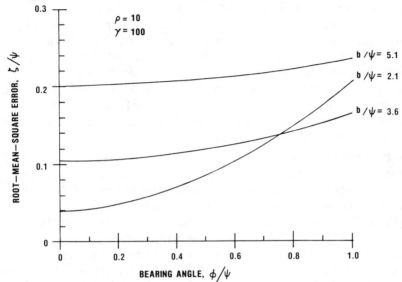

Figure 4.16/Root-mean-square error versus bearing angle for different beam widths.

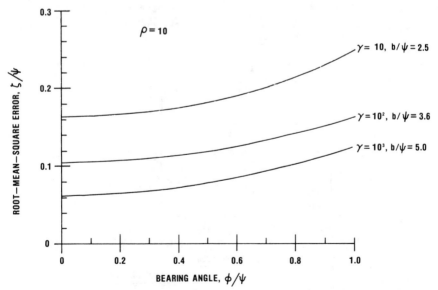

Figure 4.17/Root-mean-square error versus bearing angle for different values of γ and beam widths optimized at $\phi = \psi$.

Suppose many frequency-hopping signals are simultaneously intercepted by a channelized receiver. If it is impossible to correlate successive hopping frequencies, the direction of a signal must be estimated on the basis of the energy received in a single channel during a single hopping period. Let γ and ρ refer to a single channel and a single hopping period. As the hopping rate increases, the channel bandwidth often must be increased proportionately if most of the signal energy is to be received. Thus, γ can be kept constant as the hopping rate increases. However, ρ decreases and, consequently, Equation (4.169) indicates that ζ increases. We conclude that, in this case, direction finding becomes more difficult as the hopping rate increases.

Energy comparison with *two rotating beams* is illustrated in Figure 4.18. The receivers are radiometers that produce continuous or discrete signals. To simplify the analysis, we assume continuous signals. Detection of an intercepted signal is verified by comparing $Z = \log[(L_1 + L_2)/L_3]$ to a threshold. Since $Z(t)$ is a function of a ratio, it enables the system to reject strong signals entering through the sidelobes of the rotating beams. Following detection, the bearing angle is identified as the angle corresponding to the time when the energies received by the two displaced beams are equal, which is the time when $L_1(t) - L_2(t)$ crosses zero.

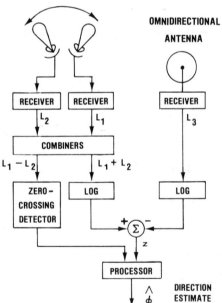

Figure 4.18/Energy comparison with two rotating beams.

Figure 4.15 illustrates the displaced beam patterns at the time of the
zero crossing if we define the angular coordinates so that the origin
corresponds to boresight. Thus, at the zero-crossing time, the bearing
angle is estimated as $\hat{\phi} = 0$. Let ϕ denote the true bearing angle relative to boresight at the zero-crossing time. Because the zero-crossing
time is a random variable, ϕ is a random variable.

We assume that the beam rotation is negligible during an observation
interval and that the signal energy produced by the source per observation interval does not vary significantly during a scan. Then at the
zero-crossing time t_0, we can make the decomposition

$$L_i(t_0) = m_i(t_0) + n_i(t_0) , \quad i = 1, 2 , \tag{4.170}$$

where $m_i(t_0)$, the expected value of $L_i(t_0)$, is given by Equation (4.163).

The zero-mean random variable $n_i(t_0)$ has a variance given by Equation
(4.164). Since $n_1(t_0)$ and $n_2(t_0)$ are produced by different receivers, it
is reasonable to assume that they are statistically independent. We further assume that ρ is sufficiently large that $\phi \ll \psi$ with high probability and

$$\rho = \frac{E}{N_0 \gamma} \gg \frac{1}{2} \exp\left(\frac{2\psi^2}{b^2}\right) , \quad \gamma \geqslant 1 . \tag{4.171}$$

It follows that $n_1(t_0)$ and $n_2(t_0)$ have nearly the same variance given by

$$\sigma^2 \cong \frac{8E}{N_0} \exp\left(-\frac{2\psi^2}{b^2}\right) + 4\gamma$$

$$\cong \frac{8E}{N_0} \exp\left(-\frac{2\psi^2}{b^2}\right) . \tag{4.172}$$

Since $L_1(t_0) = L_2(t_0)$,

$$n_2 - n_1 = m_1 - m_2 = \frac{4E}{N_0} \exp\left[-\frac{2(\phi^2 + \psi^2)}{b^2}\right] \sinh\left(\frac{4\phi\psi}{b^2}\right) , \tag{4.173}$$

where the time dependences are suppressed for notational convenience.
Since $\phi \ll \psi$ with high probability, Equation (4.173) yields the approximate solution,

$$\phi \cong \frac{b^2}{4\psi} \sinh^{-1}\left[\frac{N_0}{4E} \exp\left(\frac{2\psi^2}{b^2}\right)(n_2 - n_1) \right]. \qquad (4.174)$$

The random variable $n_2 - n_1$ has a standard deviation of $\sqrt{2}\,\sigma$. Thus, Equation (4.172) and Inequality (4.171) imply that the factor in brackets in Equation (4.174) is small with high probability. Consequently,

$$\phi \cong \frac{b^2 N_0}{16\psi E} \exp\left(\frac{2\psi^2}{b^2}\right)(n_2 - n_1) . \qquad (4.175)$$

Since $\hat{\phi} = 0$, Equation (4.150) gives $\zeta^2 = E[\phi^2]$. Thus,

$$\zeta = \frac{\sqrt{2}\,b^2 N_0\,\sigma}{16\psi E} \exp\left(\frac{2\psi^2}{b^2}\right)$$

$$= \frac{b^2}{4\psi}(\rho\gamma)^{-\frac{1}{2}} \exp\left(\frac{\psi^2}{b^2}\right), \quad \rho \gg \frac{1}{2}\exp\left(\frac{2\psi^2}{b^2}\right).$$
$$(4.176)$$

Equation (4.176) is identical to Equation (4.169). Thus, if $\phi = 0$, the stationary multibeam array performs as well as the rotating system of Figure 4.18. However, if $\phi \neq 0$, ζ increases in the multibeam case. The main disadvantage with rotating beam systems is the narrow instantaneous field of view, which may cause a signal to be missed or may decrease the possible observation time. On the other hand, when many hostile communications are present, the narrow field of view provides a valuable signal-sorting capability.

Referring to Figures 4.18 and 4.15, the threshold for $Z(t)$ is set so that, with high probability, once $Z(t)$ crosses the threshold, it stays above it until $L_1(t) - L_2(t)$ crosses zero. To achieve this high probability, it is intuitively reasonable to require that, in the absence of noise, $L_1(t) + L_2(t)$ have a local maximum near the zero-crossing time. Thus, we require $F_1(\theta) + F_2(\theta)$ to have a maximum at $\theta = 0$. Using calculus and Equations (4.152) and (4.153), we obtain $b \geqslant 2\psi$ as a necessary condition for the local maximum. Figure 4.19 depicts Equation (4.176) with $b = 2\psi$.

An alternative system uses a *single rotating beam*, as shown in Figure 4.20. Detection of a signal is verified by comparing L_1 and $Z = \log(L_1/L_2)$ to thresholds. Following detection, the direction to the signal source may be estimated as the angle corresponding to the peak value of $L_1(t)$ or $Z(t)$. Alternatively, the system may measure the angle at which L_1 or $Z(t)$ first crosses a threshold and the angle at which $L_1(t)$ or $Z(t)$ subsequently drops below this threshold; the direction estimate is the average of the two angles.

To avoid processing the noise in $L_2(t)$, it is preferable to use the threshold crossings of $L_1(t)$ rather than $Z(t)$ if the signal energy produced by the source per observation interval does not vary significantly during a scan. The threshold may be set at a fixed level to accommodate signals with a predetermined minimum energy, or adaptive thresholding may be used. *Adaptive thresholding systems* [14] can be designed so that the threshold crossings occur at the times at which the slope of $L_1(t)$ has its maximum magnitude, regardless of the signal energy. As a result, adaptive thresholding often provides more accurate measurements of threshold crossings than thresholding with a fixed level, thereby allowing an improved estimation of the bearing angle.

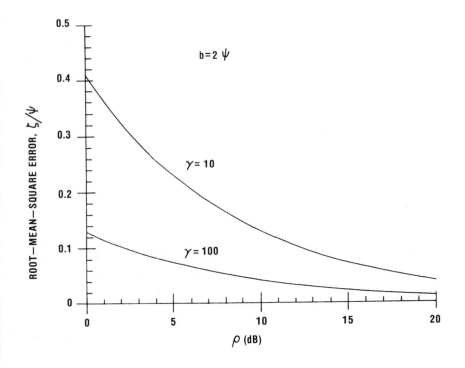

Figure 4.19/Root-mean-square error versus ρ for different values of γ.

We derive ζ for the rotating beam system with adaptive thresholding. We again assume that the beam rotation is negligible during an observation interval and that the signal energy produced by the source per observation interval does not vary significantly during a scan. Let α denote a uniform scan rate. The rotating beam has the radiation pattern

$$F(\theta) = G \exp\left(-\frac{2\theta^2}{b^2}\right). \qquad (4.177)$$

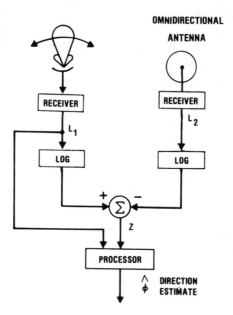

Figure 4.20/Energy comparison with single rotating beam.

In the absence of noise, $L_1(t)$ is proportional to $F(\alpha t)$, where $t = 0$ is the time of the peak value of $L_1(t)$. Let $\hat{t}_1$ and $\hat{t}_2$ denote the times at which $L_1(t)$ crosses the threshold in the presence of noise. The bearing angle estimate is

$$\hat{\phi} = \alpha\left(\frac{\hat{t}_1 + \hat{t}_2}{2}\right). \qquad (4.178)$$

We assume that the time interval between the threshold crossings is long compared to both the reciprocal of the receiver bandwidth and the duration of an observation interval. Thus, the random variables $\hat{t}_1$ and $\hat{t}_2$ may be considered statistically independent. We assume that the sources of noise do not change significantly between threshold crossings so that $\hat{t}_1$ and $\hat{t}_2$ have equal variances. Consequently, Equation (4.178) implies that

$$\text{VAR}(\hat{\phi}) = \frac{\alpha^2}{2} \ \text{VAR}(\hat{t}_1) \ . \tag{4.179}$$

To evaluate the variance of $\hat{t}_1$, we make the decomposition

$$L_1(t) = m_1(t) + n_1(t) \ , \tag{4.180}$$

where $m_1(t)$ is the expected value of $L_1(t)$. Let E denote the signal energy received when $t = 0$. Equations (4.163) and (4.177) imply that

$$m_1(t) = \frac{2E}{N_0} \ \exp\left[-\frac{2(\alpha t)^2}{b^2}\right] + 2\gamma \ . \tag{4.181}$$

The zero-mean stochastic process $n_1(t)$ is nonstationary and Gaussian for large values of γ. Using Equations (4.164) and (4.177), we obtain the mean power of $n_1(t)$:

$$\sigma^2(t) = \frac{8E}{N_0} \ \exp\left[-\frac{2(\alpha t)^2}{b^2}\right] + 4\gamma \ . \tag{4.182}$$

We interpret $m_1(t)$ as the "signal" in $L_1(t)$ and $n_1(t)$ as additive "noise".

The maximum slope magnitude of $m_1(t)$ occurs at times

$$t_1 = -\frac{b}{2\alpha} \ ; \quad t_2 = \frac{b}{2\alpha} \ . \tag{4.183}$$

At these times, the slope magnitude is

$$S = \frac{4\,\alpha\,E}{\sqrt{e}\,b\,N_0} \ . \tag{4.184}$$

If $\rho \gg 1$, $\hat{t}_1$ and $\hat{t}_2$ are near t_1 and t_2, respectively.

At times near t_1 or t_2, $n_1(t)$ can be approximated by a zero-mean stationary process with variance

$$\sigma^2 = \frac{8E}{\sqrt{e}\,N_0} + 4\gamma \ . \tag{4.185}$$

From arrival-time estimation theory, it follows that for $\rho \gg 1, \hat{t}_1$ is an unbiased estimate of t_1 with variance

$$\text{VAR}(\hat{t}_1) \cong \beta^2 \frac{\sigma^2}{S^2} , \qquad (4.186)$$

where β^2 is a constant on the order of unity [11]. Using Equations (4.184) to (4.186), we obtain

$$\text{VAR}(\hat{t}_1) \cong \beta^2 \left(\frac{8E}{\sqrt{e} \, N_0} + 4\gamma \right) \frac{e \, b^2 N_0{}^2}{16\alpha^2 E^2}$$

$$\cong \frac{\sqrt{e} \, \beta^2 b^2 N_0}{2\alpha^2 E} , \qquad \rho \gg 1 . \qquad (4.187)$$

Since $\hat{t}_1$ and $\hat{t}_2$ are unbiased estimates, $\zeta^2 = \text{VAR}(\hat{\phi})$. Combining Equations (4.168), (4.179), and (4.187) yields

$$\zeta = \frac{\sqrt[4]{e} \, \beta \, b}{2} (\rho\gamma)^{-\frac{1}{2}} , \qquad \rho \gg 1 . \qquad (4.188)$$

Since $\beta \approx 1$ in Equation (4.188), and we usually have $\psi \approx b/2$ in Equation (4.176), the two types of rotating-beam systems have approximately the same potential performance.

Interferometer

An *interferometer* consists of two or more antennas or groups of elements of a phased array that use phase or arrival-time information to estimate direction. We first consider the interferometer of Figure 4.21(a). Suppose a plane wave arrives at angle ϕ, where $|\phi| \leq \pi/2$. If two antennas are separated by distance d, then, since phase angles are modulo 2π numbers, the phase difference between the antenna outputs is

$$\theta = \frac{2\pi d \sin\phi}{\Lambda_s} - 2\pi n , \qquad |\theta| \leq \pi , \quad |\phi| \leq \frac{\pi}{2} , \qquad (4.189)$$

where Λ_s is the signal wavelength and n is an integer that ensures satisfaction of the first inequality. If $d \leq \Lambda_s/2$, then n = 0. If $d > \Lambda_s/2$, then n varies with ϕ, taking negative and positive values and the value zero. We adopt the convention that $\theta > 0$ if $\phi > 0$ and n = 0.

One antenna output provides a reference. Each of the other antenna

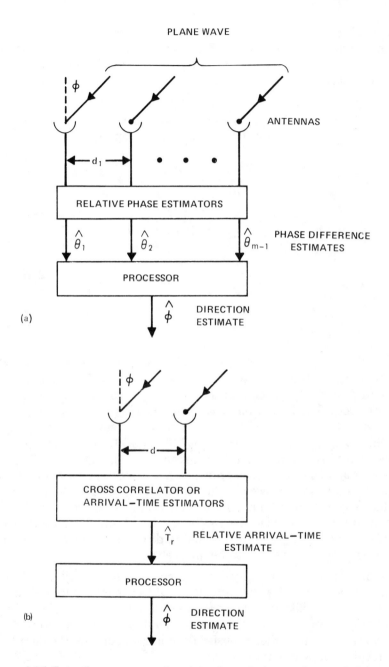

Figure 4.21/Interferometers using (a) phase information and (b) arrival-time information.

outputs is applied to a separate device that estimates its phase relative to the reference. This device may be similar to the part of the IFM receiver in Figure 4.9 that is fed by s(t) and $s_1(t)$. The estimates of the relative phases are denoted by $\hat{\theta}_i$.

Estimates of the bearing angle ϕ are calculated from the $\hat{\theta}_i$ by inverting Equation (4.189). Let $\hat{\Lambda}_s$ denote an estimate of Λ_s. If there are m antennas, the (m $-$ 1) bearing estimates are given by

$$\hat{\phi}_i = -\frac{\pi}{2}, \qquad\qquad \hat{\theta}_i + 2\pi n_i < -\frac{2\pi d_i}{\hat{\Lambda}_s},$$

$$\hat{\phi}_i = \sin^{-1}\left[\frac{\hat{\Lambda}_s}{2\pi d_i}(\hat{\theta}_i + 2\pi n_i)\right], \quad |\hat{\theta}_i + 2\pi n_i| \leqslant \frac{2\pi d_i}{\hat{\Lambda}_s},$$

$$\hat{\phi}_i = \frac{\pi}{2}, \qquad\qquad \hat{\theta}_i + 2\pi n_i > \frac{2\pi d_i}{\hat{\Lambda}_s},$$

$$i = 1, 2, \ldots, m - 1. \qquad\qquad\qquad (4.190)$$

Unless $d_i \leqslant \hat{\Lambda}_s/2$, the appropriate value of n_i is unknown. However, the accuracy of the estimate of ϕ increases with d_i. To obtain an estimate of ϕ that is both accurate and unambiguous, three or more antennas are used. The first antenna is a reference. The second antenna is separated by $d_1 \leqslant \hat{\Lambda}_s/2$, from the reference. The other antennas are separated by increasingly greater distances from the reference. The first antenna pair provides an unambiguous estimate of ϕ. The first and third antennas provide a more accurate estimate of ϕ but an ambiguous one. However, this ambiguity is resolved by the first estimate. Subsequent antennas allow increasingly accurate estimates of ϕ, provided that the ambiguities can be resolved by the less accurate estimates. In designing the interferometer, distance d_1 should correspond to the shortest wavelength to be intercepted.

Assuming that n_i is correctly determined, the probability density function and moments of $\hat{\phi}_i$ can be calculated by standard methods once the joint probability density function of $\hat{\theta}_i$ and $\hat{\Lambda}_s$ is specified. If there is a negligible error in $\hat{\Lambda}_s$, only the probability density function of $\hat{\theta}_i$ is required. Both of these density functions depend on the details of the receiver implementation.

An alternative method, depicted in Figure 4.21(b), which eliminates the need to estimate Λ_s and the need to resolve ambiguities, is based on the direct measurement of the *relative arrival time* of a plane wave at two antennas. This relative arrival time can be estimated by using a cross correlator, as in Figure 4.5, or by using two arrival-time estimators.

Assuming that a plane wave is received, the relative arrival time is given by

$$T_r = \frac{d \sin \phi}{c} \quad , \quad |\phi| \leqslant \frac{\pi}{2} \, , \tag{4.191}$$

where c is the speed of electromagnetic waves and we adopt the convention that $T_r > 0$ if $\phi > 0$. Consequently, the bearing angle estimate is

$$\hat{\phi} = -\frac{\pi}{2} \, , \qquad\qquad \hat{T}_r < -\frac{d}{c} \, ,$$

$$\hat{\phi} = \sin^{-1}\left(\frac{c\,\hat{T}_r}{d}\right) , \qquad |\hat{T}_r| \leqslant \frac{d}{c} \, , \tag{4.192}$$

$$\hat{\phi} = \frac{\pi}{2} \, , \qquad\qquad \hat{T}_r > \frac{d}{c} \, ,$$

where $\hat{T}_r$ is the relative arrival-time estimate. Retaining the first three terms of a Taylor series expansion of the arcsine function about the point T_r and using Equation (4.191), we obtain

$$\hat{\phi} \cong \phi + \frac{c}{d \cos \phi} (\hat{T}_r - T_r) + \frac{c^2 \sin \phi}{2d^2 \cos^3 \phi} (\hat{T}_r - T_r)^2 \, . \tag{4.193}$$

This approximation is reasonable if the magnitude of the right-hand side of the equation does not exceed $\pi/2$. To continue the analysis, we assume that the latter event has a high probability. If $\hat{T}_r$ provides an unbiased estimate of T_r, then

$$E[\hat{T}_r] = T_r \, . \tag{4.194}$$

It follows that

$$E[\hat{\phi}] = \phi + \frac{c^2 \sin \phi}{2d^2 \cos^3 \phi} \, \mathrm{VAR}(\hat{T}_r) \, . \tag{4.195}$$

Equation (4.195) shows that the angle estimate may be biased even if the arrival-time estimate is unbiased. A straightforward calculation yields the variance of $\hat{\phi}$.

The root-mean-square error of $\hat{\phi}$ is obtained by substituting Equation (4.193) into Equation (4.150). By retaining only the lowest order term, the result is

$$\zeta \cong \frac{c}{d \cos \phi} \; \sigma \, (\hat{T}_r) \; , \tag{4.196}$$

where $\sigma(\hat{T}_r)$ is the standard deviation of $\hat{T}_r$.

A lower bound for $\sigma(\hat{T}_r)$ or $VAR(\hat{T}_r)$ can be determined if each antenna output contains independent white Gaussian noise. The relative arrival-time estimate can be no more accurate than the arrival-time estimate for the signal at either antenna output because the former estimate would be equivalent to the latter one if one of the antenna outputs provided a perfect reference. From the Cramer-Rao bound for an unbiased arrival-time estimate [1], we have

$$VAR(\hat{T}_r) \geqslant \left(\frac{2E}{N_0} \; \beta_r^{\,2} \right)^{-1} , \tag{4.197}$$

where E/N_0 refers to the antenna output with the smallest value of this ratio, E is the energy in the signal, and $N_0/2$ is the two-sided noise power spectral density. For a narrowband signal with uniformly distributed phase,

$$\beta_r^{\,2} = \frac{2\pi \displaystyle\int_{-\infty}^{\infty} \omega^2 \, | G(\omega)|^2 \, d\omega \; - \; \left[\displaystyle\int_{-\infty}^{\infty} \omega \, | G(\omega)|^2 \, d\omega \right]^2}{2\pi \displaystyle\int_{-\infty}^{\infty} | G(\omega)|^2 \, d\omega} \tag{4.198}$$

where $G(\omega)$ is the Fourier transform of the normalized complex envelope, which is equal to the complex envelope divided by $\sqrt{2E}$.

As a simple example, we consider the signal that results from passing a pulsed sinusoid with an ideal rectangular envelope of duration T through an ideal narrowband filter of bandwidth B centered at the sinusoidal frequency. The complex envelope is a truncated sinc function. Evaluating Equation (4.198), we obtain

$$\beta_r^{\,2} \approx \frac{2B}{T} \quad , \qquad BT \gg 1 \; . \tag{4.199}$$

The left-hand antenna in Figure 4.21(b) is designated antenna 1; the right-hand antenna is designated antenna 2. The relative arrival time may be estimated by subtracting the estimated arrival time at antenna 2, $\hat{T}_2$, from the estimated arrival time at antenna 1, $\hat{T}_1$; that is,

$$\hat{T}_r = \hat{T}_1 - \hat{T}_2 \; . \tag{4.200}$$

If the arrival-time estimates are uncorrelated, then

$$VAR(\hat{T}_r) = VAR(\hat{T}_1) + VAR(\hat{T}_2) \; . \tag{4.201}$$

Each term on the right-hand side of Equation (4.201) has a lower bound similar to that in Equation (4.197). Therefore,

$$VAR(\hat{T}_r) \geqslant \frac{1}{2\beta_r^{\,2}} \left[\frac{1}{(E/N_0)_1} + \frac{1}{(E/N_0)_2} \right] \, , \tag{4.202}$$

where $(E/N_0)_1$ and $(E/N_0)_2$ refer to antennas 1 and 2, respectively. The bound in equation (4.202) is tighter than the one in Equation (4.197). Although a cross correlator does not produce $\hat{T}_r$ as in Equation (4.200), it is plausible that Equation (4.202) holds for a cross correlator also.

Arrival times may be measured by adaptive thresholding or by various other methods [14]. Suppose that a received signal at antenna 1 is applied to an envelope detector. Let $\hat{t}_1$ denote the time at which the leading edge of the detector output pulse exceeds a threshold. Let $\hat{t}_2$ denote the time at which the trailing edge of the pulse drops below the threshold. The arrival time of the signal may be estimated as

$$\hat{T}_1 = \frac{\hat{t}_1 + \hat{t}_2}{2} \; . \tag{4.203}$$

If $\hat{t}_1$ and $\hat{t}_2$ are uncorrelated and have equal variances, then

$$VAR(\hat{T}_1) = \frac{1}{2} \, VAR(\hat{t}_1) \tag{4.204}$$

If adaptive thresholding is used and the signal-to-noise ratio is large, Equation (4.186) applies. Thus,

$$\text{VAR}(\hat{T}_1) = \frac{\beta^2 \sigma_1^{\,2}}{2S_1^{\,2}} \quad , \tag{4.205}$$

where $\sigma_1^{\,2}$ is the noise power in the detector output, S_1 is the maximum slope magnitude of the pulse edges, and β^2 is a constant on the order of unity. A similar expression can be written for $\text{VAR}(\hat{T}_2)$. Using Equation (4.201), we obtain

$$\text{VAR}(\hat{T}_r) = \frac{\beta^2}{2} \left(\frac{\sigma_1^{\,2}}{S_1^{\,2}} + \frac{\sigma_2^{\,2}}{S_2^{\,2}} \right) . \tag{4.206}$$

Various expressions for ζ may be determined by combining Equation (4.197), (4.202), or (4.206) and Equation (4.196). Assuming that Equation(4.196) holds exactly, the most general expression is derived from Equation (4.197):

$$\zeta \geqslant \frac{c}{d \cos \phi} \left(\frac{2E}{N_0} \beta_r^{\,2} \right)^{-\frac{1}{2}} . \tag{4.207}$$

An interferometer using phase information can be similarly analyzed if we make two major simplifying assumptions. One assumption is that the phase ambiguities are resolved without error. The second assumption is that the intercepted signal is sufficiently narrowband and the uncertainty in the carrier frequency is sufficiently small, due to frequency estimation or *a priori* knowledge, that the signal can be approximated by a sinusoid of known frequency, $f_0 = \Lambda_s/c$. With these assumptions and Equation (4.190), a derivation similar to the one leading to Equation (4.196) results in

$$\zeta \cong \frac{c}{2\pi f_0 d \cos \phi} \, \sigma(\hat{\theta}) \, , \tag{4.208}$$

where d is the maximum separation between antennas, $\hat{\theta}$ is the corresponding estimated phase difference, and $\sigma(\hat{\theta})$ is the standard deviation of $\hat{\theta}$.

The estimated phase difference can be no more accurate than the phase estimate at either antenna output. If each antenna output contains in-

dependent white Gaussian noise, the Cramer-Rao bound for an unbiased phase estimate [4] implies that

$$\text{VAR}(\hat{\theta}) \geqslant \left(\frac{E}{N_0}\right)^{-1} , \tag{4.209}$$

where E/N_0 refers to the antenna output with the smallest value of
this ratio. Assuming that Equation (4.208) holds exactly, we have

$$\zeta \geqslant \frac{c}{2\pi f_0 d \cos \phi} \left(\frac{E}{N_0}\right)^{-\frac{1}{2}} . \tag{4.210}$$

Comparing Equation (4.210) with Equation (4.207) for equal antenna
separations, we conclude that phase comparison is potentially superior
to arrival-time processing for bearing estimation if the intercepted signal is narrowband with a small uncertainty in the carrier frequency, if
the carrier frequency satisfies

$$f_0 > \frac{\beta_r}{\sqrt{2\pi}} , \tag{4.211}$$

and if phase ambiguities can be successfully resolved with high probability.

The output of a direction-finding system can be used in reconnaissance, directional jamming, and other applications. Bearing measurements at two or more stations can be combined to estimate the location of a transmitter. However, accurate location may require large
antennas or the wide separation of interferometer elements. Consequently, location estimates are sometimes based upon signal arrival-
time measurements at three or more stations. Even in this case, bearing
measurements are usually necessary at the stations for signal sorting
when many signals are intercepted simultaneously.

The use of arrival-time measurements to estimate location is a generalization of the interferometer concept. Measurements at two stations
are combined to produce a relative arrival time that, in the absence
of noise and interference, restricts the possible transmitter location
to a hyperboloid with the corresponding pair of stations as foci.
Transmitter location is estimated from the intersections of hyper-
boloids. If the transmitter is on the earth's surface, location is
estimated from the intersections of two or more hyperbolas. In contrast, the plane wave assumption of interferometer bearing estimation
is equivalent to the approximation of a hyperbola by a straight line.

In this chapter, it has usually been assumed that little is known about the signals to be intercepted. As *a priori* information about the signals increases, the receiver designs can be improved accordingly. Detection systems may resemble the receivers being used by the intended communicators. Cross correlators may process the outputs of demodulators rather than the modulated waveforms. Simpler or more accurate methods of frequency estimation [9], such as maximum entropy methods, or of direction finding may be possible.

4.5 COUNTERMEASURES TO INTERCEPTION

By what electronic countermeasures can the communicators thwart interception? The data rates and the transmission powers can be kept to a minimum. Cables and optical fiber links are effective whenever feasible. Directional antennas help to conceal the existence of communications from the opponent. However, there are constraints on the degree of directionality that can be designed into an antenna to be used in the battlefield. An important constraint is the need to keep the antenna small to hide it from sight.

Since the antenna beam angle can be decreased by the use of a smaller wavelength as well as by a larger antenna, millimeter or even higher frequencies are sometimes viable alternatives to radio frequencies. The decision to use smaller wavelengths is tempered by such things as cost, available power, and propagation properties. The shorter wavelengths in general are attenuated more than the longer wavelengths and are more easily blocked by obstructions in their path. Furthermore, if the beam width is exceedingly narrow, it is difficult to keep it centered on another station of a communication network.

Spread-spectrum communications are inherently more difficult to intercept than are conventional communications. Time hopping, in which transmissions are increased in total duration, but contain pseudorandom time gaps, is another general countermeasure. Because of the pseudorandom gaps, an interception receiver must either process more noise energy than it would otherwise or decrease its observation interval. In either case, performance degrades.

REFERENCES

[1]   A. Whalen, *Detection of Signals in Noise.* New York: Academic Press, 1971.

[2]   H.L. Van Trees, *Detection, Estimation, and Modulation Theory,* Vol. III. New York: Wiley, 1971.

[3]   H. Urkowitz, "Energy Detection of Unknown Deterministic Signals," *Proc. IEEE* 55 (April 1967), 523.

[4]   R.E. Ziemer and W.H. Tranter, *Principles of Communications.* Boston: Houghton Mifflin, 1976.

[5]   A. Papoulis, *Signal Analysis.* New York: McGraw-Hill, 1977.

[6]   R.A. Dillard, "Detectability of Spread-Spectrum Signals," *IEEE Trans. Aerosp. Electron. Syst.* 15 (July 1979), 526.

[7]   R.A. Sprague, "A Review of Acousto-optic Signal Correlators," *Optical Engineering* 16 (Sept. 1977), 467.

[8]   D.L. Hecht, "Spectrum Analysis Using Acousto-optic Filters," *Optical Engineering* 16 (Sept. 1977), 461.

[9]   J.B.G. Roberts, G.L. Moule, and G. Parry, "Design and Application of Real-Time Spectrum Analyzer Systems," *IEE Proc.* 127, Pt. F (April 1980), 76.

[10] M.A. Jack, P.M. Grant, and J.H. Collins, "The Theory, Design, and Applications of Surface Acoustic Wave Fourier-Transform Processors," *Proc. IEEE* 68 (April 1980), 450.

[11] M.I. Skolnik, *Introduction to Radar Systems,* second ed. New York: McGraw-Hill, 1980.

[12] B.O. Steinberg, *Principles of Aperture and Array System Design.* New York: Wiley, 1976.

[13] D.C. Cooper, "Errors in Directional Measurements Using the Relative Amplitudes of Signals Received by Two Aerials," *IEE Proc.* 114 (December 1967), 1834.

[14] D.J. Torrieri, "Adaptive Thresholding Systems," *IEEE Trans. Aerosp. Electron. Syst.* 13 (May 1977), 273.

5

Adaptive Antenna Systems

5.1 INTRODUCTION

One who seeks to familiarize himself with *adaptive antenna systems* for interference rejection is confronted by a vast literature containing many different proposed systems. However, there are only a few fundamentally different concepts underlying the variations. Here, these concepts and their relationships are stressed. Adaptive systems that are not intended for interference rejection, such as retrodirective arrays, are not considered.

Special attention is given to the *sidelobe canceller*, the archetypical adaptive antenna system. The initial mathematical analysis is heuristic in order to clarify the basic principles of operation. It is shown that the adaptation in a sidelobe canceller can be interpreted not only as noise cancellation, but also as adaptive beam forming and null steering. The analysis of the sidelobe canceller leads naturally to consideration of the *multiple sidelobe canceller*. A slight modification of the sidelobe canceller yields a notch filter.

After the initial heuristic analysis of the sidelobe canceller, the remainder of this chapter contains a more rigorous mathematical analysis. Alternative adaptive systems that can handle wide-bandwidth signals are developed from the classical theory. There are two forms of the adaptive elements. In one form, the weight-adjustment mechanism responds to the system output; in the other form, the mechanism responds to the difference between the output and the desired response.

The inputs to the adaptive elements may be derived from *tapped-delay-line or frequency-domain array-processing filters.*

The detailed design of an adaptive antenna system depends upon the performance criterion selected. Two of the most useful criteria are the *signal-to-noise ratio* and the *mean-square error.* The latter criterion combined with the method of steepest descent leads to the *Widrow-Hoff algorithm.* This algorithm is often implemented in practical systems.

The *adaptive noise canceller* differs from classical adaptive systems primarily in that the estimate of the desired response is derived from a separate antenna, called the *primary antenna,* rather than from an internal generator. The sidelobe canceller is a special type of adaptive noise canceller. The *adaptive notch filter,* which removes periodic interference signals from wide-bandwidth desired signals, is another variation of the adaptive noise canceller.

Classical adaptive systems and the adaptive noise canceller sometimes exhibit unintentional cancellation of the desired signal. To preclude such a possibility, the *constrained minimum power criterion* can be used in the design of an adaptive system. The resulting system automatically limits the cancellation of the desired signal, while still adaptively filtering the interference.

5.2 SIDELOBE CANCELLER

An adaptive antenna system automatically monitors its output and adjusts its parameters accordingly. It does so in order to reduce the impact of interference that enters through the sidelobes, or possibly the mainlobe, of its antenna radiation pattern, while still allowing reception of an intended transmission. The design of an adaptive antenna system requires little *a priori* knowledge of the signal or interference characteristics.

The *sidelobe canceller* is a classic example of an adaptive antenna system. It not only is of practical importance, but also provides an introduction to the fundamental concepts of adaptive antenna systems.

Figure 5.1 shows a version of a sidelobe canceller. The *primary* and *reference* signals are outputs of two separate antennas or two different groups of elements in a single phased-array antenna. It is intended that the reference signal provide an estimate of the interference in the primary signal. After suitable processing, this estimate is subtracted from the primary signal. As a result, the interference, which may have en-

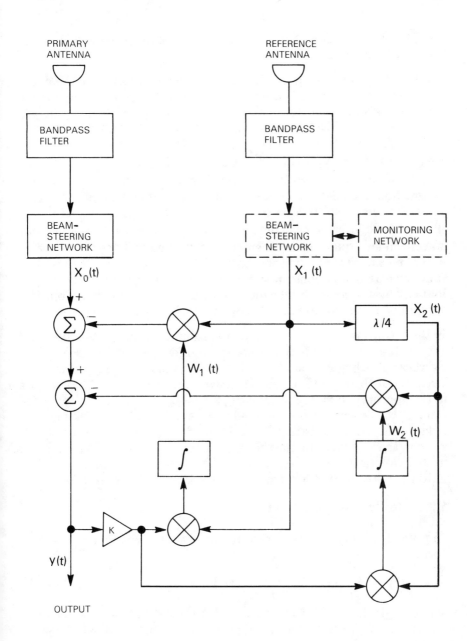

Figure 5.1/Sidelobe canceller.

tered through the sidelobes of the primary antenna, is reduced or eliminated by cancellation.

Ideally, the reference signal, $X_1(t)$, has a large interference component and a small desired signal component, whereas $X_0(t)$ may have a much larger desired signal component. The quarter-wavelength delay shown in Figure 5.1 produces a signal, $X_2(t)$, that is in phase quadrature with $X_1(t)$. (A quadrature hybrid could be used instead of the delay.) The weight functions, $W_1(t)$ and $W_2(t)$, regulate the amounts of $X_1(t)$ and $X_2(t)$ that are subtracted from $X_0(t)$. The relative magnitudes of the weight functions determine the magnitude and the phase of the total waveform that is subtracted from $X_0(t)$. If the magnitudes and the phases of the interference component of $X_0(t)$ and the total subtracted waveform are equal, the interference is cancelled and does not appear in the output, y(t). If the cancellation is nearly complete, the weight functions are nearly constants; if it is not, the weight functions vary in such a way that the total subtracted waveform gradually becomes a facsimile of the interference component of $X_0(t)$.

In the following analysis, we make no assumptions about the directionality of the primary antenna beam or the reference antenna beam. However, it is highly desirable to have the primary beam point in the direction of the desired signal. The *beam-steering network* forms a beam in the appropriate direction by using various types of *a priori* information. If the antenna is part of a radar system, the information may be radar return characteristics. If the antenna is part of a communication system, the information may be the characteristics of a pilot signal transmitted along with the message signal. The antenna system then locks onto the pilot to form a beam in the direction of the transmitter.

5.2.1 Steady-State Operation

In general, the desired signal received by the primary antenna has the form

$$s(t) = A_s(t) \cos [\omega_0 t + \phi_s(t)] , \qquad (5.1)$$

where ω_0 is the carrier frequency, and $A_s(t)$ and $\phi_s(t)$ are modulation functions. We assume that interference (which may be due to jamming), after passage through the bandpass filter of the primary branch, has the form

$$J(t) = A_j(t) \cos [\omega_1 t + \phi_j(t)] , \qquad (5.2)$$

where ω_1 is the carrier frequency, and $A_j(t)$ and $\phi_j(t)$ are modulation functions. Neglecting the thermal noise, the output of the bandpass filter of the primary branch is

$$X_0(t) = A_s(t) \cos [\omega_0 t + \phi_s(t)]$$

$$+ A_j(t) \cos [\omega_1 t + \phi_j(t)] . \tag{5.3}$$

Because of a possible difference in the radiation patterns of the two antennas, the signals received by the reference antenna may experience different amplifications than the same signals do when received by the primary antenna. Each signal has a different arrival time and, hence, a phase shift at the reference antenna relative to the same signal at the primary antenna. We assume that the antennas are close enough that the difference in arrival time of a signal at the two antennas is much less than the inverse signal bandwidth. Thus, the modulation functions are negligibly affected by this difference. We conclude that the output of the bandpass filter of the reference branch can be represented by

$$X_1(t) = C_1 A_s(t) \cos [\omega_0 t + \phi_s(t) + \theta_1]$$

$$+ C_2 A_j(t) \cos [\omega_1 t + \phi_j(t) + \theta_2] , \tag{5.4}$$

where θ_1 and θ_2 are phase angles, and C_1 and C_2 are real constants. If the sources of the desired signal and the interference are separated geometrically, then $\theta_1 \neq \theta_2$. If the sources are mobile, then θ_1 and θ_2 are functions of time. The magnitudes of the primary antenna gains in the directions of the desired signal and the interference are denoted by G_{ps} and G_{pj}, respectively. The magnitudes of the reference antenna gains in the directions of the desired signal and the interference are denoted by G_{rs} and G_{rj}, respectively. From these definitions, we have

$$C_1 = \left(\frac{G_{rs}}{G_{ps}} \right)^{1/2} , \qquad C_2 = \left(\frac{G_{rj}}{G_{pj}} \right)^{1/2} . \tag{5.5}$$

The integrators are designed to integrate over the time interval $I = [t - T, t]$, where T is such that

$$\omega_0 T \gg 1 . \tag{5.6}$$

We assume that the bandpass filter is narrowband so that

$$\omega_0 \gg 2\pi B , \tag{5.7}$$

where B is the bandwidth of the bandpass filters in hertz. Thus, the bandwidth due to the message modulation is much less than the carrier frequency. For practical values of ω_0, the bandwidths associated with any time variations of θ_1 and θ_2 are also much less than ω_0.

The quarter-wavelength delay is designed to introduce a 90-degree phase shift in the intended transmission. Since $|\omega_0 - \omega_1| < 2\pi B$, Equation (5.7) indicates that this delay also introduces nearly a 90-degree phase shift in the interference, although it does not significantly affect the modulation waveforms. Thus,

$$X_2(t) = C_1 A_s(t) \sin [\omega_0 t + \phi_s(t) + \theta_1]$$
$$+ C_2 A_j(t) \sin [\omega_1 t + \phi_j(t) + \theta_2] . \qquad (5.8)$$

The *signal-to-interference ratio at the primary input* is defined by

$$\rho_i = \frac{\dfrac{1}{T} \displaystyle\int_I s^2(u) \, du}{\dfrac{1}{T} \displaystyle\int_I J^2(u) \, du}$$

$$= \frac{\displaystyle\int_I A_s^2 \, du + \int_I A_s^2 \cos (2\omega_0 u + 2\phi_s) \, du}{\displaystyle\int_I A_j^2 \, du + \int_I A_j^2 \cos (2\omega_1 u + 2\phi_j) \, du} . \qquad (5.9)$$

In general, ρ_i is a function of time. The steady state is defined to exist when the first terms in the numerator and the denominator are nearly constant.

During steady state, Equations (5.6) and (5.7) imply that the second terms in the numerator and the denominator are negligible compared with the first terms. Thus,

$$\rho_i \cong \frac{\displaystyle\int_I A_s^2 (u) \, du}{\displaystyle\int_I A_j^2 (u) \, du} = \frac{G_{ps}}{G_{pj}} \, \rho_n \, , \qquad (5.10)$$

where ρ_n is the ratio that would exist if the primary pattern were omnidirectional. Similarly, *the signal-to-interference ratio at the reference input* is found to be

$$\rho_r \cong \left(\frac{C_1}{C_2}\right)^2 \rho_i$$

$$= \frac{G_{rs}}{G_{rj}} \rho_n \ . \tag{5.11}$$

Although ρ_i, ρ_r, and ρ_n are functions of time in general, they are nearly constant during the steady state.

From Figure 5.1, the output, $y(t)$, and the *weighting functions*, $W_1(t)$ and $W_2(t)$, are given by

$$y(t) = X_0(t) - W_1(t)X_1(t) - W_2(t)X_2(t) \ , \tag{5.12}$$

$$W_1(t) = K\int_I y(u)X_1(u) \ du \ , \tag{5.13}$$

$$W_2(t) = K\int_I y(u)X_2(u) \ du \ , \tag{5.14}$$

where the constant K is the gain of a linear amplifier. Substituting Equation (5.12) into Equation (5.13), we obtain

$$W_1(t) = K\int_I X_0(u)X_1(u) \ du - K\int_I W_1(u)X_1^2(u) \ du$$

$$- K\int_I W_2(u)X_1(u)X_2(u) \ du \ . \tag{5.15}$$

We shall show that $W_1(t)$ and $W_2(t)$ are nearly constant if ρ_r, θ_1, and θ_2 are nearly constant. In this case, $W_1(t)$ and $W_2(t)$ can be removed outside the integrals with negligible error, so that

$$W_1(t) = K\int_I X_0(u)X_1(u) \ du - KW_1(t)\int_I X_1^2(u) \ du$$

$$- KW_2(t)\int_I X_1(u)X_2(u) \ du \ . \tag{5.16}$$

In a similar manner, we obtain

$$W_2(t) = K\int_I X_0(u)X_2(u) \ du - KW_2(t)\int_I X_2^2(u)du$$

$$- KW_1(t)\int_I X_1(u)X_2(u) \ du \ . \tag{5.17}$$

Equations (5.4), (5.6), (5.7) and (5.8) and simple trigonometry show that

$$\int_I X_2^2(u) \ du \cong \int_I X_1^2(u) \ du \tag{5.18}$$

during the steady state. Using this approximation to solve Equations (5.16) and (5.17) simultaneously yields

$$W_1(t) = \frac{V_1 V_3 - V_2 V_4}{V_1^2 - V_2^2} \, , \qquad (5.19)$$

$$W_2(t) = \frac{V_1 V_4 - V_2 V_3}{V_1^2 - V_2^2} \, , \qquad (5.20)$$

where we define

$$V_1 = \frac{1}{K} + \int_I X_1^2(u) \, du \, , \qquad (5.21)$$

$$V_2 = \int_I X_1(u) X_2(u) \, du \, , \qquad (5.22)$$

$$V_3 = \int_I X_0(u) X_1(u) \, du \, , \qquad (5.23)$$

$$V_4 = \int_I X_0(u) X_2(u) \, du \, . \qquad (5.24)$$

Evaluating the integrals with Equations (5.3), (5.4), and (5.8) and substituting equations (5.19) and (5.20) into Equation (5.12) give an expression for the output in terms of the desired signal and interference.

In most cases of interest, some simplification is possible. If T and K are sufficiently large, the first term on the right-hand side of Equation (5.21) can be ignored. Substituting Equations (5.4) and (5.8) into Equation (5.22) shows that V_2 is very small during steady-state operation. Consequently, it is reasonable to neglect V_2 in Equations (5.19) and (5.20). As a result of these approximations, we have

$$W_1(t) = \frac{\int_I X_0(u) X_1(u) \, du}{\int_I X_1^2(u) \, du} \, , \qquad (5.25)$$

$$W_2(t) = \frac{\int_I X_0(u) X_2(u) \, du}{\int_I X_1^2(u) \, du} \, . \qquad (5.26)$$

Thus, the weighting functions are essentially normalized cross-correlation functions. From Equations (5.3), (5.4), (5.6), (5.7), and (5.8), we obtain

$$\int_I X_1^2(u)\, du = \int_I \left\{ \frac{C_1^2}{2} A_s^2(u) + \frac{C_2^2}{2} A_j^2(u) + C_1 C_2 A_s(u) A_j(u) \right.$$

$$\times \cos\left[(\omega_0 - \omega_1)u + \phi_s(u) - \phi_j(u) + \theta_1 \right.$$

$$\left. \left. - \theta_2 \right] \right\} du \; , \tag{5.27}$$

$$\int_I X_0(u) X_1(u)\, du = \int_I \left\{ \frac{C_1}{2} A_s^2(u) \cos\theta_1 + \frac{C_2}{2} A_j^2(u) \cos\theta_2 \right.$$

$$+ \frac{C_1}{2} A_s(u) A_j(u) \cos\left[(\omega_0 - \omega_1)u \right.$$

$$+ \phi_s(u) - \phi_j(u) + \theta_1] + \frac{C_2}{2} A_s(u) A_j(u)$$

$$\left. \times \cos\left[(\omega_0 - \omega_1)u + \phi_s(u) - \phi_j(u) - \theta_2 \right] \right\} du \; ,$$

$$\tag{5.28}$$

$$\int_I X_0(u) X_2(u)\, du = \int_I \left\{ \frac{C_1}{2} A_s^2(u) \sin\theta_1 + \frac{C_2}{2} A_j^2(u) \sin\theta_2 \right.$$

$$+ \frac{C_1}{2} A_s(u) A_j(u) \sin\left[(\omega_0 - \omega_1)u \right.$$

$$- \phi_s(u) - \phi_j(u) + \theta_1] - \frac{C_2}{2} A_s(u) A_j(u)$$

$$\left. \times \sin\left[(\omega_0 - \omega_1)u + \phi_s(u) - \phi_j(u) - \theta_2 \right] \right\} du \; .$$

$$\tag{5.29}$$

In general, since the desired signal is unsynchronized with the interference, we expect that, during steady-state operation,

$$\int_I s_1(u, \phi_1) J_1(u, \phi_2) \, du \cong 0 \ , \qquad (5.30)$$

where $s_1(u, \phi_1)$ is the desired signal with an arbitrary phase shift of ϕ_1, and $J_1(u, \phi_2)$ is the interference signal with an arbitrary phase shift of ϕ_2. If Equation (5.30) is valid, the desired signal and interference are said to be uncorrelated in the time-average sense.

Equation (5.30) implies that only the first two terms of Equations (5.27) to (5.29) need to be retained. By using Equations (5.10) and (5.11), Equations (5.25) to (5.30) yield

$$W_1 = \frac{C_1 \cos \theta_2 + C_2 \rho_r \cos \theta_1}{C_1 C_2 (1 + \rho_r)} \ , \qquad (5.31)$$

$$W_2 = \frac{C_1 \sin \theta_2 + C_2 \rho_r \sin \theta_1}{C_1 C_2 (1 + \rho_r)} \ . \qquad (5.32)$$

These equations indicate that W_1 and W_2 are approximately constant if ρ_r, θ_1, and θ_2 are approximately constant. Thus, the initial assumption that the weighting functions are constant has been verified as consistent with the other approximations made in deriving these equations.

We now substitute into Equation (5.12) and employ trigonometric identities. Using equations (5.10) and (5.11), the final result is

$$(1 + \rho_r) y(t) = A_s(t) \cos [\omega_0 t + \phi_s(t)]$$
$$- \frac{1}{\alpha} A_s(t) \cos [\omega_0 t + \phi_s(t) + \theta_1 - \theta_2]$$
$$+ \rho_r A_j(t) \cos [\omega_1 t + \phi_j(t)]$$
$$- \rho_r \alpha A_j(t) \cos [\omega_1 t + \phi_j(t) - \theta_1 + \theta_2] \ ,$$

$$\qquad (5.33)$$

where

$$\alpha = \left(\frac{G_{ps} G_{rj}}{G_{pj} G_{rs}} \right)^{1/2} . \qquad (5.34)$$

The *signal-to-interference ratio at the output* of the sidelobe canceller, ρ_0, is calculated as the ratio of the average power over interval I in the first two terms to the average power over interval I in the last two terms of the right side of Equation (5.33). If $y(t) \neq 0$, the result is the remarkably simple formula,

$$\rho_0 = \frac{1}{\rho_r} . \tag{5.35}$$

Thus, the interference component of the primary signal has been nearly cancelled if $\rho_r \ll 1$. We conclude that the output signal distortion is small when the signal power at the reference antenna is relatively low. An important approximation made in deriving Equations (5.33) and (5.35) is that the thermal noise is negligible.

If the interference source is almost directly behind the source of the desired signal, then $\alpha \cong 1$ and $\theta_1 \cong \theta_2$. Since Equation (5.33) indicates that $y(t) \cong 0$, the output signal is buried in the thermal noise. We conclude that the sidelobe canceller is ineffective in this case.

A strong desired signal in the reference channel can induce cancellation of the desired signal at the output. Specifically, if $\rho_i \rho_r \gg 1$, Equation (5.35) gives $\rho_0 \ll \rho_i$. Consequently, the adaptive system causes a performance degradation relative to the performance of the primary antenna operating alone. Equation (5.11) indicates that designing the system so that $G_{rs} \ll G_{rj}$ is helpful in ensuring small values of ρ_r. Thus, a reference antenna with a beam that points in the direction of the interference is highly desirable. One possible implementation is to use a beam-steering network that enables a reference beam to search for interfering signals of high power or special characteristics.

Since the direction of the interference is usually unknown *a priori*, and since there may be two or more spatially separated interference sources present, $G_{rs} \ll G_{rj}$ might be achieved if we deploy several reference antennas, each with a directional beam, as shown schematically in Figure 5.2. The reference beams point in various directions relative to the primary beam. The output of each reference antenna feeds a cancellation network similar to that of Figure 5.1. A configuration of this type is known as a *multiple sidelobe canceller* since it provides the possibility of cancelling multiple interfering signals entering at two or more different points of the sidelobes of the primary pattern. A less expensive multiple sidelobe canceller uses omnidirectional reference antennas [1].

Even if $G_{rs} \ll G_{rj}$, serious cancellation of the desired signal can occur if the interference is so small that $\rho_r \gg 1$. To prevent this disaster, the reference input can be monitored and its propagation can be blocked unless its amplitude or power exceeds a fixed threshold. Thus, the adaptive mechanism is disabled unless the interference is strong enough to warrant its use.

If the reference antenna is disconnected and an unmodulated carrier is injected as $X_1(t)$, the adaptive antenna system behaves as a notch filter at the carrier frequency. To demonstrate this effect, we set C_1 = 0 and assume that $A_j(t)$ and $\phi_j(t)$ are constants in Equations (5.3) and (5.4). If Equation (5.30) is valid, we obtain y(t) = s(t), indicating complete cancellation of the interfering carrier. However, Equation (5.30) is not valid if $A_s(t)$ and $\phi_s(t)$ are constants and $\omega_0 = \omega_1$. In this case, a straightforward but tedious calculation using Equations (5.3), (5.4), (5.8), (5.12), and (5.25) to (5.29) gives y(t) $\cong$ 0, indicating complete cancellation of the primary input.

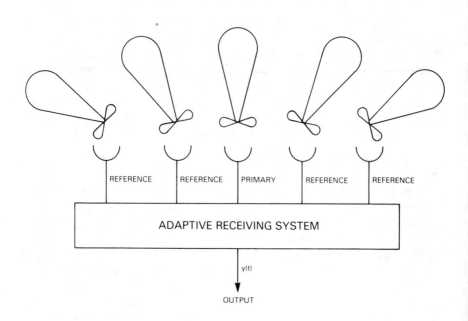

Figure 5.2/Multiple sidelobe canceller.

5.2.2 Adaptive Null Steering

We can interpret the operation of the adaptive antenna system in terms of *adaptive null steering*. Since we are not seeking to obtain new results, but only to interpret old ones, we simplify the mathematics by assuming that $\alpha \gg 1$. Thus, the second term of Equation (5.33) is negligible compared with the first, and the third term is negligible compared with the fourth. Decomposing the first and fourth terms yields

$$y(t) \cong [s(t) + J_1(t)]$$
$$- \left[\frac{\rho_r}{1 + \rho_r} s(t) + \left(1 + \frac{\rho_r \alpha}{1 + \rho_r} \right) J_1(t) \right],$$
$$\alpha \gg 1,$$

$$(5.36)$$

where

$$J_1(t) = A_j(t) \cos[\omega_1 t + \phi_j(t) - \theta_1 + \theta_2] \qquad (5.37)$$

is a phase-shifted version of $J(t)$. The first bracketed term on the right-hand side of Equation (5.36) can be interpreted as the response due to the primary antenna with gains G_{ps} and G_{pj} in the directions of the desired signal and interference, respectively. The second bracketed term can be interpreted as the response due to an equivalent pattern, the output of which is subtracted from the primary output to give $y(t)$.

With this interpretation, the *equivalent cancellation pattern* or *adaptive beam* has gains

$$G_s' = \left(\frac{\rho_r}{1 + \rho_r} \right)^2 G_{ps}, \quad \alpha \gg 1, \qquad (5.38)$$

$$G_j' = \left(1 + \frac{\rho_r \alpha}{1 + \rho_r} \right)^2 G_{pj}, \quad \alpha \gg 1, \qquad (5.39)$$

in the directions of the desired signal and interference, respectively.

The equivalent overall pattern of the adaptive antenna system provides the gains

$$G_s'' = \left(\sqrt{G_{ps}} - \sqrt{G_s'} \right)^2 = \left(\frac{1}{1 + \rho_r} \right)^2 G_{ps} \, ,$$

$$\alpha \gg 1 \, , \qquad (5.40)$$

$$G_j'' = \left(\sqrt{G_{pj}} - \sqrt{G_j'} \right)^2 = \left(\frac{\rho_r \alpha}{1 + \rho_r} \right)^2 G_{pj} \, ,$$

$$\alpha \gg 1 \, , \qquad (5.41)$$

in the directions of the desired signal and interference, respectively. If ρ_r is small, Equation (5.40) gives $G_s'' \cong G_{ps}$. If ρ_r is so small that $\rho_r \alpha \ll 1$, Equation (5.41) indicates that G_j'' is much smaller than G_{pj}. Thus, an approximate null can be created in the direction of the interference. For this reason, the action of an adaptive antenna system is sometimes called null steering. A pictorial representation is given in Figure 5.3.

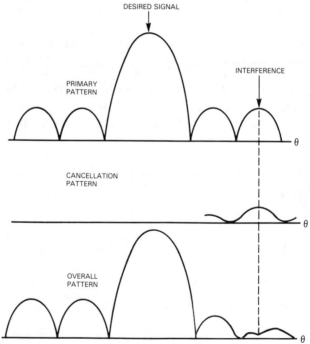

Figure 5.3/Adaptive beam forming and null steering.

An analysis based upon the *Wiener-Hopf equation*, which is derived in Section 5.3, shows that if the narrowband condition given by Equation (5.7) is not satisfied, then the performance of the sidelobe canceller of Figure 5.1 deteriorates [2]. Consequently, adaptive systems intended to handle wide-bandwidth signals must use more elaborate processing, such as that provided by delay lines with multiple taps.

Although the major features of the sidelobe canceller have been determined, the theoretical motivation for the configuration of Figure 5.1 has not been discussed. For this purpose and to explore alternative configurations, we consider the classical theory of adaptive antenna systems.

5.3 CLASSICAL THEORY

An adaptive antenna system consists of an antenna array, fixed processing elements, and *adaptive elements*. Its purpose is to remove externally generated interference from a receiver signal. The adaptive elements have one of the forms shown in Figure 5.4. In Figure 5.4(a), the weight adjustment mechanism responds to the output; in Figure 5.4(b), it responds to the error, which is the difference between the *desired response* and the output. Ideally, the desired response, d, is the received signal minus the interference and the noise. In practice, d is a signal with the general characteristics, but not the detailed structure, of the signals that the antenna system is attempting to receive. The forms in Figure 5.4 are not necessarily optimal, but are used because of their simplicity and compatibility with computer-controlled systems. The inputs, X_1, X_2, . . ., X_N, are derived from fixed processing elements and may be either continuous or discrete-time signals. The inputs are applied to weights W_1, W_2, . . ., W_N, which are continually adjusted as a function of the output or the error. The basic adaptive elements can be used in a variety of different systems.

The inputs may be derived from a *tapped delay line*, as shown in Figure 5.5. Each of the K antenna outputs is filtered, delayed, and then applied to a line consisting of L tap points and L $-$ 1 ideal time delays of δ seconds each. The number of inputs to the adaptive weights is N = KL.

Each input of Figure 5.4 may be the discrete Fourier transform at a specific frequency, say f_j, of an antenna output. With this interpretation for Figure 5.4(b), the desired response is the discrete Fourier

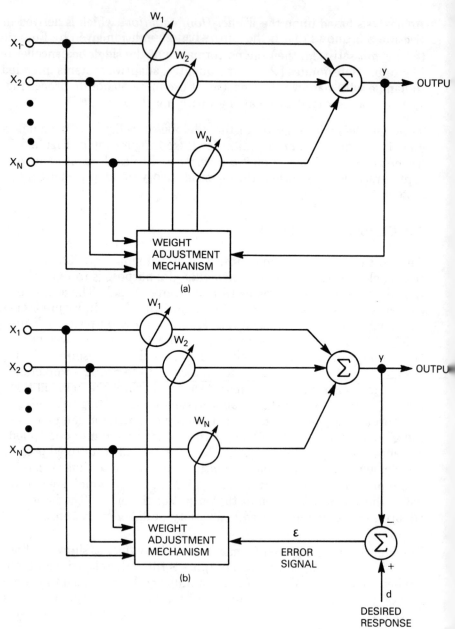

Figure 5.4/Basic adaptive elements. Weight adjustment is controlled by (a) output or (b) error signal.

transform at f_i of the desired waveform. A complete *frequency-domain array-processing filter* feeds K of the adaptive elements — one for each of K discrete frequencies, as illustrated in Figure 5.6. This filter may be attractive if the desired waveform is a complicated function of time, but has a simple Fourier transform.

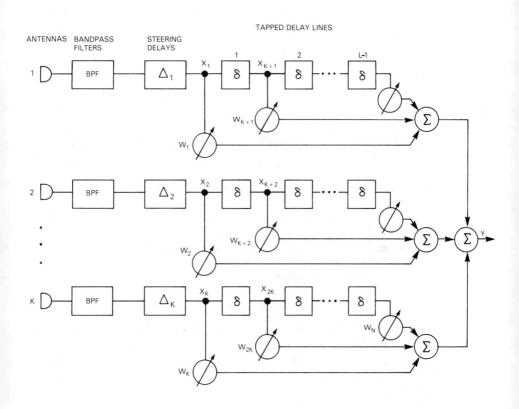

Figure 5.5/General form of tapped delay-line array-processing filter.

To develop adaptive algorithms, we first determine the optimal fixed weights. Then adaptive algorithms can be determined that yield weights converging to the optimal fixed weights.

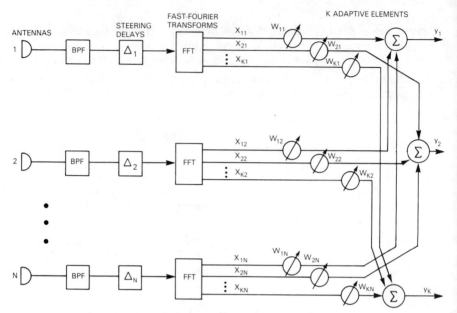

Figure 5.6/General form of frequency-domain array-processing filter.

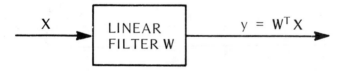

Figure 5.7/Optimization problem.

The derivation of the optimal fixed weights depends upon the specification of a performance criterion or estimation procedure and the modeling of the signals received by the antennas. For fixed weights, the optimization problem is illustrated in Figure 5.7. The input and weight vectors are

$$X = \begin{bmatrix} X_1 \\ X_2 \\ \cdot \\ \cdot \\ \cdot \\ X_N \end{bmatrix}, \quad W = \begin{bmatrix} W_1 \\ W_2 \\ \cdot \\ \cdot \\ \cdot \\ W_N \end{bmatrix} \cdot \tag{5.42}$$

The input is a function of the desired signal, interference, and thermal noise. The scalar output is

$$y = W^T X , \qquad (5.43)$$

where the superscript T denotes the transpose. The output is an estimate of the desired response, d. The filter or combiner of Figure 5.7 is linear because the weights are fixed. Since their characteristics change in response to changes in the characteristics of their inputs, adaptive systems are intrinsically nonlinear. However, adaptive systems can be designed that approximate the optimal linear filter after a sufficient amount of adaptation.

Several different estimators of d can be implemented by the linear filter of Figure 5.7. If the received vector, X, is assumed to have a Gaussian distribution, maximum likelihood estimation of the desired signal components of the received waveform leads to an estimator that is a linear function of X. However, the Gaussian assumption is unwarranted when interference is present. Estimators that depend only upon the second-order moments of X can be derived using performance criteria based upon the *signal-to-noise ratio* or the *mean-square error* of the filter output. Consequently, maximum likelihood estimation is not pursued further in this chapter. Griffiths [3] compares the maximum likelihood filter and the *Wiener filter*, which is described below.

5.3.1 Signal-to-Noise Ratio Criterion

A reasonable design criterion for adaptive radar systems is the maximization of the probability of detection for fixed probability of false alarm [4]. This maximization has been shown to be equivalent to a maximization of a generalized signal-to-noise ratio, which is itself an intuitively appealing design criterion.

Consider the maximization of the signal-to-noise ratio at the output of the adaptive element of Figure 5.4(a) [5]. By noise, we mean the combined thermal noise and externally generated interference. We assume that the input vector, X, is the sum of two components,

$$X = Hd + n , \qquad (5.44)$$

where H is an N-dimensional column vector of constants, n is an N-dimensional column vector of noise components that are derived from stationary processes, and d is the deterministic desired signal. We treat all vector components and scalars as complex variables. Consequently, our results apply to adaptive elements fed by the system of Figure 5.6

and to narrowband systems for which d is the complex envelope representation of the desired signal.

The component of the output, y, that is due to the desired signal is

$$y_s = W^T H d \ , \tag{5.45}$$

and the component of y that is due to the noise is

$$y_n = W^T n = n^T W \ . \tag{5.46}$$

At a single instant of time, the signal power at the output is

$$R_s = |y_s|^2 = |W^T H d|^2 \ . \tag{5.47}$$

Let a prime denote the conjugate transpose and an asterisk denote the conjugate. The mean noise power in the output is

$$R_n = E\left[(n^T W)' (n^T W)\right] = W' R_{nn} W \ , \tag{5.48}$$

where $E[x]$ is the expected value of x and $R_{nn} = E[n^* n^T]$ is the correlation matrix of the noise. The signal-to-noise ratio is

$$P = \frac{R_s}{R_n} = \frac{|W^T H d|^2}{W' R_{nn} W} \ . \tag{5.49}$$

Assuming that $R_n > 0$ for all W, R_{nn} is positive definite. From its definition, R_{nn} is Hermitian (See Appendix D).

A positive definite Hermitian matrix has positive eigenvalues. Thus, it can be diagonalized to the identity matrix. We define the nonsingular N x N matrix,

$$D = \left[\frac{e_1}{\sqrt{\lambda_1}} \quad \frac{e_2}{\sqrt{\lambda_2}} \quad \cdots \quad \frac{e_N}{\sqrt{\lambda_N}} \right] \ , \tag{5.50}$$

where the λ_i are the eigenvalues and the e_i are the corresponding orthonormal eigenvectors of R_{nn}. Straightforward matrix algebra yields

$$I = D' R_{nn} D \ , \tag{5.51}$$

where I is the identity matrix.

Combining this result with Equation (5.48) gives

$$R_n = W'(D')^{-1} D' R_{nn} D D^{-1} W$$

$$= (D^{-1} W)' (D^{-1} W) = \| D^{-1} W \|^2 \ , \tag{5.52}$$

where $\| x \|^2 = x' x$ is the squared Euclidean norm of the vector x. Using the Cauchy-Schwarz inequality, Equation (5.47) yields

$$R_s = |W^T(D^T)^{-1}D^THd|^2$$

$$= |(D^{-1}W)^TD^THd|^2$$

$$= |(D^{-1}W)'D'H^*|^2 |d|^2$$

$$\leqslant \| D^{-1}W \|^2 \| D'H^* \|^2 |d|^2 . \tag{5.53}$$

Equality in this equation is attained if

$$D^{-1}W = cD'H^* , \tag{5.54}$$

where c is an arbitrary constant. Substituting Equations (5.52) and (5.53) into Equation (5.49), it follows that

$$P \leqslant \| D'H^* \|^2 |d|^2 . \tag{5.55}$$

The maximum value of P is attained if Equation (5.54) is satisfied. Thus, the optimal choice of W is

$$W_0 = cDD'H^* . \tag{5.56}$$

By using Equation (5.51), this relation becomes

$$W_0 = cR_{nn}^{-1}H^* . \tag{5.57}$$

The value of P corresponding to optimal weights is

$$P_0 = \| D'H^* \|^2 |d|^2$$

$$= H^TDD'H^*|d|^2 = H^TR_{nn}^{-1}H^* |d|^2 . \tag{5.58}$$

To implement Equation (5.57), we must know the values of the components of H. Since adaptive systems have more than one antenna (or array element), this knowledge implies that the direction of arrival of the desired signal is known.

5.3.2 Mean-Square Error Criterion

The most widely used method of estimation is based on the minimization of the mean-square error [6]. Instead of assuming a known direction of arrival, we assume that a facsimile of the desired response is supplied. We assume that X and d are derived from stationary stochastic processes. Similar results can be obtained by modeling X and d as continuous-time or discrete-time deterministic variables and minimizing the time- or sample-average square error.

Because it is convenient and because the results are usually applied to systems of the form of Figure 5.5, we assume that all scalars and matrix components are real. Referring to Figure 5.4(b), the difference between the desired response and the output is the error signal,

$$\epsilon = d - W^T X . \tag{5.59}$$

We square both sides of this equation and take the expected value. Regarding W as fixed and noting that $W^T X = X^T W$, the mean-square error is

$$E[\epsilon^2] = E[(d - W^T X)^2]$$
$$= E[d^2] + W^T R_{xx} W - 2W^T R_{xd} , \tag{5.60}$$

where

$$R_{xx} = E[XX^T] \tag{5.61}$$

is the symmetric correlation matrix of X, and

$$R_{xd} = E[Xd] \tag{5.62}$$

is a vector of cross correlations between the input signals and the desired response. Taking the gradient of Equation (5.60) with respect to W yields the column vector

$$\nabla E[\epsilon^2] = 2R_{xx} W - 2R_{xd} . \tag{5.63}$$

Setting the gradient equal to zero, we obtain a necessary condition for the optimal weight vector W_0. Assuming that the output is nonzero, R_{xx} is positive definite. Thus, it is nonsingular so that we obtain

$$W_0 = R_{xx}^{-1} R_{xd} . \tag{5.64}$$

This equation is the *Wiener-Hopf equation* for the optimal weight vector. The associated linear filter is called the *Wiener filter*. To show that W_0 produces the minimum mean-square error, we set $W = W_0$ in Equation (5.60) to obtain the mean-square error corresponding to W_0,

$$E_R = E[d^2] - W_0^T R_{xx} W_0$$
$$= E[d^2] - R_{xd}^T R_{xx}^{-1} R_{xd} . \tag{5.65}$$

Substituting Equation (5.65) into Equation (5.60) and using Equation (5.64) to eliminate R_{xd}, we may express the mean-square error in the form

$$E[\epsilon^2] = E_R + (W - W_0)^T R_{xx}(W - W_0) . \tag{5.66}$$

Since R_{xx} is positive definite, this expression shows that W_0 is a unique optimal weight vector and E_R is the minimum mean-square error. Equation (5.66) describes a multidimensional quadratic function of the weights that can be visualized in two dimensions as a bowl-shaped surface. The purpose of adaptation is to continually seek the bottom of the bowl.

5.3.3 Steepest Descent

In the implementation of either Equation (5.57) or Equation (5.64), the presence of interference means that the correlation matrix, R_{nn} or R_{xx} , is unknown. For this reason, approximations of the equations must be determined. Since the computational difficulties of the matrix inversions are considerable when the number of weights is large or time-varying signal statistics require frequent computations, most of the approximations developed involve recursion relations and gradient or random search techniques [7]. However, for sampled data systems, direct implementation of the equations after suitable approximations of the matrix elements has been shown to exhibit rapid convergence in certain circumstances [8].

Because the theory has been extensively investigated and it has often been implemented, we consider the approximation of Equation (5.64) by the *method of steepest descent*. The approximation of Equation (5.57) implies a similar adaptive weight adjustment mechanism [4]. We treat X, W, and d as discrete-time, sampled-value variables and use the index k to denote a particular sampling instant or *adaptation cycle*. The results for continuous-time systems are analogous.

In the method of steepest descent, the weight vector is changed along the direction of the negative gradient of the mean-square error. Using Equation (5.63), we obtain

$$W(k + 1) = W(k) - \mu\nabla E[\epsilon^2]$$
$$= W(k) - 2\mu [R_{xx}W(k) - R_{xd}] , \qquad (5.67)$$

where the scalar constant μ controls the rate of convergence and stability. The adaptation cycle begins with an arbitrary initial weight. As it stands, this method eliminates the need to compute the inverse of R_{xx} , but still requires approximation of R_{xx} and R_{xd} .

The *Griffiths algorithm* [9] results if R_{xx} is replaced by $X(k)X^T(k)$ and R_{xd} is directly estimated; that is, we use

$$W(k + 1) \quad = \quad W(k) - 2\mu\,[X(k)X^T(k)W(k) - \hat{R}_{xd}]$$

$$= \quad W(k) - 2\mu\,[X(k)y(k) - \hat{R}_{xd}]\ , \qquad (5.68)$$

where $\hat{R}_{xd}$ is an estimate of R_{xd}. The problem with this algorithm is that an accurate estimate of R_{xd} is difficult if the amplitude of the desired signal component of X is unknown.

The *Widrow-Hoff algorithm* [6], also known as the *least-mean-square* (LMS) *algorithm*, approximates R_{xd} by $X(k)d(k)$ so that

$$W(k + 1) \quad = \quad W(k) - 2\mu[X(k)X^T(k)W(k) - X(k)d(k)]$$

$$= \quad W(k) + 2\mu\epsilon(k)X(k)\ . \qquad (5.69)$$

This iteration rule states that the next weight vector is obtained by adding to the present weight vector the input vector scaled by the amount of error. It is shown in Section 5.6 that, for an appropriate value of μ, the mean of the weight vector converges to the optimal value given by the Wiener-Hopf equation. Figure 5.8 shows a block-diagram representation of Equation (5.69) for one component of the weight vector.

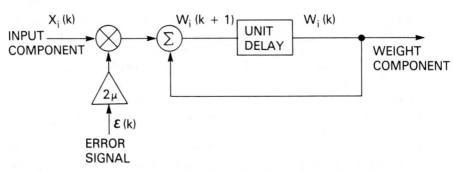

Figure 5.8/Digital realization of Widrow-Hoff algorithm.

In analog implementations of continuous systems, Equation (5.69) becomes the differential equation

$$\frac{d}{dt}\,W(t) \quad = \quad 2\mu\epsilon(t)X(t)\ . \qquad (5.70)$$

Equivalently, if $W(0) = 0$,

$$W(t) \quad = \quad 2\mu\int_0^t \epsilon(\tau)X(\tau)\,d\tau\ . \qquad (5.71)$$

Figure 5.9 shows a realization of one component of this equation.

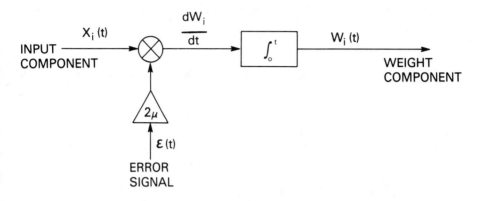

Figure 5.9/Analog realization of Widrow-Hoff algorithm.

One potential problem with the Widrow-Hoff algorithm can be explained in terms of the overall equivalent radiation pattern of the antenna array. Adaptation causes the array to form a beam in the direction of the desired signal, while reducing or nulling the array response in the direction of the interference. If the desired signal is not transmitted, the adaptation may reduce the response in the direction of this signal so that communication is hindered or disabled when transmission is resumed. To alleviate this problem, a *pilot signal* may be used.

A pilot signal is a vector, each component of which is an estimate of the desired signal that would appear at an antenna output if no interference or noise were present. In other words, the pilot signal is constructed to have spectral and directional characteristics similar to those of the incoming signal of interest. Two different algorithms that use the pilot signal have been proposed. In the *two-mode algorithm*, adaptation alternates between adapting only on the pilot signal and adapting only on the signals actually received by the array. The *one-mode algorithm* adapts on the sum of the pilot signal and the received signal. Details of the performance of the pilot signal method can be found in the literature [6, 9].

The desired response, d, is required at each iteration of Equation (5.69). An estimate of the desired response, denoted by $\hat{d}$, can be generated for some types of communications by feedback systems of the forms shown in Figure 5.10. For effective operation, $\hat{d}$ does not have to be a perfect replica of the desired response; if it were, we would not need the adaptive antenna system. However, the Wiener-Hopf equation, which we would like to approximately satisfy, indicates that $\hat{d}$ should be such that

$$R_{x\hat{d}} \cong R_{xd} \;. \tag{5.72}$$

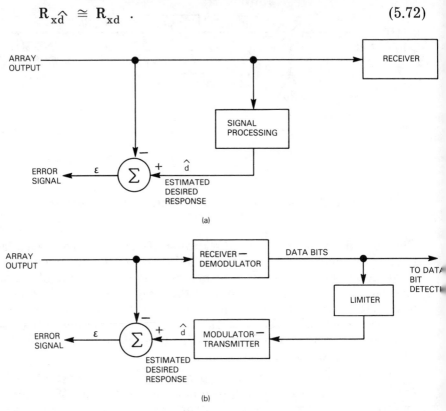

Figure 5.10/Generators of desired response.

Stable operation is achieved only if $\hat{d}$ is independent of the amplitude of the component proportional to the desired signal in the array output. If it is not, the array weights may increase indefinitely or decrease to zero. The presence of the limiter in Figure 5.10(b) controls the amplitude of $\hat{d}$. The delay due to the feedback generation of $\hat{d}$ should be considerably less than the data-modulation period. Details of the operation of an adaptive array in a spread-spectrum communication system and with feedback generation of the desired response are described by Compton [10]. For this system, the interference suppression due to the adaptive array is available in addition to the suppression afforded by the waveform processing.

5.4 ADAPTIVE NOISE CANCELLING

The adaptive element of a noise-cancelling system [11] is a special
case of Figure 5.4(a). However, a noise-cancelling system has such
distinctive features that it is treated separately in this section. In
adaptive noise-cancelling systems, illustrated in Figure 5.11, the desired response is replaced by the primary input, which is derived from
a separate antenna. The primary input is excluded from weight vector

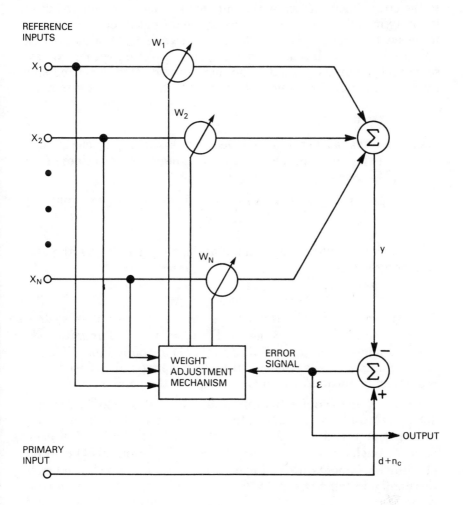

Figure 5.11/Adaptive noise canceller.

calculations. Thus, the optimal weight vector for minimizing the mean-square error signal is given by the Wiener-Hopf equation,

$$W_0 = R_{xx}^{-1} R_{xp} \, , \tag{5.73}$$

where we interpret R_{xx} as the correlation matrix of the reference inputs and R_{xp} is the correlation vector of the reference inputs with the primary input.

The system output for the adaptive noise-cancelling system is identical to the error signal. We show that minimizing the mean-square output is approximately equivalent to causing the output to be a minimum mean-square error estimate of the desired signal, d, if the adaptive filter output, y, is such that it has negligible correlation with d. We assume that the primary input is the sum of the desired signal and uncorrelated noise, n_0. Referring to Figure 5.11, the canceller output is

$$\epsilon = d + n_0 - y \, . \tag{5.74}$$

We assume that all signals are derived from stationary stochastic processes. Taking the expected value of the squares of both sides of Equation (5.74) gives

$$E[\epsilon^2] = E[d^2] + E[(n_0 - y)^2] + 2E[dn_0] - 2E[dy] \, . \tag{5.75}$$

If d is uncorrelated with n_0 and has negligible correlation with y, this equation reduces to

$$E[\epsilon^2] = E[d^2] + E[(n_0 - y)^2] \, . \tag{5.76}$$

The signal power, $E[d^2]$, is unaffected as the adaptive filter is adjusted to minimize $E[\epsilon^2]$. Consequently, $E[(n_0 - y)^2]$ is minimized when $E[\epsilon^2]$ is minimized. From Equation (5.74), it follows that $E[(\epsilon - d)^2]$ also is minimized. We conclude that the adaptive noise-canceller output is a minimum mean-square-error estimate of the desired signal.

Since the Wiener-Hopf equation is valid, the Widrow-Hoff algorithm applies. Consider a continuous-time system with a two-dimensional reference vector, $X^T = [X_1, X_2]$, where $X_2(t)$ is the result of passing $X_1(t)$ through a quarter-wavelength delay. Equation (5.71) then implies the implementation of Figure 5.1. Thus, we have shown how this configuration arises and why its performance can be expected to be nearly optimal. Using the Wiener-Hopf equation, Widrow [11] derived a Z-transform, sampled-data version of Equation (5.35).

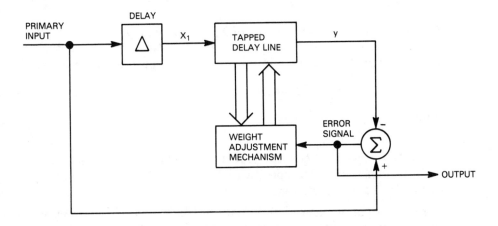

Figure 5.12/Adaptive notch filter.

The adaptive noise canceller can be used as an *adaptive notch filter*, which is useful in applications such as removing periodic interference from spread-spectrum communications. The adaptive notch filter has the form depicted in Figure 5.12, which results from Figure 5.11 when the reference inputs are derived from a tapped delay line that is fed by the delayed primary input. The delay, Δ, is sufficiently long to cause the desired wideband signal component of X_1 to become uncorrelated with the corresponding components of the primary input. As a result, the tapped delay line adaptively forms a filter such that y is composed primarily of the periodic interference components. If the filter bandwidth is sufficiently narrow, the system output is the desired wideband signal with little distortion.

As shown in Section 5.1, adaptive noise cancelling results in a small amount of cancellation of the desired signal. In terms of the overall antenna pattern, this cancellation is caused by the changes in sensitivity of the main beam in the steering direction. These changes can occur because the mainlobe pattern is not constrained by the adaptive process.

5.5 CONSTRAINED MINIMUM POWER CRITERION

A performance criterion that inherently limits the cancellation of the desired signal is the *constrained minimum power criterion*, which is applied to systems with adaptive elements of the form of Figure 5.4(a).

We assume that the components of X are derived from stationary stochastic processes. The correlation matrix is defined by $R_{xx} = E[X^*X^T]$. The criterion requires the minimization of the mean output power,

$$E[\,|y|^2\,] = W'R_{xx}W \, , \qquad\qquad (5.77)$$

subject to the constraint

$$C'W = F \, , \qquad\qquad (5.78)$$

where F is a specified constraint vector and C is a matrix associated with the constraint. The specification of C and F depends upon the form of the adaptive system.

For the system of Figure 5.6, Equations (5.77) and (5.78) are applied to each summer output. Consider a specific summer and let W represent the associated complex weight vector and X the associated complex input vector. Assuming that the steering delays are such that the antenna array pattern points in the direction of the desired signal, the elements of X differ from each other only because of the interference and the noise. Thus, if we require Equation (5.78) with

$$C' = [1\ 1\ \ldots\ 1], \quad F = f \, , \qquad\qquad (5.79)$$

where f is a scalar, this constraint forces the desired signal component of the summer output to be a conventional coherent sum. Minimization of the output power then minimizes the interference power obtained from directions other than the main beam direction. W has $2N$ degrees of freedom because of the N magnitudes and N phases of its elements. The complex constraint equation removes two of these degrees of freedom, but leaves $2N - 2$ to be used in limiting the interference.

For the system of Figure 5.5, the constraint is somewhat different. We assume that identical desired signal components arriving on a plane wave front appear at the first K taps simultaneously. Consequently, the filter response to the signal is equivalent to the response of a single tapped delay line in which each weight is equal to the sum of the weights in the corresponding vertical column of the adaptive element. These summation weights in the equivalent line are selected to give a desired frequency response. Thus, we require that

$$C_i'\,W = f_i \, , \quad i = 1, 2, \ldots, L \, , \qquad\qquad (5.80)$$

where f_i is a desired summation weight and C_i' is an N-dimensional vector of the form

$$C_i' = [0\ 0\ \ldots\ 1\ 1\ \ldots\ 1\ 0\ 0\ \ldots\ 0] \, . \qquad\qquad (5.81)$$

The 1's correspond to the ith vertical column of K weights. To put Equation (5.80) in matrix form, the constraint matrix is defined as

$$C = [C_1 \ C_2 \ \ldots \ C_L] \ , \tag{5.82}$$

which has the dimensions N by L. The L-dimensional vector of weights of the equivalent line is

$$F = \begin{bmatrix} f_1 \\ f_2 \\ . \\ . \\ . \\ f_L \end{bmatrix} . \tag{5.83}$$

With these definitions, the constraints can be combined into a single matrix equation of the form of Equation (5.78). Once again, the constrained minimization ensures that the output power from all directions except boresight is minimized.

Having shown how the constraint equation is constructed, we proceed to a derivation of the optimal weight vector, assuming that the weights are fixed constants. For simplicity, we assume that all scalars and matrix components are real. By the method of Lagrange multipliers, we minimize

$$H = W^T R_{xx} W + \Upsilon^T (C^T W - F) \ , \tag{5.84}$$

where Υ is a column vector of Lagrange multipliers.

Taking the gradient of Equation (5.84) with respect to the vector W yields the column vector

$$\nabla H = 2R_{xx} W + C \Upsilon . \tag{5.85}$$

A necessary condition for the minimum is determined by setting ∇H equal to zero. Thus,

$$W_0 = -\frac{1}{2} R_{xx}^{-1} C \Upsilon . \tag{5.86}$$

Since W_0 must satisfy the constraint, we substitute Equation (5.86) into Equation (5.78) with the result

$$-\frac{1}{2} C^T R_{xx}^{-1} C \Upsilon = F . \tag{5.87}$$

This equation can be solved for Υ. Substituting the solution into Equation (5.86) gives

$$W_0 = R_{xx}^{-1} C(C^T R_{xx}^{-1} C)^{-1} F ,\qquad(5.88)$$

where we assume that the indicated inverse exists.

Frost's adaptive algorithm [12] is based upon approximating Equation (5.88) by the method of steepest descent. The weight vector during the $(k + 1)$ st adaptation cycle is related to the weight vector during the k th adaptation cycle by

$$W(k + 1) = W(k) - \frac{1}{2} \mu \nabla H$$

$$= W(k) - \mu \left[R_{xx} W(k) + \frac{1}{2} C \Upsilon(k) \right] ,\qquad(5.89)$$

where μ is a constant that regulates the convergence rate, and the factor 1/2 has been inserted for convenience. This equation is similar to Equation (5.67), except that the gradient of H is used instead of the gradient of the mean-square error. The Lagrange-multiplier vector, $\Upsilon(k)$, is allowed to vary with the adaptation cycle in such a way that the constraint is satisfied for $W(k + 1)$; that is, $\Upsilon(k)$ is chosen so that

$$C^T W(k + 1) = F .\qquad(5.90)$$

Substituting Equation (5.89) into Equation (5.90) and solving for $\Upsilon(k)$ yields

$$\Upsilon(k) = \frac{2}{\mu} (C^T C)^{-1}[C^T W(k) - F] - 2(C^T C)^{-1} C^T R_{xx} W(k) ,$$

$$(5.91)$$

where the indicated inverse is assumed to exist. We define the constant matrices:

$$A = I - C(C^T C)^{-1}C^T ,$$

$$B = C(C^T C)^{-1}F .\qquad(5.92)$$

Substituting Equations (5.91) and (5.92) into Equation (5.89), we obtain

$$W(k + 1) = A [W(k) - \mu R_{xx} W(k)] + B .\qquad(5.93)$$

This equation provides a deterministic algorithm that would be used if R_{xx} were known. Since it is not, we approximate R_{xx} by $X(k)X^T(k)$

and use Equation (5.43). The initial weight W(0) is somewhat arbitrary. However, a good choice is W(0) = B because B must be computed anyway and this choice satisfies the constraint $C^T W(0) = F$. Thus, Frost's adaptive algorithm is

$$W(0) = B , \qquad\qquad\qquad\qquad\qquad\qquad\qquad (5.94)$$

$$W(k + 1) = A[W(k) - \mu y(k) X(k)] + B . \qquad\qquad (5.95)$$

An important feature of the algorithm is that each iteration automatically corrects for computational errors in the weight vector that prevented exact satisfaction of the constraint during the preceding iteration. These errors often occur during an interation because of truncation, roundoff, or quantization errors in the computer implementation of the algorithm. If the errors are not corrected, they may have a significant cumulative effect after a few iterations. The error-correcting capability of the algorithm is due to the fact that the factor ($C^T W(k)$ — F) was not set to zero in Equation (5.91). Thus, apart from other sources of error, $C^T W(k + 1) = F$ even if $C^T W(k) \neq F$.

Neither pilot signals nor generators of the desired response are needed in constrained-minimum-power systems. However, in defining the constraint, knowledge of the direction of the desired signal is necessary. If the direction is unknown, it may be estimated by methods similar to those described in Chapter 4. Thus, although the generators of Figure 5.10 are unnecessary, adaptive systems based on the constrained-minimum-power or the signal-to-noise-ratio criterion usually require auxiliary direction-finding circuitry.

5.6 CONVERGENCE OF WIDROW-HOFF ALGORITHM

No matter how plausible the construction of an adaptive algorithm, it must be checked to verify that the weights converge in some sense to optimal or nearly optimal values. Since the adaptive weights are random if the input signals are random, it is usually appropriate to examine convergence of the mean weights.

We prove convergence for the discrete-time Widrow-Hoff algorithm under the assumption that samples of the input vector are statistically independent. This assumption is not necessary, but greatly facilitates the analysis. The assumption is valid at least when the input vector is sampled at intervals that are large compared to the correlation time of the input process plus the maximum time delay between input vector components.

If $X(k + 1)$ is independent of $X(n)$ and $d(n)$, $n \leqslant k$, Equation (5.69) implies that $X(k + 1)$ is independent of $W(k + 1)$. Thus, the expected value of the weight vector satisfies

$$E[W(k+1)] = (I - 2\mu R_{xx})E[W(k)] + 2\mu R_{xd} . \qquad (5.96)$$

This discrete-time equation is linear and time invariant. Its equilibrium point is easily calculated to be W_0, the optimal weight vector. From the theory of linear time-invariant equations, it follows that $E[W(k)]$ converges to W_0 if and only if the eigenvalues of $I - 2\mu R_{xx}$ have magnitudes less than unity. Since R_{xx} is symmetric and positive definite, its eigenvalues, $\lambda_1, \lambda_2, \ldots, \lambda_n$, are positive. Therefore, the eigenvalues of $I - 2\mu R_{xx}$, which are $1 - 2\mu\lambda_1, 1 - 2\mu\lambda_2, \ldots, 1 - 2\mu\lambda_n$, have magnitudes less than unity if

$$|1 - 2\mu\lambda_m| < 1 , \qquad (5.97)$$

where λ_m is the maximum eigenvalue of R_{xx}. This equation yields the convergence condition

$$0 < \mu < \frac{1}{\lambda_m} . \qquad (5.98)$$

The sum of the eigenvalues of a square matrix is equal to its trace. Thus,

$$\sum_{i=1}^{N} \lambda_i = \text{trace}(R_{xx}) = \sum_{i=1}^{N} E[x_i^2] = R_T , \qquad (5.99)$$

where R_T denotes the total input power. Since $\lambda_m \leqslant R_T$, Equation (5.98) implies that

$$0 < \mu < \frac{1}{R_T} \qquad (5.100)$$

is sufficient for convergence of $E[W(k)]$ to W_0.

During adaptation, the weights undergo transients that vary as sums of terms of the form $(1 - 2\mu\lambda_i)^k$. These transients determine the rate of convergence. If an adaptive antenna system is designed to combat jamming, μ must be chosen, in accordance with Equation (5.100), to allow for the potential value of R_T when the jamming is present.

In the development of the adaptive algorithms, it has always been assumed that the noise processes are stationary. However, the main purpose of adaptive systems is to automatically adjust to nonstationary inputs, especially when the stochastic properties are unknown *a priori*. Fortunately, experimental results and tentative theoretical results seem to indicate that adaptive algorithms retain their usefulness in many realistic environments with nonstationarv inputs [13].

In addition to the stochastic properties of the inputs, we have tacitly assumed plane-wave signals, an ideal propagation medium, and distortionless receivers. Since these assumptions may not be valid under actual operating conditions, Vural has investigated the effects of signal, medium, and system deviations from the usual assumptions [14].

Adaptive antenna systems have many applications. In general, adaptation is potentially helpful for communications or radar when the desired signal and the interference are distinguishable *a priori*. The discriminant may be the direction of arrival, a waveform characteristic, or even signal polarization.

5.7 ADAPTIVE POLARIZATION DISCRIMINATION

To discriminate on the basis of polarization [1], the signal is received on two linearly polarized antennas, as represented in Figure 5.13. The outputs of the primary and reference antennas provide the primary and reference inputs, respectively, to an adaptive noise canceller, as shown in Figure 5.14. Because there is no significant difference in the arrival times of a received signal at the two antennas, the reference input can be processed directly, without the need for producing the quadrature components of Figure 5.1. We assume a linearly polarized desired signal. The primary antenna is aligned as accurately as possible with the polarization of the desired signal. If the alignment is perfect and the reference antenna is perpendicular to the primary antenna, the desired signal produces no response in the reference antenna. Thus, Equation (5.35) implies that, if the thermal noise is negligible, a single linearly polarized interference signal can be completely rejected by the adaptive system. If the antennas are not perpendicular or if the primary antenna and the desired signal polarization are offset by a known positive angle, then a reference input with no signal component can be produced by subtracting the weighted primary signal from the reference signal, as illustrated in Figure 5.14. However, to avoid the extra circuitry, it appears preferable to have perpendicular antennas, which we assume in the following analysis.

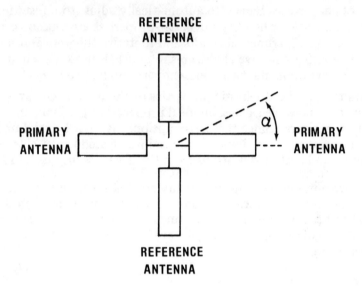

Figure 5.13/Two linearly polarized antennas.

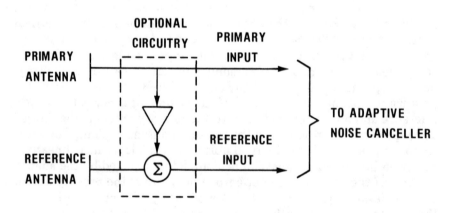

Figure 5.14/Adaptive system for polarization discrimination.

Interference and thermal noise cause an error in the alignment of the primary antenna with the polarization of the desired signal. Let α denote the unknown polarization angle of the desired signal relative to the primary antenna, as indicated in Figure 5.13. Suppose the desired signal, s(t), is received along with various linearly polarized interference signals, $J_i(t)$, that have polarization angles β_i relative to the primary antenna. Neglecting thermal noise, the primary input to the adaptive noise canceller is

$$X_0(t) = s(t) \cos \alpha + \sum_i J_i(t) \cos \beta_i . \qquad (5.101)$$

The reference input is

$$X_1(t) = s(t) \sin \alpha + \sum_i J_i(t) \sin \beta_i . \qquad (5.102)$$

The optimal weight vector is a scalar, W_0, given by Equation (5.73). We model s(t) and the $J_i(t)$ as uncorrelated, stationary, zero-mean, stochastic processes. It follows that

$$W_0 = \frac{E[s^2]\ \sin \alpha \cos \alpha + \sum_i E[J_i^2] \sin \beta_i \cos \beta_i}{E[s^2]\ \sin^2 \alpha + \sum_i E[J_i^2] \sin^2 \beta_i} . \qquad (5.103)$$

If ideal adaptation occurs, the output of the adaptive noise canceller (Figure 5.11) is

$$\begin{aligned}
\epsilon &= X_0 - W_0 X_1 \\
&= s(t)(\cos \alpha - W_0 \sin \alpha) + \sum_i J_i(t)(\cos \beta_i - W_0 \sin \beta_i).
\end{aligned}$$
$$(5.104)$$

Thus, the signal-to-interference ratio at the output is

$$\rho_0 = \frac{E[s^2]\ (\cos \alpha - W_0 \sin \alpha)^2}{\sum_i E[J_i^2]\ (\cos \beta_i - W_0 \sin \beta_i)^2} . \qquad (5.105)$$

Substituting Equation (5.103) into Equation (5.105) and using algebraic and trigonometric simplification, we obtain

$$\rho_0 = \frac{E[s^2]\left\{\sum_i E[J_i^2]\sin\beta_i\sin(\beta_i-\alpha)\right\}^2}{\sum_k E[J_k^2]\left\{E[s^2]\sin\alpha\sin(\beta_k-\alpha)+\sum_i E[J_i^2]\sin\beta_i\sin(\beta_i-\beta_k)\right\}}$$

(5.106)

If only one interference signal is received, Equation (5.106) reduces to

$$\rho_0 = \frac{E[J_1^2]\sin^2\beta_1}{E[s^2]\sin^2\alpha}.$$

(5.107)

This result is similar to what would have been obtained by applying equation (5.35) to Equation (5.102). Equation (5.107) shows explicitly that imperfect knowledge of the desired signal's polarization degrades the interference rejection capability of the adaptive system. However, for small values of α, the rejection of a single interfering signal is nearly complete.

Even if the antenna alignment is perfect, the interference rejection capability of an adaptive system is usually greatly diminished if two or more interference signals with different polarizations are received. Setting $\alpha = 0$ in Equation (5.106) yields

$$\rho_0 = \frac{E[s^2]\left\{\sum_i E[J_i^2]\sin^2\beta_i\right\}^2}{\sum_k E[J_k^2]\left\{\sum_i E[J_i^2]\sin\beta_i\sin(\beta_i-\beta_k)\right\}^2}.$$

(5.108)

This equation indicates that complete interference rejection is usually impossible unless the β_i are all equal. This condition requires identical polarizations of the interference signals.

Suppose an adaptive system receives two uncorrelated jamming signals of equal powers and orthogonal polarizations. Thus, $E[J_1^2] = E[J_2^2] = E[J_T^2]/2$, where $J_T = J_1 + J_2$, and $\beta_1 = \beta_2 + \pi/2$ radians. Equation (5.108) becomes

$$\rho_0 = \frac{2E[s^2]}{E[J_T^2]}.$$

(5.109)

Thus, the interference rejection capability of the adaptive system is small in this case. Nevertheless, *adaptive polarization discrimination* is potentially a useful supplement to an adaptive antenna system because it provides at least some interference rejection when the desired signal and jamming signals have similar directions and waveforms.

REFERENCES

[1]   B.D. Steinberg, *Principles of Aperture and Array System Design*, Wiley, 1976.

[2]   W.E. Rodgers and R.J. Compton, "Adaptive Array Bandwidth with Tapped Delay-Line Processing," *IEEE Trans. Aerospace Electron. Syst.* AES-15 (January 1979), 21.

[3]   L.J. Griffiths, "A Comparison of Multidimensional Wiener and Maximum-Likelihood Filters for Antenna Arrays," *Proc. IEEE* 55 (November 1967), 2045.

[4]   L.E. Brennan and I.S. Reed, "Theory of Adaptive Radar," *IEEE Trans. Aerospace Electron. Syst.* AES-9 (March 1973), 237.

[5]   S.P. Applebaum, "Adaptive Arrays," *IEEE Trans. Antennas Prop.* AP-24 (September 1976), 585.

[6]   B. Widrow, *et al.*, "Adaptive Antenna Systems," *Proc. IEEE* 55 (December 1967), 2143.

[7]   B. Widrow and J.M. McCool, "A Comparison of Adaptive Algorithms Based on the Methods of Steepest Descent and Random Search," *IEEE Trans. Antennas Prop.* AP-24 (September 1976), 615.

[8]   I.S. Reed, *et al.*, Rapid Convergence Rates in Adaptive Arrays," *IEEE Trans. Aerospace Electron. Syst.* AES-10 (November 1974), 853.

[9]   L.J. Griffiths, "A Simple Adaptive Algorithm for Real-Time Processing in Antenna Arrays," *Proc. IEEE* 57 (October 1969), 1696.

[10] R.J. Compton, "An Adaptive Array in a Spread-Spectrum Communication System," *Proc. IEEE* 66 (March 1978), 289.

[11] B. Widrow, *et al.*, "Adaptive Noise Cancelling: Principles and Applications," *Proc. IEEE* 63 (December 1975), 1692.

[12] O.L. Frost, "An Algorithm for Linearly Constrained Adaptive Array Processing," *Proc. IEEE* 60 (August 1972), 926.

[13] B. Widrow, *et al.*, "Stationary and Nonstationary Learning Characteristics of the LMS Adaptive Filter," *Proc. IEEE* 64 (August 1976), 1151.

[14] A.M. Vural, "Effects of Perturbations on the Performance of Optimum/Adaptive Arrays," *IEEE Trans. Aerospace Electron. Syst.* AES-15 (January 1979), 76.

Cryptographic
Digital
Communications

6.1 CIPHERS AND CRYPTANALYSIS

Cryptography is used to ensure the secrecy of messages when hostile personnel have the technical capability of intercepting and correctly interpreting a message. Although modern cryptographic techniques can eliminate the possibility of eavesdropping, cryptographic communications have a greater susceptibility to jamming than ordinary ones.

Diffie and Hellman [1] have comprehensively reviewed cryptography in a general setting. Here, we concentrate upon the most important aspects of cryptographic digital communications.

Practical cryptographic systems must produce a cryptogram that not only resists cryptanalysis, but also is efficiently deciphered by authorized personnel. These requirements have been much more satisfactorily fulfilled by digital techniques than by analog ones. Thus, if secure voice or other analog information is to be communicated, analog-to-digital conversion before transmission is desirable.

For each class of cryptographic systems, the set of parameters that determine the specific cryptographic transformation to be employed is called the *key*. Cryptographic systems are designed so that their security depends upon the inability of the cryptanalyst to determine the key even if he has knowledge of the basic structure of the cryptographic system.

There are two distinct cryptographic transformations that can be applied to the message bits or *plaintext: coding* and *enciphering.* Coding consists of the substitution of groups of bits of variable length for plain-text groups of variable length. Enciphering consists of the substitution of fixed-length groups of bits for fixed-length plaintext groups. Coding is too slow for high-density data transmission, and the frequent code changes necessary for secrecy are often technically difficult. Since en-ciphering systems provide high-speed capabilities and are easily modi-fied, they are nearly always used for cryptographic digital communica-tions.

Messages can be enciphered or *encrypted* by a *block cipher,* a *stream cipher,* or a combination of these ciphers. A block cipher is a system that divides the plaintext into separate blocks of m bits and associates with each block $(x_i, x_{i+1}, \ldots, x_{i+m-1})$ of plaintext a block $(y_i, y_{i+1}, \ldots, y_{i+n-1})$ of n bits of *ciphertext.* Thus, we can write

$$y_k = f_k(x_i, x_{i+1}, \ldots, x_{i+m-1}), \quad i \leqslant k \leqslant i + n - 1,$$

$$(6.1)$$

where the f_k are functions. Messages are deciphered with inverse func-tions. For unambiguous deciphering, $n \geqslant m$ is necessary; for ease of automation, $n = m$ is preferred.

A stream cipher performs bit-by-bit modulo-two addition of the plain-text and a set of bits called the *keystream.* In modulo-two arithmetic, $a \oplus b = c$ implies $a = b \oplus c$. Thus, ciphertext is deciphered by add-ing the keystream bits to the corresponding enciphered bits. The key-stream may be a function of the ciphertext itself. Thus, a stream cipher associates with each stream $(x_1, x_2, \ldots, x_i, x_{i+1}, \ldots)$ of plaintext a stream $(y_1, y_2, \ldots, y_i, y_{i+1}, \ldots)$ of ciphertext such that

$$y_k = \begin{cases} x_k \oplus f_k(y_{k-1}, y_{k-2}, \ldots, y_{k-n}), & k \geqslant n, \\ \\ x_k \oplus f_k(y_{k-1}, y_{k-2}, \ldots y_1), & k < n. \end{cases}$$

$$(6.2)$$

In addition, y_k may be a function of the initial conditions of the crypto-graphic system.

Block ciphers are basically digital substitution ciphers. Hence, they are potentially susceptible to classical frequency analysis of the blocks. Se-curity is achieved by using large blocks that include at least four data words. The generic form of a system for enciphering or deciphering blocks is shown in Figure 6.1.

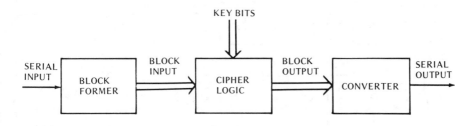

Figure 6.1/Generic form of system for enciphering or deciphering blocks.

A practical difficulty of secure block ciphers is the large number of key bits required to specify the block transformations. If the blocks are n bits long, there are 2^n distinct blocks and $2^n!$ possible transformations for which inverses exist. The number of key bits needed to specify a particular transformation is $\log_2 (2^n!) \approx n2^n$. To reduce the number of required key bits, a fixed form of cipher logic may be used. As an example, Figure 6.2 illustrates one form of a block cipher [2]. The plaintext block is transformed by successive stages that alternate between a set of *substitution* (S) boxes and a single *permutation* (P) box. A key bit determines which one of two possible transformations each substitution box performs. The permutation boxes rearrange or transpose their input bits. If the permutation boxes are not defined by the key, the number of required key bits for this cipher is equal to the total number of substitution boxes. Deciphering is accomplished by running the data backward through the inverses of the boxes. The permutation boxes ensure the cryptographic complexity of the cipher by preventing the overall transformation from being equivalent to a single stage of substitution boxes.

There are two types of stream ciphers: those for which the keystream is independent of the ciphertext and those for which the keystream is not. Independently keyed ciphers are often called *synchronous ciphers* because they require synchronization between the keystream and the ciphertext for successful deciphering. Stream ciphers for which the

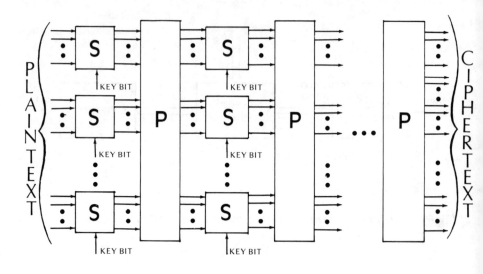

Figure 6.2/Block cipher with alternating stages.

keystream is a function of the ciphertext and, thus, the plaintext are here called *data-keyed ciphers.*

The only definitely secure cipher is a synchronous cipher that generates a completely random keystream as long as the message. Since the key, which is the same as the keystream in this case, cannot be reused, this cipher is called the *one-time tape.* The necessity of long, frequently changed keys renders the one-time tape impractical for most applications. Thus, most synchronous ciphers use feedback shift registers to generate pseudorandom keystreams with long periods (see Section 2.2). The generic form of synchronous enciphering or deciphering systems is diagrammed in Figure 6.3, where the indicated addition is modulo-two.

A feedback shift register is called *linear* if the feedback logic consists entirely of modulo-two adders (Exclusive OR gates). Linear feedback shift registers can generate long sequences with desirable random properties such as a nearly even balance of *zeros* and *ones*. However, the structure of these linear generators makes them susceptible to cryptanalysis unless the number of shift-register stages is at least half as long as the data sequence to be enciphered. Since there are practical limits to the number of shift-register stages, shift registers with nonlinear feedback or nonlinear operations on the shift-register outputs are needed to produce secure keystreams. Algorithms exist for constructing a linear feedback shift register to generate any periodic binary sequence. However, nonlinear generators with relatively few shift-register stages can produce sequences that require a prohibitively large number of stages in the *equivalent linear generator*, which is defined as the linear generator with the smallest number of stages.

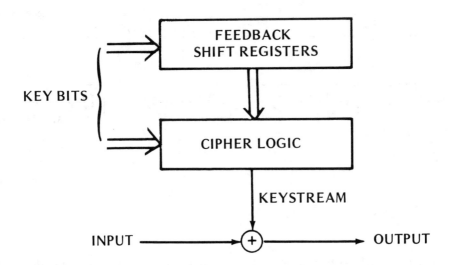

Figure 6.3/Generic form of synchronous enciphering or deciphering system.

Figures 6.4 and 6.5 depict nonlinear keystream generators and their linear equivalents [3]. The initial contents of the shift-register stages are indicated by binary numbers. In Figure 6.4(a), a linear feedback shift register is used, but the outputs of two stages are nonlinearly combined to produce the keystream. In Figure 6.5(a), two linear feedback shift registers have their outputs nonlinearly combined to produce the keystream.

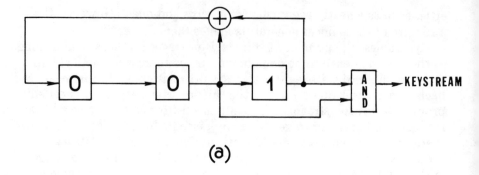

(a)

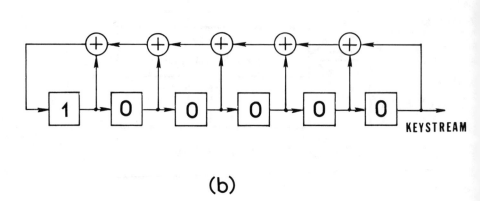

(b)

Figure 6.4/(a) Nonlinear generator using single shift register, and (b) its linear equivalent.

The generic forms of data-keyed enciphering and deciphering systems are shown in Figures 6.6 and 6.7. The ciphertext is applied to the first stages of the shift registers. Since the keystream depends upon the ciphertext and, thus, the plaintext, data-keyed ciphers are potentially self-synchronizing. A data-keyed cipher is called *linear* if the cipher logic, which is equivalent to feedback logic, consists entirely of modulo-two adders.

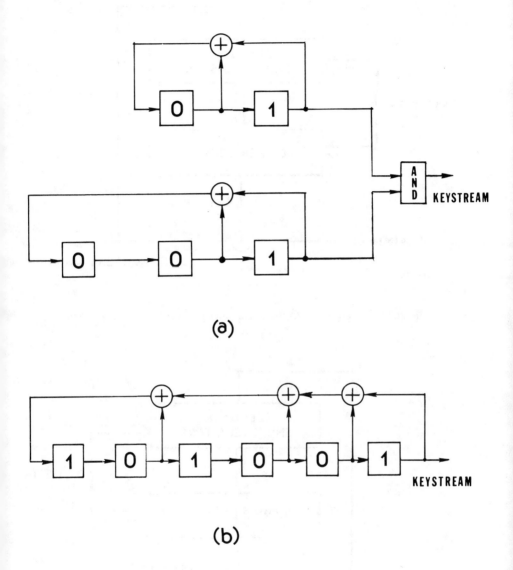

(a)

(b)

*Figure 6.5/(a) Nonlinear generator using two shift registers, and (b)
its linear equivalent.*

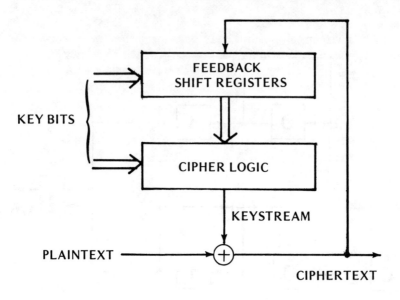

Figure 6.6/Generic form of data-keyed enciphering system.

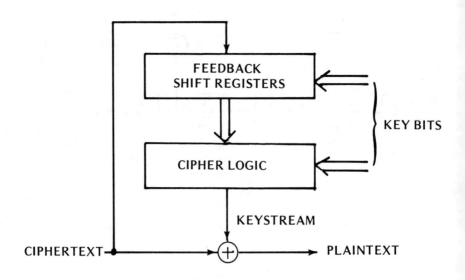

Figure 6.7/Generic form of data-keyed deciphering system.

The key bits of a stream cipher not only determine the cipher and feedback logic, but also may set the initial contents of the shift registers. The cipher logic of a stream cipher may include a block cipher with a block size equal to the number of shift-register outputs.

As a specific example of a data-keyed cipher, we consider a linear enciphering system with four stages, as shown in Figure 6.8. For each distinct setting of the switches, there is a different enciphered output stream. The corresponding deciphering system is shown in Figure 6.9. The switches in both figures could consist of AND gates controlled by the key bits. It is assumed that the bit transitions of the input sequence are synchronized by the shift-register clock.

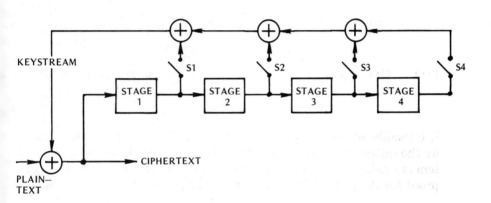

Figure 6.8/Linear data-keyed enciphering system.

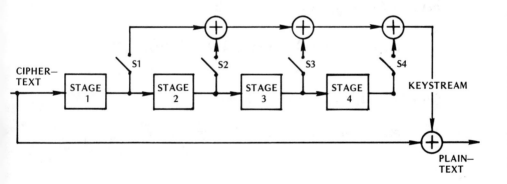

Figure 6.9/Linear data-keyed deciphering system.

We define $p(t)$ as the sequence of plaintext bits entering the enciphering system and $c(t)$ as the corresponding output. We define the operation $\oplus$ as modulo-two addition. Multiplication is defined as usual. The operator D is defined by $Dp(t) = p(t - T)$, where T is the clock (bit) period. The discrete variables s_i may take the values 0 or 1, depending on whether the corresponding switches in the enciphering and deciphering systems are open or closed, respectively. With the preceding definitions and the system of Figure 6.8, we observe that, during *steady state operation*,

$$c(t) = p(t) \oplus s_1 Dc(t) \oplus s_2 D^2 c(t) \oplus s_3 D^3 c(t) \oplus s_4 D^4 c(t) .$$

(6.3)

Since $a \oplus b = c$ implies $a = b \oplus c$, Equation (6.3) implies

$$p(t) = c(t) \oplus s_1 Dc(t) \oplus s_2 D^2 c(t) \oplus s_3 D^3 c(t) \oplus s_4 D^4 c(t) .$$

(6.4)

It is readily verified that if $c(t)$ is the input, Equation (6.4) is satisfied by the output of Figure 6.9. Thus, the output of the deciphering system is a delayed version of the input to the enciphering system. The proof for the general linear system of m shift-register stages is analogous.

Consider the discrete time t_i, where $t_i = t_{i-1} + T$, and t_1 corresponds to the start of operation. For a general linear system of m stages, we have the following steady-state relations:

$$p(t_i) = c(t_i) \oplus s_1 Dc(t_i) \oplus \ldots \oplus s_m D^m c(t_i) ,$$

$$i > m . \quad (6.5)$$

Since $D^n c(t_i) = c(t_{i-n})$, we obtain

$$p(t_i) = c(t_i) \oplus s_1 c(t_{i-1}) \oplus \ldots \oplus s_m c(t_{i-m}) ,$$

$$i > m . \quad (6.6)$$

If the initial content of stage i is Z_i, linear enciphering systems of the form of Figure 6.8 yield the relations:

$$p(t_1) = c(t_1) \oplus s_1 Z_1 \oplus s_2 Z_2 \oplus \cdots \oplus s_m Z_m \; ,$$
$$p(t_2) = c(t_2) \oplus s_1 c(t_1) \oplus s_2 Z_1 \oplus \cdots \oplus s_m Z_{m-1} \; ,$$

.

.

.

$$p(t_m) = c(t_m) \oplus s_1 c(t_{m-1}) \oplus s_2 c(t_{m-2}) \oplus \cdots \oplus s_m Z_1$$

$$(6.7)$$

In the absence of an input, a system of the form of Figure 6.8 generates a periodic output sequence. The maximum length of the sequence before pattern repetition is $2^m - 1$, where m is the total number of functioning shift-register stages. The maximal-length sequence occurs only for certain switch settings and only if the initial contents of the stages are not all zero. If m = 20, a pseudorandom sequence of over a million bits in length may be generated. The object of cryptanalysis is to determine the key, which is the set of bits representing the switch settings and the initial contents. It might seem that cryptanalysis would require at least $2^m - 1$ intercepted bits so that it would be very difficult if m > 20. However, the key can be determined with as few as 2m pairs of corresponding ciphertext and plaintext bits.

As an example, consider the case where m = 4 and we acquire the following corresponding sequences of plaintext and ciphertext bits:

$p(t_i)$:   1 0 1 0 1 0 1 0 ,

$$(6.8)$$

$c(t_i)$:   1 0 1 1 0 0 0 1 .

Using Equations (6.6) and (6.7), starting with i = 8, we obtain

$$0 = 1 \oplus s_4 \, ,$$

$$1 = s_3 \oplus s_4 \, ,$$

$$0 = s_2 \oplus s_3 \, ,$$

$$1 = s_1 \oplus s_2 \oplus s_4 \, , \qquad\qquad (6.9)$$

$$0 = 1 \oplus s_1 \oplus s_3 \oplus s_4 Z_1 \, ,$$

$$1 = 1 \oplus s_2 \oplus s_3 Z_1 \oplus s_4 Z_2 \, ,$$

$$0 = s_1 \oplus s_2 Z_1 \oplus s_3 Z_2 \oplus s_4 Z_3 \, ,$$

$$1 = 1 \oplus s_1 Z_1 \oplus s_2 Z_2 \oplus s_3 Z_3 \oplus s_4 Z_4 \, .$$

We determine the s_i from the first four of these equations and then solve for the Z_i from the last four equations. The results are

$$s_1 = 0, \quad s_2 = 0, \quad s_3 = 0, \quad s_4 = 1 \, ,$$

$$\qquad\qquad (6.10)$$

$$Z_1 = 1, \quad Z_2 = 0, \quad Z_3 = 0, \quad Z_4 = 0 \, .$$

Thus, the key has been completely determined with $2m = 8$ pairs of corresponding ciphertext and plaintext bits.

In any digital communication system, the received bits and words have certain error probabilities. Except for synchronous ciphers, enciphering causes these error probabilities to increase if other system parameters remain unchanged. In block-enciphered systems, each deciphered bit is a function of all the enciphered bits in the corresponding block. Therefore, a single erroneous received bit is practically certain to cause many erroneous deciphered bits. In systems with data-keyed ciphers, a received bit error is carried through shift registers, causing additional bit errors down the line. The characteristic increase in the bit errors due to block or data-keyed ciphers is called *error extension* or *error propagation*.

Theoretically, the system of Figure 6.9 could serve as an enciphering system, while the system of Figure 6.8 serves as the corresponding deciphering system. However, this choice is not a good one in practice since a single bit error at the deciphering system input would cause an indefinite number of errors at the output. In the original configuration, at most four output bits are affected by a single bit error in the deciphering system input.

6.2 ERROR PROBABILITY BOUNDS AND ENSEMBLE AVERAGES FOR STREAM CIPHERS

We denote the bit error probability at a receiver output by P_b. Assuming that the bit errors occur independently of each other, the word error probability for binary communications is:

$$P_w = 1 - (1 - P_b)^k , \qquad (6.11)$$

where k denotes the number of bits per word. If the receiver output is ciphertext, it is applied to a deciphering system. The k bits of a ciphertext word entering the deciphering system are referred to as the *input word*. The corresponding k plaintext bits emerging from the deciphering system are designated the *output word*. The probability of one or more erroneous bits in the output word is denoted by P_{cw}. For synchronous ciphers, $P_{cw} = P_w$. For data-keyed ciphers, error extension causes an increase in P_{cw} relative to P_w.

Suppose a ciphertext bit is erroneously received as a result of random noise or other interference. As the erroneous bit proceeds through the deciphering system, each of n consecutive output bits may be affected. We define a *train* to be this set of n consecutive bits emerging from the deciphering system. The parameter n defines a subset of stream ciphers. For a synchronous cipher, n = 1; for a data-keyed cipher, n > 1.

We say that a train is of *external origin* with respect to an output word if the first bit of the train occurs before the first bit of the word. The joint probability of a word error and a train of external origin extending into the word is denoted by P(w,t). If no train of external origin extends into the word, the conditional probability of a word error is denoted by $P(w/\bar{t})$. The probability that a train of external origin does not extend into a word is denoted by $P(\bar{t})$. From the theorem of total probability,

$$P_{cw} = P(w,t) + P(w/\bar{t})P(\bar{t}). \qquad (6.12)$$

A train extends into an output word if and only if one of the n − 1 input bits immediately preceding the corresponding input word is in error. Thus, assuming input bit errors are independent,

$$P(\bar{t}) = (1 - P_b)^{n-1} . \qquad (6.13)$$

When no train is present, an error in one of the bits of the input word causes an error in the corresponding bit of the output word. Thus,

$P(w/\bar{t})$ is the same as the probability of a word error for plaintext; that is,

$$P(w/\bar{t}) = 1 - (1 - P_b)^k \ . \tag{6.14}$$

If i bits of a train of external origin extend into a word, we denote this event by the symbols tb = i. For example, $P(tb = i)$ denotes the probability that a word contains i externally generated train bits. Since $P(w,t/tb = i) = P(w/tb = i)$, we can write

$$P(w,t) = P(w/tb = k)P(tb = k)$$
$$+ \sum_{i=1}^{k-1} P(w/tb = i)P(tb = i) \ . \tag{6.15}$$

If at least one of the $n - k$ bits preceding an input word is in error and $n > k$, then tb = k. Thus,

$$P(tb = k) = \begin{cases} 1 - (1 - P_b)^{n-k} \ , & n > k \ , \\ 0 \ , & n \leqslant k \ . \end{cases} \tag{6.16}$$

For tb = i, where $1 \leqslant i < k$, it is necessary that there be an error precisely $n - i$ bits prior to the word but no erroneous bits among the next $n - i - 1$ bits. Therefore, for $1 \leqslant i < k$,

$$P(tb = i) = \begin{cases} P_b(1 - P_b)^{n-i-1} \ , & n > i \ , \\ 0 \ , & n \leqslant i \ . \end{cases} \tag{6.17}$$

Substitution of Equations (6.13) through (6.17) into Equation (6.12) yields the decomposition

$$P_{cw} = P(w/tb = k)\left[1 - (1 - P_b)^{n-k}\right] u(n - k)$$
$$+ \sum_{i=1}^{\min(k-1,n-1)} P(w/tb = i)P_b(1 - P_b)^{n-i-1}$$
$$+ \left[1 - (1 - P_b)^k\right](1 - P_b)^{n-1} \ , \tag{6.18}$$

where $u(n - k)$ is a step function; that is, $u(n - k)$ is 0 for $n < k$ and is 1 for $n \geqslant k$. In the summation term, i extends to the least of the two integers $k - 1$ and $n - 1$.

To evaluate the decomposition, the exact configuration of the crypto-graphic system has to be specified. However, an upper bound can be obtained by simply observing that $P(w/tb = k)$ and $P(w/tb = i)$ must be less than or equal to unity. After some algebraic simplification, Equation (6.18) yields the bound (which can be derived directly)

$$P_{cw} \leqslant 1 - (1 - P_b)^{n+k-1} . \tag{6.19}$$

We show that there is a simpler bound:

$$P_{cw} \leqslant (n + k - 1)P_b . \tag{6.20}$$

Consider the function of x defined by

$$y = m x + (1 - x)^m - 1 , \quad 0 \leqslant x \leqslant 1 , m \geqslant 1 . \tag{6.21}$$

Clearly, $y = 0$ at $x = 0$. Since $m \geqslant 1$, y has a nonnegative derivative for all x such that $0 \leqslant x \leqslant 1$. Thus, $y \geqslant 0$. We conclude that

$$m x \geqslant 1 - (1 - x)^m , \quad 0 \leqslant x \leqslant 1, m \geqslant 1 . \tag{6.22}$$

Applying this inequality to Equation (6.19) yields Equation (6.20).

A second measure of performance for data-keyed ciphers is obtained by averaging P_{cw} over *ensembles of deciphering systems for which, at most, n output bits are affected by an input bit error.* Suppose that an erroneous bit starts a train. Let X denote the ensemble-average probability that a subsequent train bit, called an *interior train bit,* is in the correct state. Let Y denote the ensemble-average probability that a subsequent keystream bit corresponding to an interior train bit is in the correct state. Since an input bit is added to a keystream bit to produce a train bit, we have

$$X = (1 - P_b)Y + P_b(1 - Y) . \tag{6.23}$$

To determine the value of Y, we first consider linear systems. Over the ensemble of deciphering systems of the form of Figure 6.9, it is equally likely that S1 is open or closed. Suppose that after three or more correct input bits, an erroneous bit is received. If S1 is open, the next keystream bit will be correct. If S1 is closed, the next keystream bit will be in error. Thus, the ensemble-average probability that the next keystream bit will be correct is one-half. Continuing this type of reasoning, we see that $Y = 1/2$ for ensembles of linear data-keyed ciphers.

For a restricted ensemble of nonlinear ciphers, Y may be different from one-half. However, the most important cipher ensembles are those for which cryptanalysis is very difficult. Setting Y equal to one-half for these ensembles appears to be an excellent approximation.

We indicate an ensemble-average probability by a bar over a P. When $k = 1$, $\overline{P}(w/tb = k) = 1 - X$. Thus, Equation (6.18) yields the ensemble-average bit error probability

$$\overline{P}_{cb} = (1 - X)\left[1 - (1 - P_b)^{n-1}\right] + P_b(1 - P_b)^{n-1} \; .$$

(6.24)

Substituting Equation (6.23) into Equation (6.24) gives

$$\overline{P}_{cb} = (1 - Y)\left[1 - (1 - P_b)^{n-1} + 2P_b(1 - P_b)^{n-1}\right]$$
$$- P_b(1 - 2Y) \; .$$

(6.25)

In this equation, we have kept the unspecified parameter Y because its retention does not complicate the expression significantly. However, for the reasons mentioned and for easier derivation, we always assume $Y = 1/2$ in determining the ensemble-average word error probability.

If $Y = 1/2$, Equation (6.23) indicates that $X = 1/2$. Furthermore, if $Y = 1/2$, the probability that an interior train bit is correct is one-half, regardless of the states of the input bits.

Given $tb = i$, we denote the event that one or more of the first i bits of an input word is in error by the symbol α and the opposite event by $\overline{\alpha}$. Using the theorem of total probability, we can write

$$\overline{P}(w \mid tb = i) = \overline{P}(w,\alpha \mid tb = i) + \overline{P}(w \mid tb = i,\overline{\alpha})P(\overline{\alpha} \mid tb = i) \; .$$

(6.26)

If $tb = i$ and α is false, the ensemble-average probability of no error in the first i bits of the output word is $(1/2)^i$. The last $k - i$ output bits are not part of a train generated by the first i input bits. Consequently, the first error in the last $k - i$ input bits causes an output bit error. Therefore, the probability of no error in the last $k - i$ output bits is equal to the probability of no error in the corresponding input bits. From the independence of input bit errors, we conclude that

$$\overline{P}(w \mid tb = i,\overline{\alpha}) = 1 - 2^{-i}(1 - P_b)^{k-i}$$

(6.27)

and

$$P(\overline{\alpha} \mid tb = i) = (1 - P_b)^i \; .$$

(6.28)

Given tb = i, let the symbol β = ℓ denote the event that the last bit error among the first i input bits occurs at input bit ℓ, where $1 \leqslant \ell \leqslant$ i. If β = ℓ, then α is true; thus, we make the decomposition

$$\overline{P}(w,\alpha | tb = i) = \sum_{\ell = 1}^{i} \overline{P}(w | tb = i, \beta = \ell) \, P(\beta = \ell | tb = i) \ .$$

(6.29)

The probability that β = ℓ given tb = i is equal to the probability that input bit ℓ is erroneous and input bits ℓ + 1 through i are correct. We conclude that

$$P(\beta = \ell | tb = i) = P_b (1 - P_b)^{i - \ell}, \quad 1 \leqslant \ell \leqslant i \ . \quad (6.30)$$

Given tb = i, the probability that the first i output bits are correct has an ensemble average equal to $(1/2)^i$. The probability that the last k $-$ i output bits are correct depends on the event β = ℓ, which implies that a train of n + ℓ $-$ i $-$ 1 bits extends into the final k $-$ i bits. Let $w_{k - i}$ denote the event that an error occurs in a word consisting of k $-$ i output bits. From the previous discussion, it follows that

$$\overline{P}(w | tb = i, \beta = \ell) = 1 - 2^{-i} [1 - \overline{P}(w_{k - i} | tb = n + \ell - i - 1)] \ .$$

(6.31)

Combining Equations (6.26) to (6.31), we obtain

$$\overline{P}(w | tb = i) = 1 - 2^{-i}(1 - P_b)^k - 2^{-i}[1 - (1 - P_b)^i]$$

$$+ 2^{-i} P_b \sum_{\ell = 1}^{i} (1 - P_b)^{i - \ell}$$

$$\times \overline{P}(w_{k - i} | tb = n + \ell - i - 1) \ . \quad (6.32)$$

The factor $\overline{P}(w_{k - i} | tb = n + \ell - i - 1)$ can be evaluated by the same procedure as that leading to Equation (6.32) itself. If n $<$ k, we have a finite hierarchy of equations. The *ensemble-average cryptographic word error probability* follows on substitution of Equation (6.32) into the ensemble average of Equation (6.18).

In practical communication systems with data-keyed ciphers, we nearly always have n $\geqslant$ k. In this case, all of the final k $-$ i bits are part of a train when tb = n + ℓ $-$ i $-$ 1. Thus,

$$\overline{P}(w_{k-i} \mid tb = n + \ell - i - 1) = 1 - 2^{-(k-i)},$$

$$1 \leqslant \ell \leqslant i \leqslant k \leqslant n. \quad (6.33)$$

Substituting Equations (6.32) and (6.33) into the ensemble average of Equation (6.18), performing summations, and regrouping terms, we obtain for $n \geqslant k$,

$$\overline{P}_{cw} = 1 - 2^{-k} + k2^{-k} P_b(1 - P_b)^{n-1}$$

$$- \frac{(1 - P_b)^n [(1 - P_b)^k - 2^{-k}]}{1 - 2P_b}, P_b \neq 1/2;$$

$$\overline{P}_{cw} = 1 - 2^{-k}, \qquad\qquad\qquad P_b = 1/2.$$

$$(6.34)$$

A simple approximation to this equation, which is accurate over the usual range of interest, can be obtained by deriving a Taylor-series expansion about the point $P_b = 0$ and retaining only the first order term. The result is

$$\overline{P}_{cw} \approx [n + k - 2 - 2^{-k}(n - k - 2)] P_b, \quad n \geqslant k. $$

$$(6.35)$$

From the remainder terms in the Taylor series expansions of the factors in Equation (6.34), it is found that the simple condition

$$P_b \ll (n + k - 2)^{-1}, \qquad\qquad\qquad (6.36)$$

is sufficient for the validity of Equation (6.35). Using the same method on Equation (6.25), we obtain

$$\overline{P}_{cb} \approx [n(1 - Y) + Y] P_b, \qquad\qquad (6.37)$$

where Equation (6.36) with $k = 1$ provides a sufficient condition for validity.

To obtain an approximate equation for $\overline{P}_{cw}$ when $n < k$, we note that the last term in Equation (6.32) cannot contribute to the first-order term in a Taylor-series expansion of $\overline{P}_{cw}$. Thus, Equations (6.32) and (6.18) give

$$\overline{P}_{cw} \approx [\, n + k - 2(1 - 2^{-n})\,]\, P_b \,, \quad n < k \,, \quad (6.38)$$

where Equation (6.36) provides a sufficient condition for validity. For a synchronous cipher, $\overline{P}_{cw} = P_{cw} = P_w$. If P_b is small, Equation (6.11) yields $P_{cw} \approx k P_b$. Since the same approximation results when we set $n = 1$ in Equations (6.35) and (6.38), we can use the latter equations for both types of stream ciphers.

6.3 ERROR PROBABILITY BOUNDS AND ENSEMBLE AVERAGES FOR BLOCK CIPHERS

In the conventional block cipher, a plaintext block of m total bits, comprising an integral number of words of k bits each, is enciphered as a block of n total bits. After transmission and reception, the plaintext block is restored as the output of the deciphering system. No output words are in error unless the received ciphertext block contains an error in at least one of its n bits. Assuming the independence of input bit errors,

$$P_{cw} = P(w\,|\,be)\,[\, 1 - (1 - P_b)^n\,] \,, \qquad (6.39)$$

where $P(w\,|\,be)$ is the probability of an error in an output word, given that there is a block error at the input of the deciphering system. Setting $P(w\,|\,be) = 1$ and using Equation (6.22), we obtain

$$P_{cw} \leqslant 1 - (1 - P_b)^n \leqslant n\, P_b \,. \qquad (6.40)$$

Usually block ciphers do not involve a size change; that is, $n = m$. We obtain the ensemble-average cryptographic error probabilities for this case. Due to the one-to-one correspondence between the ciphertext blocks and plaintext blocks, an error in a received ciphertext block is certain to cause at least one erroneous bit in the output block. Consequently, over the ensemble of block ciphers of size n, there are $2^n - 1$ equally likely output blocks corresponding to an erroneous ciphertext block. Consider any fixed bit in these output blocks. In $2^{n-1} - 1$ of the possible output blocks, this bit is correct, that is, in the same state that it would have been in if no error had occurred in the enciphered block. We conclude that given a block error, there is an ensemble-average probability that a bit is correct equal to $(2^{n-1} - 1)/(2^n - 1)$. Consider a second fixed output bit. Given that there is a block error and that the first fixed output bit is correct, it follows from an extension of the previous reasoning that there is an ensemble-average probability that the second fixed bit is correct equal to $(2^{n-2} - 1)/(2^{n-1} - 1)$. If $x_1, x_2, \ldots, x_n$ are events, the probability of all these events is equal to the product of conditional probabilities:

$$P(x_1, x_2, \ldots, x_n) = P(x_n | x_{n-1}, \ldots, x_1) \ldots P(x_2 | x_1) P(x_1) .$$

$$(6.41)$$

Using this equation and repeating the analysis for successive output bits, we conclude that

$$\overline{P}(w | be) = 1 - \prod_{i=1}^{k} \frac{2^{n-i} - 1}{2^{n+1-i} - 1}$$

$$= \frac{2^n (1 - 2^{-k})}{2^n - 1} .$$

$$(6.42)$$

Combining this relation with Equation (6.39), we obtain the ensemble-average cryptographic word error probability for block ciphers,

$$\overline{P}_{cw} = (1 - 2^{-n})^{-1} (1 - 2^{-k}) [1 - (1 - P_b)^n] .$$

$$(6.43)$$

A Taylor-series expansion yields

$$\overline{P}_{cw} \approx (1 - 2^{-n})^{-1} (1 - 2^{-k}) n P_b ,$$

$$(6.44)$$

which is accurate if

$$P_b \ll 2(n - 1)^{-1} .$$

$$(6.45)$$

The ensemble-average cryptographic bit error probability for block ciphers is obtained by setting $k = 1$ in Equation (6.43) or (6.44). Although these equations hold for all values of n and k, $n \geq 4k$ is usually required to safeguard against the frequency analysis of block patterns.

6.4 DEGRADATION DUE TO CRYPTOGRAPHY

The bit error probability for binary communications is a function of the mean energy per bit, E_b. In general, we may write

$$P_b = f(E_b) \, , \tag{6.46}$$

where f is a function. If this equation is substituted into the equations for the cryptographic error probabilities, there result equations in terms of E_b. By comparing these equations with Equations (6.11) and (6.46), we can determine the increase in energy required to obtain the same error probability from a cryptographic system as provided by the corresponding plaintext system. This increase provides a quantitative measure of *cryptographic degradation.* The degradation in decibels is defined to be

$$D = 10 \log_{10} E_b' - 10 \log_{10} E_b = 10 \log_{10} \left(\frac{E_b'}{E_b} \right) \, , \tag{6.47}$$

where E_b' is the energy required to produce a value of $\overline{P}_{cw}$ that equals the value of P_w when the energy is E_b.

It is often convenient to have a simple approximate formula for the degradation. To derive such a formula, note that for small values of P_b, Equation (6.11) becomes

$$P_w \cong k P_b, \quad P_b \ll 2(k-1)^{-1} \, . \tag{6.48}$$

With this approximation, the ensemble-average word error probabilities for small values of P_b have the form

$$\overline{P}_{cw} \cong g(n,k) \, P_w \, , \quad P_b \ll (n+k-2)^{-1} \, . \tag{6.49}$$

The parameter n is the number of output bits that may be affected by an error in a received ciphertext bit. For stream ciphers,

$$g(n,1) = n(1-Y) + Y \tag{6.50}$$

for bits and

$$g(n,k) = \begin{cases} \dfrac{n+k-2-2^{-k}(n-k-2)}{k} \, , & n \geq k \, , \\[4mm] \dfrac{n+k-2(1-2^{-n})}{k} \, , & n < k \, , \end{cases} \tag{6.51}$$

for words with $Y = 1/2$. For block ciphers,

$$g(n,k) = \frac{(1 - 2^{-k})\, n}{(1 - 2^{-n})\, k} \ . \tag{6.52}$$

According to the definition of E_b', it is implicitly related to E_b by

$$\overline{P}_{cw}(E_b') = P_w(E_b) \ . \tag{6.53}$$

Combining Equations (6.46), (6.48), (6.49), and (6.53), it follows that the degradation can be determined analytically by solving

$$g(n,k)\, f\,(E_b') = f\,(E_b) \ . \tag{6.54}$$

Many noncoherent and differentially coherent systems operating in Gaussian noise or interference have bit error probabilities of the form

$$P_b = f(E_b) = b \exp\,(-cE_b) \ , \tag{6.55}$$

where b and c are independent of E_b, but depend on the modulation type and the noise power. Substituting Equation (6.55) into Equation (6.54), solving for E_b'/E_b, and using the result in Equation (6.47), we obtain

$$D = 10 \log_{10} \left[1 + \frac{\ln g(n,k)}{cE_b} \right]. \tag{6.56}$$

Substituting Equations (6.48) and (6.55) into Equation (6.56) yields

$$D = 10 \log_{10} \left[1 - \frac{\ln g(n,k)}{\ln \left(\dfrac{P_w}{bk} \right)} \right]. \tag{6.57}$$

In this form, D can be calculated without specifying the constant c. For a uniform noise spectrum, we usually have $b = 1/2$. Although Equations (6.56) and (6.57) were derived assuming Equation (6.55), they are usually quite accurate for coherent systems if $cE_b > 10$.

To illustrate various aspects of ciphers, Figures 6.10 and 6.11 plot the degradation of ensemble-average bit error probabilities when $b = 1/2$. In Figure 6.10, we set $n = 100$ and plot D as a function of P_b. The impact of changing $Y = 1/2$ to $Y = 3/4$ is observed to be

relatively minor. Thus, the reduced degradation is usually not sufficient to warrant limiting the cryptographic ensemble to a cipher subset with $Y = 3/4$.

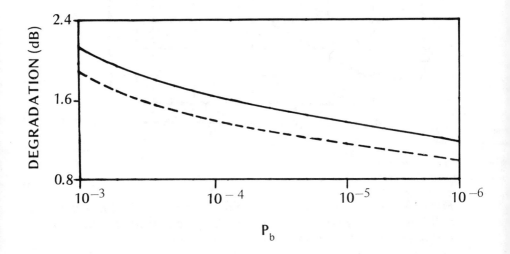

Figure 6.10/Degradation as function of P_b for n = 100 and b = 1/2.
Solid curve: block cipher or stream cipher with Y = 1/2. Dashed
curve: stream cipher with Y = 3/4.

In Figure 6.11, we see the effects of increasing n when $P_b = 10^{-3}$.
The degradations of block and stream ciphers converge as n increases.
Since n is a measure of the security of the cryptographic system, the
figure illustrates the price paid in degradation for increased security.

6.5 ERROR CORRECTION

To reduce the word error probability and the jamming susceptibility of
a cryptographic system, an error-correcting code can be superimposed
on the enciphering. Figure 6.12 illustrates one possible system configuration. The data bits are first enciphered and then encoded; after transmission and reception, the bits are first decoded and then deciphered.

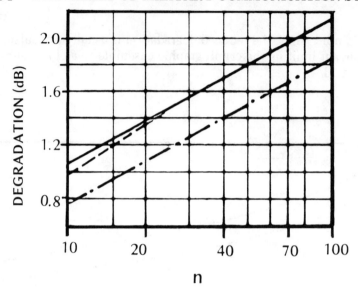

Figure 6.11/Degradation as function of n for P_b = 10^{-3} and b = 1/2.
Solid curve: stream cipher with Y = 1/2. Dashed curve: block cipher.
Dot-dashed curve: stream cipher with Y = 3/4.

If a synchronous cipher is used with an error-correcting code, an equally effective system configuration usually results when the inner and outer blocks are interchanged. However, if a data-keyed or block cipher is used in combination with an error-correcting code, an interchange is usually inappropriate for military communications because error extension might overwhelm the error-correcting capability of the decoding system.

The preceding derivations of cryptographic error probabilities depend upon the assumption of independent bit errors at the input to the deciphering system. When this input is the output from a decoding system that corrects word errors, the input bit errors are not independent, but occur in clusters. Thus, the preceding equations for the cryptographic error probabilities do not apply. However, assuming the independence of the input word errors, we can relate the word error probabilities at the outputs of deciphering systems to the word error probabilities at the inputs. This assumption is valid when block codes are used for error correction and the bit errors at the input to the decoding system are independent.

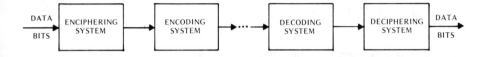

Figure 6.12/Encoding superimposed on enciphering.

For stream ciphers, we define the parameter h as the number of input words that can cause a train of external origin in an output word. Thus,

$$h = intl\left(\frac{n-1}{k}\right) + 1 , \qquad (6.58)$$

where intl(x) is the largest integer less than x. Let P(t) denote the probability that a train of external origin extends into an output word. From Equation (6.12), we obtain $P_{cw} \leqslant P(t) + P_w$. Therefore,

$$P_{cw} \leqslant 1 - (1 - P_w)^h + P_w \leqslant (h + 1) P_w , \qquad (6.59)$$

where P_w and P_{cw} are the error probabilities of the input and output words, respectively. These upper bounds can be used in approximate calculations of the cryptographic degradation.

For block ciphers, we use the methods of Section 6.3 to obtain

$$P_{cw} \leqslant 1 - (1 - P_w)^{n/k} \leqslant \frac{n}{k} P_w , \qquad (6.60)$$

and

$$\overline{P}_{cw} = (1 - 2^{-n})^{-1} (1 - 2^{-k})[1 - (1 - P_w)^{n/k}] , \qquad (6.61)$$

where the integer n/k is the number of words in a block. A Taylor-series expansion yields the approximation

$$\overline{P}_{cw} \approx (1 - 2^{-n})^{-1} (1 - 2^{-k}) \frac{n}{k} P_w , \tag{6.62}$$

which is accurate if

$$P_w \ll 2k(n - k)^{-1}. \tag{6.63}$$

6.6 SYNCHRONIZATION AND JAMMING

The operation of communication systems using synchronous ciphers depends upon the perfect alignment of the keystream and received bits in the deciphering system. Once misalignment occurs, special measures must be employed to restore synchronization. In contrast, communication systems with data-keyed ciphers restore alignment of the bits automatically since the keystream is continually produced by the received bits. Synchronization is lost in a data-keyed system whenever the receiver incorrectly identifies the word boundaries. Synchronization is lost in a block-enciphered system whenever the receiver incorrectly identifies the block boundaries. Both data-keyed and block-enciphered systems often can resynchronize automatically as soon as the next frame identification bits are received.

Loss of synchronization in a receiver for a synchronous cipher can occur when a burst of energy causes the clock output of a bit synchronizer to skip a pulse or generate an extra pulse. Alternatively, synchronization can be lost when interference causes a sufficient number of frame synchronization bits to be received erroneously. When this event is recognized, the receiver assumes that a misalignment has occurred and initiates the resynchronization procedure.

Suppose strong jamming of pulse duration T_D occurs every T_B seconds during the reception of a synchronous cipher. If a jamming pulse causes a loss of synchronization in the receiver, time is lost while the communication system recognizes the loss of synchronization, initiates the resynchronization procedure, and reestablishes synchronization between the received ciphertext and the keystream. We call this lost time the *reacquisition time* and denote its average duration by T_R. Since reacquisition cannot be completed until the jamming has ceased, $T_R > T_D$, as illustrated in Figure 6.13. In general, T_R is a function of T_D. When T_D is sufficiently large, it is reasonable to expect that $T_R \cong T_D + C$, where C is a constant.

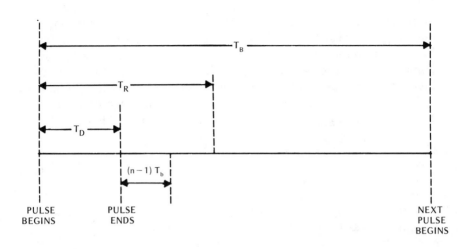

Figure 6.13/Timing diagram for pulsed jamming of cryptographic communications.

During the reacquisition time, the probability of error of the deciphered bits in the receiver is one-half, since the transmitted information has been entirely destroyed. (If the receiver output is disabled upon recognition of a synchronization loss, the missing bits must be guessed, so the equivalent bit error probability is one-half.) After reacquisition, assuming there is no further loss of synchronization before the occurrence of the next jamming pulse, the bit error probability at the output of the deciphering system becomes P_b, the usual channel bit error probability. To ignore the relative time alignment of the bit edges and the jamming pulses, we assume that

$$T_R \gg T_b \ , \quad T_B - T_R \gg T_b \ , \tag{6.64}$$

where T_b is the bit duration. It follows that the expected number of bit errors over a jamming pulse period for a synchronous cipher is

$$N_S \cong \left(\frac{T_R}{T_b} \right) \frac{1}{2} + \left(\frac{T_B - T_R}{T_b} \right) P_b \ . \tag{6.65}$$

Suppose that the same pulsed jamming temporarily disrupts a data-keyed cipher with $Y = 1/2$, but word synchronization is maintained. For the pulse duration and $n - 1$ bits following the cessation of the jamming pulse, the bit error probability is one-half. The remaining bits before the next pulse have an ensemble-average error probability of $\overline{P}_{cb}$. As seen in Figure 6.13, the relative time alignments of the bit edges and the pulses may be ignored by assuming that

$$T_D + (n - 1)T_b \gg T_b \; ,$$

$$T_B - T_D - (n - 1)T_b \gg T_b \; . \tag{6.66}$$

It follows that the expected number of bit errors over a pulse period for a data-keyed cipher is

$$N_D \cong \left[\frac{T_D + (n - 1)T_b}{T_b} \right] \frac{1}{2} + \left[\frac{T_B - T_D - (n - 1)T_b}{T_b} \right] \overline{P}_{cb} \; . \tag{6.67}$$

Assuming that word synchronization is maintained, a data-keyed cipher has a lower bit error probability than a synchronous cipher if $N_D < N_S$. From Equations (6.65) and (6.67), we see that this situation exists if

$$T_B < \frac{T_R \left(\dfrac{1}{2} - P_b \right) - \left[T_D + (n - 1)T_b \right] \left(\dfrac{1}{2} - \overline{P}_{cb} \right)}{\overline{P}_{cb} - P_b} \; . \tag{6.68}$$

For most practical communication systems using a data-keyed cipher, this inequality can be approximated by

$$T_B < \frac{T_R - T_D - (n - 1)T_b}{2\overline{P}_{cb}} \; , \quad P_b \ll \overline{P}_{cb} \ll \frac{1}{2} \; . \tag{6.69}$$

Equations (6.64), (6.66), and either (6.68) or (6.69) constitute sufficient conditions for a data-keyed cipher to outperform a synchronous cipher when pulsed jamming is present and word synchronization is maintained. If word synchronization is not maintained in a data-keyed cipher, the sufficient conditions are obtained by substituting T_F in place of $(n - 1)T_b$, where T_F is the average time until frame identification bits allow resynchronization.

As an example, suppose $n = 101$, $T_D = 900\ T_b$, $T_R = 10^4\ T_b$, and $P_b = 10^{-4}$. Since $k = 1$ and Equation (6.36) is satisfied, Equation (6.37) with $Y = 1/2$ gives $\overline{P}_{cb} = 5.1 \times 10^{-3}$. Equation (6.69) applies and yields $T_B < 0.9 \times 10^6\ T_b$. Equations (6.64) and (6.66) are satisfied if $T_B > 1.1 \times 10^4\ T_b$.

Another type of jamming, called *playback*, occurs if intercepted cryptographic communications are retransmitted at a later time with sufficiently high power to capture the victim receiver. Although synchronous ciphers are inherently immune to playback, block and data-keyed ciphers require special protective measures. If the key of a data-keyed cipher has not been changed since the interception, the first n receiver output bits due to playback are affected by error extension, but subsequent output bits constitute an erroneous, but comprehensible, message. A countermeasure that is effective for data-keyed ciphers is to intersperse the plaintext with the date and time of day or other time varying authentication information.

This approach may be effective for block ciphers unless an opponent can isolate the specific blocks that contain the authentication information and appropriately alter these blocks before retransmission. To preclude this possibility and similar threats, interdependence between adjacent blocks may be introduced. In *block chaining*, each successive plaintext block contains a number of bits from the previous ciphertext block. A deciphered block is checked to ensure that these authentication bits match the corresponding bits of the previous ciphertext block. The problem with block chaining is that an adequate number of authentication bits may significantly reduce the transmission rate of information bits. To eliminate this problem, *cipher-block chaining* may be used. In this method, the bits of a ciphertext block are related to the plaintext bits and the bits of the previous ciphertext block by a generalization of Equation (6.1) for $m = n$:

$$y_k = f_k(z_i, z_{i+1}, \ldots, z_{i+n-1}) , \quad i \leqslant k \leqslant i + n - 1 ,$$
$$(6.70)$$

where

$$z_k = x_k \oplus y_{k-n} , \quad i \leqslant k \leqslant i + n - 1 . \qquad (6.71)$$

These equations indicate that cipher-block chaining can be interpreted as a hybrid of a stream cipher and a block cipher. The forms of the enciphering and deciphering systems are depicted in Figures 6.14 and 6.15. In addition to the error extension within blocks, there is a limited error propagation between adjacent blocks. For example, suppose there is a single bit error in a received ciphertext block and no errors in the next one. After deciphering, the first corresponding plaintext block will usually contain many bit errors, but the second plaintext block will contain exactly one bit error.

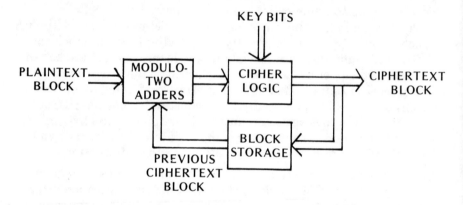

Figure 6.14/Enciphering system for cipher-block chaining.

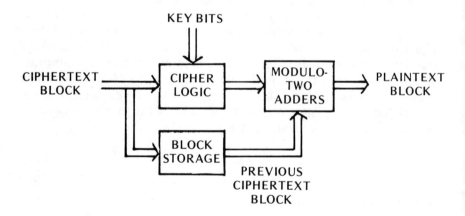

Figure 6.15/Deciphering system for cipher-block chaining.

6.7 SECURITY

The susceptibility of a synchronous cipher to cryptanalysis is greatly increased if the same part of the keystream is used to produce two or more different ciphertexts. The reason is that the modulo-two sum of two ciphertexts equals the modulo-two sum of the corresponding plaintexts, which can often be cryptanalyzed by well-known methods [1]. In a network of more than two communicators sharing the same key, an *indicator* can be used to prevent reuse of a keystream. An indicator is transmitted data that a communicator sends, in plaintext or ciphertext form, to enable a receiver to decipher a message. The initial contents of the shift register stages are usually a suitable indicator for either a synchronous or a data-keyed cipher.

Keys are usually distributed to communicators by means that are the most secure possible, such as couriers, but that are too slow for the transmission of all messages. There are several ways to allocate keys in a network. All potential pairs of communicators may receive appropriate keys. If this procedure entails too many different keys, an alternative is to distribute a single master key to each network element. Each master key enables an element to communicate with a *key distribution center*. When two elements to wish to communicate, they request a *session key* from the key distribution center, which transmits the session key to the elements in their master keys. In this configuration, the overall security of the network depends upon the security of the key distribution center.

It is sometimes necessary for communications to pass through intermediate nodes. If the message is enciphered at the source and deciphered only at its destination, with only the address or identification of the destination transmitted as plaintext, the procedure is called *end-to-end encryption*.

Another way to allocate keys and communicate within a network, called *link encryption*, is to provide each element with a single key for communicating with a central node or a local node. A message is successively deciphered and then enciphered by use of the node key as the message passes through each successive node until it reaches its final destination. The security of a message depends upon the security of the intermediate nodes.

The use of cryptography can ensure communication security, but system performance degrades, susceptibility to jamming increases, reliability decreases, and cost rises.

REFERENCES

[1]   W. Diffie and M.E. Hellman, "Privacy and Authentication: An Introduction to Cryptography," *Proc. IEEE* 67 (March 1979), 397.

[2]   H. Feistel, W.A. Notz, and J.L. Smith, "Some Cryptographic Techniques for Machine-to-Machine Data Communications," *Proc. IEEE* 63 (November 1975), 1545.

[3]   E.L. Key, "An Analysis of the Structure and Complexity of Nonlinear Binary Sequence Generators," *IEEE Trans. Inform. Theory* IT-22 (November 1976), 732.

Appendix A

DERIVATIONS OF CONDITIONAL BIT ERROR
PROBABILITIES FOR FREQUENCY-SHIFT KEYING

A noncoherent binary frequency-shift-keying (FSK) demodulator is
displayed in Figure A.1. We assume that Gaussian noise enters each
bandpass filter and that the noise spectrum is flat across the filter passband.

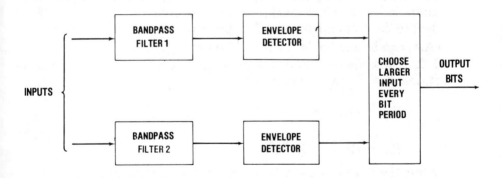

Figure A.1 /Noncoherent frequency-shift-keying demodulator.

At the output of bandpass filter i, the bandlimited white Gaussian
noise has the narrowband representation [1]

$$n_i(t) = n_{ci}(t) \cos \omega_i t - n_{si}(t) \sin \omega_i t, \quad i = 1, 2, \qquad (A.1)$$

where ω_i is the center frequency and $n_{ci}(t)$ and $n_{si}(t)$ are independent Gaussian processes with noise powers equal to N_i. We assume that jamming signals of the form

$$J_i(t) = B_i(t) \cos [\omega_i t + \phi_i(t)] , \quad i = 1, 2 , \qquad (A.2)$$

emerge from the bandpass filters. Suppose that a binary symbol represented by

$$s_1(t) = A \cos \omega_1 t \qquad (A.3)$$

is received and passes through bandpass filter 1 with negligible distortion. The total signals at the outputs of the two bandpass filters are

$$X_1(t) = A_1 \cos \omega_1 t + B_1 \cos (\omega_1 t + \phi_1) + n_{c1} \cos \omega_1 t$$
$$- n_{s1} \sin \omega_1 t ,$$
$$X_2(t) = B_2 \cos (\omega_2 t + \phi_2) + n_{c2} \cos \omega_2 t - n_{c2} \sin \omega_2 t .$$
$$(A.4)$$

We consider a typical bit interval, which is defined by $0 \leqslant t \leqslant T_b$ The sampling time, the time at which a bit decision is made, could theoretically be any time within this interval because of the idealized form assumed in Equation (A.3). In practice, a sampling time at the midpoint of the bit interval is likely to provide the best results. We denote the sampling time by T_1. By using trigonometry, Equations (A.4) can be written in the form $X_i(t) = R_i(t) \cos (\omega_i t + \psi_i)$, $i = 1, 2$. Thus, the outputs of the envelope detectors of the two branches at time $t = T_1$ are found to be

$$R_1 = (Z_1^2 + Z_2^2)^{\frac{1}{2}} ,$$
$$R_2 = (Z_3^2 + Z_4^2)^{\frac{1}{2}} , \qquad (A.5)$$

where the following definitions are made for notational convenience:

$$Z_1 = A + B_1(T_1) \cos [\phi_1(T_1)] + n_{c1}(T_1) ,$$
$$Z_2 = B_1(T_1) \sin [\phi_1(T_1)] + n_{s1}(T_1) ,$$
$$Z_3 = B_2(T_1) \cos [\phi_2(T_1)] + n_{c2}(T_1) , \qquad (A.6)$$
$$Z_4 = B_2(T_1) \sin [\phi_2(T_1)] + n_{s2}(T_1) .$$

Since the $n_i(t)$ are assumed to be zero-mean processes, all the noise variables in Equations (A.6) are zero mean. Denoting the expected value of Z_i by M_i, we have

$$M_1 = A + B_1(T_1) \cos [\phi_1(T_1)] ,$$
$$M_2 = B_1(T_1) \sin [\phi_1(T_1)] ,$$
$$M_3 = B_2(T_1) \cos [\phi_2(T_1)] ,$$
$$M_4 = B_2(T_1) \sin [\phi_2(T_1)] .$$

(A.7)

Assuming that $B_1(T_1)$ and $\phi_1(T_1)$ are given, the joint probability density function of Z_1 and Z_2 is

$$g_1(z_1, z_2) = \frac{1}{2\pi N_1} \exp \left[-\frac{(z_1 - M_1)^2 + (z_2 - M_2)^2}{2N_1} \right].$$

(A.8)

If we define $Z_1 = R_1 \cos \Theta$ and $Z_2 = R_1 \sin \Theta$, it follows that the joint density of R_1 and Θ is

$$g_2(r_1, \theta) = \frac{r_1}{2\pi N_1}$$

$$\times \exp \left(-\frac{r_1^2 - 2r_1 M_1 \cos \theta - 2r_1 M_2 \sin \theta + M_1^2 + M_2^2}{2N_1} \right),$$

$$r_1 \geq 0, \ |\theta| \leq \pi .$$

(A.9)

The density of the envelope R_1 is obtained by integration over θ. First we note that the modified Bessel function of the first kind and zero order satisfies

$$I_0(x) = \frac{1}{2\pi} \int_0^{2\pi} \exp [x \cos (u + v)] \, du ,$$

(A.10)

regardless of the value of v. Consequently, after suitable trigonometric manipulation, the integral of Equation (A.9) over θ can be reduced to

$$f_1(r_1) = \frac{r_1}{N_1} \exp \left(-\frac{D_1^2 + r_1^2}{2N_1} \right) I_0 \left(\frac{D_1 r_1}{N_1} \right), \quad r_1 \geq 0 ,$$

(A.11)

where we define

$$D_1{}^2 = M_1{}^2 + M_2{}^2 = A^2 + B_1{}^2(T_1) + 2AB_1(T_1) \cos[\phi_1(T_1)] \ . \tag{A.12}$$

In a similar manner, the output at time $t = T_1$ of the envelope detector in the other branch of the FSK demodulator has the density given by

$$f_2(r_2) = \frac{r_2}{N_2} \exp\left(-\frac{B_2{}^2 + r_2{}^2}{2N_2}\right) I_0\left(\frac{B_2 r_2}{N_2}\right), \quad r_2 \geqslant 0 \ . \tag{A.13}$$

Since $s_1(t)$ has been transmitted, an error occurs if $R_2 > R_1$. Thus, the probability of an error is

$$P(E/1) = \int_0^\infty f_1(r_1) \left[\int_{r_1}^\infty f_2(r_2)\, dr_2\right] dr_1 \ . \tag{A.14}$$

Substituting Equations (A.11) and (A.13) into Equation (A.14), we obtain

$$P(E/1) = \int_0^\infty q\left(\frac{D_1}{\sqrt{N_1}}, x\right) Q\left(\frac{B_2}{\sqrt{N_2}}, \frac{\sqrt{N_1}\, x}{\sqrt{N_2}}\right) dx \ , \tag{A.15}$$

where we have defined the Rician function

$$q(\alpha, x) = x \exp\left(-\frac{x^2 + \alpha^2}{2}\right) I_0(\alpha x) \tag{A.16}$$

and the Q-function

$$Q(\alpha, \beta) = \int_\beta^\infty q(\alpha, x)\, dx \ . \tag{A.17}$$

The integral in Equation (A.15) can be evaluated by using the identity [2]

$$\int_0^\infty q(a, x)\, Q(b, rx)\, dx = Q(v_2, v_1) - \frac{r^2}{1 + r^2}$$

$$\times \exp\left[-\frac{a^2 r^2 + b^2}{2(1 + r^2)}\right] I_0\left(\frac{abr}{1 + r^2}\right),$$

$$(A.18)$$

where

$$v_1 = \frac{ar}{\sqrt{1 + r^2}}, \qquad v_2 = \frac{b}{\sqrt{1 + r^2}}.$$

Carrying out the algebra, we obtain

$$P(E/1) = Q\left(\frac{B_2}{\sqrt{N_1 + N_2}}, \frac{D_1}{\sqrt{N_1 + N_2}}\right) - \frac{N_1}{N_1 + N_2}$$

$$\times \exp\left[-\frac{B_2{}^2 + D_1{}^2}{2(N_1 + N_2)}\right] I_0\left(\frac{B_2 D_1}{N_1 + N_2}\right). \quad (A.19)$$

This expression gives $P(E/1)$ for fixed values of the $B_i(T_1)$ and $\phi_1(T_1)$. From bit interval to bit interval, these parameters generally vary in value. If these parameters are modeled as random variables, an aggregate $P(E/1)$ can be calculated by integrating the product of Equation (A.19) and the joint density of the $B_i(T_1)$ and $\phi_1(T_1)$. To obtain reasonably simple results, we assume that narrowband angle-modulated jamming is present so that $B_i(t) = B_i(T_1) = B_i$, a constant. If $\phi_1(t)$ is nonsynchronous with the carrier frequency of $s_1(t)$, it is logical to model $\phi_1(T_1)$ as uniformly distributed from 0 to 2π radians. Thus, the aggregate probability of error, given that $s_1(t)$ was transmitted, is

$$\overline{P}(E/1) = \frac{1}{2\pi} \int_0^{2\pi} P(E/1)\, d\phi_1. \qquad (A.20)$$

When a symbol represented by

$$s_2(t) = A \cos \omega_2 t \qquad (A.21)$$

is received, the bit error probabilities can be determined by an analogous procedure. Defining

$$D_2{}^2 = A^2 + B_2{}^2(T_1) + 2AB_2(T_1) \cos [\phi_2(T_1)] , \qquad (A.22)$$

we obtain

$$P(E/2) = Q\left(\frac{B_1}{\sqrt{N_1 + N_2}}, \frac{D_2}{\sqrt{N_1 + N_2}}\right) - \frac{N_2}{N_1 + N_2}$$

$$\times \exp\left[-\frac{B_1{}^2 + D_2{}^2}{2(N_1 + N_2)}\right] I_0\left(\frac{B_1 D_2}{N_1 + N_2}\right). \qquad (A.23)$$

If $B_i(t) = B_i(T_1) = B_i$, a constant, and $\phi_2(T_1)$ is uniformly distributed, then

$$\overline{P}(E/2) = \frac{1}{2\pi} \int_0^{2\pi} P(E/2) \, d\phi_2 . \qquad (A.24)$$

If the transmission of $s_1(t)$ or $s_2(t)$ is equally likely, the probability of a bit error is

$$\overline{P}(E) = \frac{1}{2} \overline{P}(E/1) + \frac{1}{2} \overline{P}(E/2) . \qquad (A.25)$$

Substitution of the previous equations into Equation (A.25) yields

$$\overline{P}(E) = \frac{1}{4\pi} \int_0^{2\pi} dx \left\{ Q\left[\frac{B_2}{\sqrt{N_1 + N_2}}, \frac{D_1(x)}{\sqrt{N_1 + N_2}}\right] \right.$$

$$+ Q\left[\frac{B_1}{\sqrt{N_1 + N_2}}, \frac{D_2(x)}{\sqrt{N_1 + N_2}}\right] - \frac{N_1}{N_1 + N_2}$$

$$\times \exp\left[-\frac{B_2{}^2 + D_1{}^2(x)}{2(N_1 + N_2)}\right] I_0\left[\frac{B_2 D_1(x)}{N_1 + N_2}\right] - \frac{N_2}{N_1 +}$$

$$\times \exp\left[-\frac{B_1{}^2 + D_2{}^2(x)}{2(N_1 + N_2)}\right] I_0\left[\frac{B_1 D_2(x)}{N_1 + N_2}\right]\right\}, \qquad (A.2$$

where

$$D_i^2(x) = A^2 + B_i^2 + 2AB_i \cos x , \quad i = 1, 2 .$$

This equation is a slight generalization of one derived by Pettit [3].

The various conditional bit error probabilities can be calculated from the above equations. The passband of each bandpass filter is called a channel. The probability of a bit error given that an equal amount of narrowband jamming power enters both channels, S_2, is determined by setting $B_1 = B_2 = \sqrt{2R_j}$ in Equation (A.26), where R_j is the jamming power. Setting $A = \sqrt{2R_s}$, where R_s is the received signal power, we obtain

$$S_2 = \frac{1}{2\pi} \int_0^{2\pi} dx \left\{ Q \left[\sqrt{\frac{2R_j}{N_1 + N_2}} , \frac{D(x)}{\sqrt{N_1 + N_2}} \right] \right.$$

$$\left. - \frac{1}{2} \exp \left[-\frac{2R_j + D^2(x)}{2(N_1 + N_2)} \right] I_0 \left[\frac{\sqrt{2R_j} \, D(x)}{N_1 + N_2} \right] \right\} , \quad (A.27)$$

where

$$D^2(x) = 2R_s + 2R_j + 4\sqrt{R_s R_j} \cos x .$$

The probability of a bit error given that narrowband jamming enters a single channel, S_1, is determined by setting $B_1 = \sqrt{2R_j}$ and $B_2 = 0$ in Equation (A.26). To simplify the result, we use Equation (A.10), $I_0(0) = 1$, and

$$Q(0, \beta) = \exp \left(-\frac{\beta^2}{2} \right) \qquad (A.28)$$

to obtain

$$S_1 = \frac{1}{2} Q \left(\sqrt{\frac{2R_j}{N_1 + N_2}} , \sqrt{\frac{2R_s}{N_1 + N_2}} \right) , \qquad (A.29)$$

where N_1 is the noise power in the jammed channel and N_2 is the noise power in the unjammed channel.

The probability of a bit error given that narrowband jamming enters the same channel as the desired signal, S_t, is determined by setting

$B_1 = \sqrt{2R_j}$ and $B_2 = 0$ in Equations (A.19) and (A.20). Using Equations (A.10), (A.12), and (A.28) yields

$$S_t = \frac{N_2}{N_1 + N_2} \exp\left(-\frac{R_s + R_j}{N_1 + N_2}\right) I_0\left(\frac{2\sqrt{R_s R_j}}{N_1 + N_2}\right), \quad (A.30)$$

where N_1 is the noise power in the same channel as the desired signal and N_2 is the noise power in the unjammed channel.

The probability of a bit error given that narrowband jamming enters the channel without the desired signal, S_c, is determined by setting $B_1 = 0$ and $B_2 = \sqrt{2R_j}$ in Equations (A.19) and (A.20). After simplification, the result is

$$S_c = Q\left(\sqrt{\frac{2R_j}{N_1 + N_2}}, \sqrt{\frac{2R_s}{N_1 + N_2}}\right) - \frac{N_1}{N_1 + N_2}$$

$$\times \exp\left(-\frac{R_s + R_j}{N_1 + N_2}\right) I_0\left(\frac{2\sqrt{R_s R_j}}{N_1 + N_2}\right), \quad (A.31)$$

where N_1 is the noise power in the same channel as the desired signal and N_2 is the noise power in the jammed channel.

The probability of a bit error given that narrowband jamming is absent can be obtained by setting $R_j = 0$ in Equation (A.27) and using Equation (A.28). The result is

$$P(E) = \frac{1}{2} \exp\left(-\frac{R_s}{N_1 + N_2}\right), \quad R_j = 0. \quad (A.32)$$

REFERENCES

[1]   R.E. Ziemer and W.H. Tranter, *Principles of Communications.* Boston: Houghton Mifflin, 1976.

[2]   C. Helstrom, *Statistical Theory of Signal Detection,* 2nd ed. New York: Pergamon Press, 1968.

[3]   R. Pettit, "Error Probability for NCFSK with Linear FM Jamming," *IEEE Trans. Aerosp. Electron. Syst.* AES-8 (September 1972), 609.

Appendix B

NONCENTRAL CHI-SQUARED DISTRIBUTION

Consider the sum of random variables

$$Z = \sum_{i=1}^{N} A_i^2 \, , \tag{B.1}$$

where the A_i are independent, identically distributed, Gaussian random variables with means m_i and unit variances. The random variable Z is said to have a noncentral chi-squared (χ^2) distribution with N degrees of freedom and a noncentral parameter

$$\lambda = \sum_{i=1}^{N} m_i^2 \tag{B.2}$$

To derive the density function of Z, we first note that each A_i has the density function

$$p_{Ai}(x) = \frac{1}{\sqrt{2\pi}} \, \exp\left[-\frac{(x - m_i)^2}{2} \right] . \tag{B.3}$$

From elementary probability, the density of $Y_i = A_i^2$ is

$$p_{Yi}(x) = \frac{1}{2\sqrt{x}} \, [\, p_{Ai}(\sqrt{x}) + p_{Ai}(-\sqrt{x}) \,] \, u(x) \, , \tag{B.4}$$

where u(x) = 1, x $\geqslant$ 0, and u(x) = 0, x $<$ 0. Substituting Equation (B.3) into Equation (B.4), expanding the exponentials, and simplifying, we obtain the density

$$p_{Yi}(x) = \frac{1}{\sqrt{2\pi x}} \exp\left(-\frac{x + m_i^2}{2}\right) \cosh(m_i\sqrt{x})\, u(x) \ .$$

(B.5)

The characteristic function of a random variable X is defined as

$$M_X(j\nu) = E[e^{j\nu X}] = \int_{-\infty}^{\infty} p_X(x) \exp(j\nu x)\, dx \ ,$$

(B.6)

where E[ ] denotes the expected value, j = $\sqrt{-1}$, and $p_X(x)$ is the density of X. Since $M_X(j\nu)$ is the conjugate Fourier transform of $p_X(x)$,

$$p_X(x) = \frac{1}{2\pi} \int_{-\infty}^{\infty} M_X(j\nu) \exp(-j\nu x)\, d\nu \ .$$

(B.7)

Using Equation (B.6) and LaPlace or Fourier transform tables, we determine the characteristic function of $p_{Yi}(x)$ to be

$$M_{Yi}(j\nu) = \exp\left(-\frac{m_i^2}{2}\right) (1 - j2\nu)^{-\frac{1}{2}} \exp\left[\frac{m_i^2}{2(1 - j2\nu)}\right] \ .$$

(B.8)

The characteristic function of a sum of independent random variables is equal to the product of the individual characteristic functions. Since Z is the sum of the Y_i, the characteristic function of Z is

$$M_Z(j\nu) = \exp\left(-\frac{\lambda}{2}\right) (1 - j2\nu)^{-N/2} \exp\left[\frac{\lambda}{2(1 - j2\nu)}\right] \ ,$$

(B.9)

where we have used Equation (B.2). From Equation (B.7) and LaPlace or Fourier transform tables, we obtain

$$p_Z(x) = \frac{1}{2}\left(\frac{x}{\lambda}\right)^{(N-2)/4} \exp\left(-\frac{x + \lambda}{2}\right) I_{N/2 - 1}(\sqrt{x\lambda})\, u(x) \ ,$$

(B.10)

where $I_n(\ )$ is the modified Bessel function of the first kind and order n. Equation (B.10) is the density function of a noncentral χ^2 random variable with N degrees of freedom and a noncentral parameter λ. Using the series expansion in λ of the Bessel function and setting $\lambda = 0$, we obtain

$$p_Z(x) = \frac{1}{2^{N/2}\, \Gamma(N/2)}\, x^{N/2-1}\, \exp\left(-\frac{x}{2}\right) u(x) \ , \ \lambda = 0 \ .$$

$$(B.11)$$

Alternatively, we can obtain Equation (B.11) by setting $\lambda = 0$ in Equation (B.9) and using transform tables. Equation (B.11) is the density function for a central χ^2 random variable with N degrees of freedom. This density is widely used in statistics.

The moments of Z can be determined by integrations and Equation (B.10) or from the properties of Gaussian random variables and Equation (B.1). The mean and variance are

$$E(Z) = \lambda + N \ , \tag{B.12}$$

$$VAR(Z) = 4\lambda + 2N \ . \tag{B.13}$$

From the properties of characteristic functions, it follows that the sum of two independent noncentral χ^2 random variables with N_1 and N_2 degrees of freedom and noncentral parameters λ_1 and λ_2, respectively, is a noncentral χ^2 random variable with $N_1 + N_2$ degrees of freedom and noncentral parameter $\lambda_1 + \lambda_2$.

Computations of the noncentral chi-squared distribution involve the integral

$$L = \int_V^{\infty} \frac{1}{2}\left(\frac{x}{\lambda}\right)^{(N-2)/4} \exp\left(-\frac{x+\lambda}{2}\right) I_{N/2-1}(\sqrt{x\lambda})\ dx \ ,$$

$$(B.14)$$

where $V \geqslant 0$. A change of coordinates yields

$$L = Q_{N/2}(\sqrt{\lambda}, \sqrt{V}) \ , \tag{B.15}$$

where

$$Q_M(\alpha, \beta) = \int_{\beta}^{\infty} x \left(\frac{x}{\alpha}\right)^{M-1} \exp\left(-\frac{x^2 + \alpha^2}{2}\right) I_{M-1}(\alpha x) \, dx$$

(B.16)

The function $Q_M(\alpha,\beta)$ is called the generalized Q-function. Methods for its approximate evaluation are presented in the references.

REFERENCES

[1]   A.D. Whalen, *Detection of Signals in Noise.* New York: Academic Press, 1971.

[2]   C.W. Helstrom, *Statistical Theory of Signal Detection*, 2nd ed., New York: Pergamon Press, 1968.

Appendix C

THE DISCRETE FOURIER TRANSFORM AND
THE SIGNAL SPECTRUM

In this appendix, we establish the relation between the discrete and continuous Fourier transforms. The continuous Fourier transform or spectrum of a signal $g(t)$ is defined as

$$G(\omega) = \int_{-\infty}^{\infty} g(t) \exp(-j\omega t) \, dt \,, \tag{C.1}$$

where $j = \sqrt{-1}$. We form the periodic function

$$\overline{G}(\omega) = \sum_{n=-\infty}^{\infty} G(\omega + n\omega_1) \,. \tag{C.2}$$

Since the period of $\overline{G}(\omega)$ is ω_1, $\overline{G}(\omega)$ can be expressed as a complex Fourier series. We have

$$\overline{G}(\omega) = \sum_{k=-\infty}^{\infty} c_k \exp\left(-j2\pi k \frac{\omega}{\omega_1}\right), \tag{C.3}$$

where c_k is the Fourier coefficient, which is given by

$$c_k = \frac{1}{\omega_1} \int_{-\omega_1/2}^{\omega_1/2} \overline{G}(\omega) \exp\left(j2\pi k \frac{\omega}{\omega_1}\right) d\omega \,. \tag{C.4}$$

Substituting Equation (C.2) into Equation (C.4) and interchanging the order of the summation and integration yields

$$c_k = \frac{1}{\omega_1} \sum_{n=-\infty}^{\infty} \int_{-\omega_1/2}^{\omega_1/2} G(\omega + n\omega_1) \exp\left(j2\pi k \frac{\omega}{\omega_1}\right) d\omega \; .$$

(C.5)

We change coordinates and observe that $\exp(j2\pi k n) = 1$ to obtain

$$c_k = \frac{1}{\omega_1} \sum_{n=-\infty}^{\infty} \int_{-\omega_1/2 + n\omega_1}^{\omega_1/2 + n\omega_1} G(\omega) \exp\left(j2\pi k \frac{\omega}{\omega_1}\right.$$

$$\left. - j2\pi k n\right) d\omega$$

$$= \frac{1}{\omega_1} \int_{-\infty}^{\infty} G(\omega) \exp\left(j2\pi k \frac{\omega}{\omega_1}\right) d\omega \; .$$

(C.6)

The function $g(t)$ can be expressed as the inverse Fourier transform:

$$g(t) = \frac{1}{2\pi} \int_{-\infty}^{\infty} G(\omega) \exp(j\omega t) d\omega \; .$$

(C.7)

Thus, Equation (C.6) implies that

$$c_k = \frac{2\pi}{\omega_1} g\left(\frac{2\pi k}{\omega_1}\right) \; .$$

(C.8)

Substituting Equation (C.8) into Equation (C.3) yields

$$\overline{G}(\omega) = \frac{2\pi}{\omega_1} \sum_{k=-\infty}^{\infty} g\left(\frac{2\pi k}{\omega_1}\right) \exp\left(-j2\pi k \frac{\omega}{\omega_1}\right) \; .$$

(C.9)

Let K denote a positive integer. Equation (C.9) gives

$$\overline{G}\left(\frac{i\omega_1}{K}\right) = \frac{2\pi}{\omega_1} \sum_{k=-\infty}^{\infty} g\left(\frac{2\pi k}{\omega_1}\right) \Omega_K^{ik} , \quad i = 0, 1, \ldots, K - 1 ,$$

(C.10)

where

$$\Omega_K = \exp\left(-\frac{j2\pi}{K}\right)$$

(C.11)

Any integer k can be expressed as $k = mK + n$, where m is some integer and n is an integer such that $0 \leqslant n \leqslant K - 1$. Therefore, Equation (C.10) can be written as

$$\overline{G}\left(\frac{i\omega_1}{K}\right) = \frac{2\pi}{\omega_1} \sum_{n=0}^{K-1} \sum_{m=-\infty}^{\infty} g\left(\frac{2\pi n + 2\pi mK}{\omega_1}\right) \Omega_K^{i(n+mK)} .$$

(C.12)

Defining the periodic function

$$\overline{g}(t) = \sum_{m=-\infty}^{\infty} g\left(t + m\frac{2\pi K}{\omega_1}\right),$$

(C.13)

and observing that

$$\Omega_K^{imK} = 1 ,$$

(C.14)

we obtain

$$\overline{G}\left(\frac{i\omega_1}{K}\right) = \frac{2\pi}{\omega_1} \sum_{n=0}^{K-1} \overline{g}\left(\frac{2\pi n}{\omega_1}\right) \Omega_K^{in} , \quad i = 0, 1, \ldots, K-1 .$$

(C.15)

This equation relates a periodic extension of the signal spectrum to the discrete Fourier transform of a periodic extension of the signal.

Appendix D

MATRIX ANALYSIS

This appendix summarizes the results from matrix analysis that are needed in Chapter 5.

D.1 ELEMENTARY RESULTS

An m $\times$ n (m by n) matrix is a rectangular array of mn elements arranged in m rows and n columns. If m $=$ n, the matrix is called a square matrix. A column vector is a set of n elements arranged in a column; thus, it is an n $\times$ 1 matrix. A row vector is a 1 $\times$ n matrix. A diagonal matrix is a square matrix in which only the elements along the main diagonal are nonzero. If these diagonal elements are all equal to unity, the matrix is called the identity matrix and is denoted by I. If a_{ij} is an element of an m $\times$ n matrix A and b_{ij} is an element of an n $\times$ p matrix B, then the product of A and B is defined to be the m $\times$ p matrix C $=$ AB having elements

$$c_{ij} = \sum_{k=1}^{n} a_{ik} b_{kj} , \quad i = 1, 2, \ldots, m, \quad j = 1, 2, \ldots, p .$$

(D.1)

The transpose of a matrix A is formed by interchanging the rows and columns. It is denoted by A^T. The transpose of a column vector is a row vector; the transpose of a row vector is a column vector. If A is an m × n matrix and B is an n × p matrix, the transpose of AB is a p × m matrix such that

$$(AB)^T = B^T A^T . \tag{D.2}$$

This result follows from the definition of matrix multiplication. We denote the complex conjugate of a quantity by an asterisk. The complex conjugate of A^T is denoted by A'; that is,

$$A' = (A^T)^* . \tag{D.3}$$

A square matrix A is called singular if the determinant of its elements, which is denoted by det [A], is zero. If A is a nonsingular matrix, there exists a unique inverse matrix, denoted by A^{-1}, such that

$$AA^{-1} = A^{-1} A = I . \tag{D.4}$$

If A and B are nonsingular square matrices, a direct application of Equation (D.4) proves that the product AB has an inverse that can be expressed as

$$(AB)^{-1} = B^{-1} A^{-1} . \tag{D.5}$$

For a nonsingular matrix A, it follows from Equation (D.2) that

$$I = I^T = (AA^{-1})^T = (A^{-1})^T A^T . \tag{D.6}$$

Similarly,

$$I = A^T (A^{-1})^T . \tag{D.7}$$

Thus, we have

$$(A^{-1})^T = (A^T)^{-1} . \tag{D.8}$$

The Euclidean norm of a column vector x is a nonnegative scalar defined as

$$\| x \| = (x'x)^{\frac{1}{2}} \tag{D.9}$$

The Cauchy-Schwarz inequality states that column vectors x and y satisfy

$$|x'y|^2 \leqslant \| x \|^2 \| y \|^2 . \tag{D.10}$$

Equality exists if $x = \alpha y$ for some scalar α.

An eigenvector of a square matrix A is any nontrivial column vector x that satisfies

$$Ax = \lambda x \tag{D.11}$$

for some scalar λ. Each value of λ associated with an eigenvector is called an eigenvalue. The set of eigenvalues is determined by solving the characteristic equation, which is

$$\det [A - \lambda I] = 0 .$$

(D.12)

If A and I are $n \times n$ matrices, we expand the determinant to obtain

$$
\det \begin{bmatrix}
a_{11} - \lambda & a_{12} & \cdots & a_{1n} \\
a_{21} & a_{22} - \lambda & \cdots & a_{2n} \\
\cdot & \cdot & & \cdot \\
\cdot & \cdot & & \cdot \\
\cdot & \cdot & & \cdot \\
a_{n1} & a_{n2} & \cdots & a_{nn} - \lambda
\end{bmatrix}
$$

$$= (-1)^n \lambda^n + c_1 \lambda^{n-1} + c_2 \lambda^{n-2} + \ldots + c_n ,$$

(D.13)

where the c_k are functions of the a_{ij}. The polynomial in Equation (D.13) is called the characteristic polynomial of the matrix A. It follows from the fundamental theorem of algebra that the characteristic polynomial can be written in factored form as

$$(-1)^n \lambda^n + c_1 \lambda^{n-1} + \ldots + c_n = (-1)^n \prod_{i=1}^{n} (\lambda - \lambda_i) ,$$

(D.14)

where the λ_i are the roots of the polynomial. Since the roots correspond to the eigenvalues, we conclude that an $n \times n$ matrix has n eigenvalues, $\lambda_1, \lambda_2, \ldots, \lambda_n$, which are not necessarily all distinct.

The expansion of the determinant in Equation (D.13) gives

$$c_1 = (-1)^{n-1} \sum_{i=1}^{n} a_{ii} .$$

(D.15)

Setting $\lambda = 0$ in Equation (D.13), we obtain

$$c_n = \det [A] .$$

(D.16)

Equating terms with the same power of λ on both sides of Equation (D.14), we obtain

$$c_1 = (-1)^{n+1} \sum_{i=1}^{n} \lambda_i ,$$

(D.17)

$$c_n = \prod_{i=1}^{n} \lambda_i . \tag{D.18}$$

The trace of a square matrix is defined to be the sum of its diagonal elements. Comparing Equations (D.15) and (D.17), we conclude that the trace of a matrix is equal to the sum of its eigenvalues; that is,

$$\text{trace } [A] = \sum_{i=1}^{n} \lambda_i . \tag{D.19}$$

Equations (D.16) and (D.18) yield

$$\det [A] = \prod_{i=1}^{n} \lambda_i , \tag{D.20}$$

which states that the determinant of a matrix is equal to the product of its eigenvalues.

D.2 HERMITIAN AND QUADRATIC FORMS

A Hermitian matrix is a square matrix that satisfies

$$A' = A , \tag{D.21}$$

or, equivalently,

$$A^T = A^* . \tag{D.22}$$

Let λ_i and e_i represent an eigenvalue and its corresponding eigenvector. From Equation (D.11), we have

$$A e_i = \lambda_i e_i . \tag{D.23}$$

Multiplying this equation by the conjugate transpose of an eigenvector e_j yields

$$e_j' A e_i = \lambda_i e_j' e_i . \tag{D.24}$$

If λ_j is the eigenvalue corresponding to e_j, we also have

$$e_i' A e_j = \lambda_j e_i' e_j . \tag{D.25}$$

Taking the conjugate transpose of Equation (D.25) and using Equations (D.2) and (D.21) yield

$$e_j' A e_i = \lambda_j^* e_j' e_i . \tag{D.26}$$

Subtracting Equation (D.26) from Equation (D.24) gives

$$(\lambda_i - \lambda_j^*)\, e_j'\, e_i = 0 \ . \tag{D.27}$$

If $j = i$, this equation becomes

$$(\lambda_i - \lambda_i^*)\, e_i'\, e_i = 0 \ . \tag{D.28}$$

Since e_i is not the zero vector, this equation can be satisfied only if $\lambda_i = \lambda_i^*$. Thus, we conclude that the eigenvalues of a Hermitian matrix are real. If $j \neq i$ and $\lambda_i \neq \lambda_j$, Equation (D.27) implies that e_j and e_i are orthogonal; that is, the two vectors satisfy $e_j'\, e_i = e_i'\, e_j = 0$. Thus, the eigenvectors corresponding to distinct eigenvalues are orthogonal. In general, it can be shown that an $n \times n$ Hermitian matrix has n eigenvectors such that

$$e_i'\, e_j = 0, \quad i \neq j \ , \quad i, j = 1, 2, \ldots, n \ ,$$

$$e_i'\, e_i = 1, \quad i = 1, 2, \ldots, n \ . \tag{D.29}$$

Eigenvectors satisfying these equations are called orthonormal eigenvectors.

Let U denote a matrix with columns that are the orthonormal eigenvectors of a Hermitian matrix A:

$$U = [e_1\ e_2\ \ldots\ e_n] \ . \tag{D.30}$$

Straightforward calculations using the orthonormality yield

$$U'\, U = U\, U' = I \ . \tag{D.31}$$

Therefore,

$$U' = U^{-1} \ . \tag{D.32}$$

A matrix that satisfies Equation (D.32) is called a unitary matrix. A straightforward calculation using Equations (D.23), (D.29), and (D.30) gives

$$U'\, A\, U = \lambda \ , \tag{D.33}$$

where λ is the diagonal matrix of eigenvalues:

$$\lambda = \begin{bmatrix} \lambda_1 & 0 & 0 & \ldots & 0 \\ 0 & \lambda_2 & 0 & \ldots & 0 \\ 0 & 0 & \lambda_3 & \ldots & 0 \\ \cdot & \cdot & \cdot & & \cdot \\ \cdot & \cdot & \cdot & & \cdot \\ \cdot & \cdot & \cdot & & \cdot \\ 0 & 0 & 0 & \ldots & \lambda_n \end{bmatrix} \ . \tag{D.34}$$

The matrix A is said to be diagonalized to λ by the operation on the left-hand side of Equation (D.33).

A Hermitian form is a function that takes scalar values and has the form

$$H = x' A x , \tag{D.35}$$

where A is an $n \times n$ Hermitian matrix and x is a column vector with n elements. It can easily be verified that $H = H^*$. Thus, a Hermitian form always assumes real values.

A Hermitian matrix is said to be positive definite if its corresponding Hermitian form is positive for every $x \neq 0$. We define the column vector

$$y = U' x , \tag{D.36}$$

where U is the unitary matrix defined in Equation (D.30). From Equation (D.32), it follows that

$$x = U y . \tag{D.37}$$

Using Equations (D.32) to (D.36), we obtain

$$
\begin{aligned}
H &= x'U U^{-1} A U U^{-1} x \\
&= (U' x)' (U' A U) (U' x) \\
&= y' \lambda y \\
&= \sum_{i=1}^{n} \lambda_i |y_i|^2 .
\end{aligned}
\tag{D.38}
$$

Thus, if all the eigenvalues are positive, then $H > 0$ unless $y = 0$, which implies $x = 0$ by Equation (D.37). Therefore, $H > 0$ for every $x \neq 0$ if all the eigenvalues are positive. Conversely, suppose that some eigenvalue, λ_j is negative or zero. If we set $y_i = 0, i \neq j$, and $y_j = 1$, we obtain $H \leqslant 0$; the corresponding value of x is $x = U y = e_j \neq 0$. Thus, $H > 0$ for every $x \neq 0$ only if the eigenvalues are all positive. We conclude that a Hermitian matrix is positive definite if and only if all its eigenvalues are positive.

Since the eigenvalues are positive, Equation (D.20) indicates that the determinant of a positive definite Hermitian matrix is positive. Therefore, the matrix has an inverse.

A symmetric matrix is a square matrix with real elements that satisfies

$$A^T = A .$$

(D.39)

A symmetric matrix can be considered a special case of a Hermitian matrix. Thus, the properties of Hermitian matrices apply to symmetric matrices.

The eigenvalues of a symmetric matrix are real. There exist n real orthonormal eigenvectors such that

$$e_i^T e_j = 0 , \quad i \neq j , \quad i, j = 1, 2, \ldots, n,$$

$$e_i^T e_i = 1 , \quad i = 1, 2, \ldots, n .$$

(D.40)

If x is a real n-dimensional column vector and A is a real n × n matrix, then

$$Q = x^T A x$$

(D.41)

is called a quadratic form. A symmetric matrix is said to be positive definite if its corresponding quadratic form is positive for every $x \neq 0$. If a symmetric matrix is positive definite, its inverse exists. A symmetric matrix is positive definite if and only if all its eigenvalues are positive.

The positive definite matrices of Chapter 5 arise in a special way. Consider the product $x^T y = y^T x$, where x is an n-dimensional column vector of random variables and y is an n-dimensional column vector of arbitrary constants. The magnitude of the product is nonnegative. Suppose that it is known that the expected value of the magnitude squared is positive if $y \neq 0$. Then

$$0 < E[|x^T y|^2] = E[(y^T x)^* (x^T y)] = E[y' x^* x^T y]$$

(D.42)

for every $y \neq 0$. Therefore,

$$y' E[x^* x^T] y > 0 , \quad y \neq 0 ,$$

(D.43)

which indicates that $E[x^* x^T]$ is positive definite.

D.3 THE GRADIENT

Differentiation of a scalar function f with respect to a real vector x is called the gradient of f with respect to x, and is defined to be the column vector

$$\nabla_x f = \begin{bmatrix} \dfrac{\partial f}{\partial x_1} \\[2mm] \dfrac{\partial f}{\partial x_2} \\[2mm] . \\ . \\ . \\[2mm] \dfrac{\partial f}{\partial x_n} \end{bmatrix} \qquad (D.44)$$

From this definition, it follows that for column vectors x and y, we have

$$\nabla_x(x^T y) = \nabla_x(y^T x) = y . \qquad (D.45)$$

Let A represent an n × n matrix with elements a_{ij} . Then

$$\frac{\partial}{\partial x_i} (x^T A x) = \sum_{j=1}^{n} x_j A_{ji} + \sum_{j=1}^{n} A_{ij} x_j ,$$

$$i = 1, 2, \ldots, n, \qquad (D.46)$$

which implies that

$$\nabla_x (x^T A x) = A^T x + A x . \qquad (D.47)$$

When A is symmetric, then

$$\nabla_x (x^T A x) = 2 A x . \qquad (D.48)$$

D.4 LINEAR DISCRETE-TIME EQUATIONS

Consider a system of linear discrete-time equations that can be written in the form

$$x(k + 1) = A x (k) + b , \qquad (D.49)$$

where A is a square matrix of constants, b is a column vector of constants, and k is the discrete-time variable. Thus, Equation (D.49) describes a linear time-invariant dynamic system. A vector x_0 is an equilibrium point of the dynamic system if $x(k) = x_0$ implies $x(k + 1) = x_0$. Therefore, an equilibrium point must satisfy the equation

$$x_0 = A x_0 + b . \qquad (D.50)$$

If the matrix $(I - A)$ is nonsingular, Equation (D.50) has a unique solution:

$$x_0 = (I - A)^{-1} b. \qquad (D.51)$$

An equilibrium point is said to be asymptotically stable if $x(k)$ converges to x_0 as k increases. A necessary and sufficient condition for an equilibrium point to be asymptotically stable is that the eigenvalues of A all have magnitudes less than unity.

REFERENCES

[1]   F.B. Hildebrand, *Methods of Applied Mathematics*, 2nd ed. Englewood Cliffs, New Jersey: Prentice-Hall, 1965.

[2]   D.G. Luenberger, *Introduction to Dynamic Systems*. New York: Wiley, 1979.

Index

Acousto-optics, 140, 152-154
Acquisition
  by serial search, 54-55, 94
  by matched filter, 55-56, 94-95
  of frequency-hopping code, 94-95
  of pseudonoise code, 53-56
Adaptive antenna systems, 191-228
Adaptive element, 205-206
Adaptive noise cancelling, 217-219
Adaptive notch filter, 219
Adaptive null steering, 203-204
Adaptive polarization
  discrimination, 225-228
Adaptive thresholding, 177
Adjacent splatter ratio, 110, 116
Amplitude comparison, 167
Amplitude modulation (AM), 6-8, 11
Analog communications, 6-11
Arrival-time estimation, 141,
  181-187
Asymptotic stability, 293
Autocorrelation
  average, 38
  of maximal sequence, 34-36
  of periodic function, 34
  of stochastic process, 38

Bit error probability, see Error
  probability
Bit interleaving, 20
Block chaining, 259
Block cipher, 232-234, 249-256,
  259-260
Block code, 49-51, 68, 70, 78-79
Bragg cell, 152-154
Burst of errors, 19-20

Cable communications, 1-2, 188
Cancellation pattern, 203-204
Capture of receiver, 11, 259
Cauchy-Schwarz inequality, 286

Channel
  complementary, 68
  frequency-hopping, 65
  transmission, 68
Channelized cross correlator, 147
Channelized radiometer, 135-140
Channelized receiver, 148-149
Chi-squared distribution
  central, 277
  noncentral, 275-278
Chip, 25, 79
Chip-rate ratio, 49
Chirp filter, 161
Chirp transform processor, 164-166
Cipher
  block, 232-234, 249-256, 259-260
  data-keyed, 234, 236, 238-249,
    251-259, 261
  stream, 232-249, 251-259, 261
  synchronous, 233-237, 243, 249,
    251-259, 261
Cipher-block chaining, 259-260
Close interferers, 114-116
Code
  block, 49-51, 68, 70, 78-79
  burst-error correcting, 19-20
  convolutional, 49
  cross correlation of codes, 56-58
  cryptographic, 231-232
  Gold, 57
  pseudonoise, 23, 30-36
  repetition, 79
  synchronization, 53-56, 94-95
Code-shift keying, 28, 30, 60
Commutator, 149
Complementary channel, 68
Complementary error function, 43
Compression ratio, 163
Concealment of pseudonoise
  waveforms, 36-41
Constrained minimum power
  criterion, 219-223

Continuous-phase frequency-shift
    keying (CPFSK), 90, 101-102
Correlator, 126-127
Cramer-Rao bound
    for arrival-time estimate, 184
    for phase angle estimate, 187
Cross correlator, 140-147
Cryptanalysis, 241-242
Cryptographic degradation, 250-254
Cryptographic digital
    communications 231-261
Cryptographic error correction,
    253-256
Cryptography, 231

Data-keyed cipher, 234, 236,
    238-249, 251-259, 261
Deemphasis, 10-11
Degrees of freedom, 275
Deployment, 108-109
Desired response, 205-206
    generators of, 215-216
Detection, 126-147, 188
Deviation ratio, 101
Digital communications, see
    specific types
Direct-sequence system, 25-28
Directional antenna, 188
Direction finding
    amplitude comparison, 167
    energy comparison, 167-180
    interferometer, 180-187
Duty cycle, 104
Duty factor, 104

Eigenvalue, 286
Eigenvector, 286
Enciphering, see Cipher
Encryption, see Cipher
    end-to-end, 261
    link, 261
Energy comparison, 167-180
    stationary multibeam, 168-174
    with single rotating beam, 176-180
    with two rotating beams, 174-176
Energy detector, 128-140

Ensembles of deciphering systems,
    245
Error-correcting code, see Code
Error extension, 242
Error probability
    cryptographic, 243-250
    frequency-hopping, 70-94, 98-100,
        102-121
    frequency-shift keying, 11-18
    pseudonoise, 41-50, 58, 98-100
    quadriphase pseudonoise, 50-52
Error propagation, 242
Equilibrium point, 293
Equivalent linear generator, 235-237
Equivalent channels, 110
Estimation
    arrival-time, 141, 181-187
    bearing, 167-187
    frequency, 147-167
    location, 187
    maximum likelihood, 209
    maximum signal-to-noise ratio,
        209-211
    minimum mean-square error,
        211-213
    phase, 180-182, 186-187

Fast frequency hopping, 66-68
Feedback shift register, 31-33
Fractional out-of-band power,
    114-115
Frequency-domain array-processing
    filter, 207-208
Frequency estimation, 147-167
Frequency hopping, 65-121, 135,
    138, 147, 152, 154, 167, 174
Frequency-hopping network, 100-121
Frequency-hopping pseudonoise
    system, 96-97
Frequency modulation (FM), 6-7, 9-11
Frequency-shift keying (FSK), 11-18,
    68-70, 89-90, 101
Frost's adaptive algorithm, 222-223

Generalized Q-function, 278
Gold code, 57

Gradient, 292
Griffiths algorithm, 213-214

Hermitian form, 290-291
Hermitian matrix, 288-289
Hybrid system, 96-97

Indicator, 261
Input word, 243
Instantaneous frequency measurement, 154-155
Intelligibility, 16-17
Interception, 125-188
Interference, see Jamming
Interference parameter, 45
Interferometer, 180-187
Interleaving, 20

Jamming, basic characteristics
    narrowband, 2, 13-18
    noise, 12-18
    partial-band, 79, 82-84
    playback, 259
    pseudonoise, 53
    pulsed, 17-20, 256-259
    repeater, 85-89
    swept-frequency, 17
    tone, 8-11, 53
    wideband, 3

Key, 231
Key distribution center, 261
Keystream, 232

Least-mean-square algorithm, see
    Widrow-Hoff algorithm
Link encryption, 261
Location estimation, 187
Longley-Rice model, 3

Matrix analysis, 285-293
Maximal sequence, 33-36
Mean-square error criterion, 211-213
Message privacy, 25
Microscan receiver, 161-167

Minimum-shift keying (MSK), 90, 102, 115-116
Modulation, see specific types
Multipath, 36
Multiple frequency-shift keying (MFSK), 65, 89-90, 135, 152, 154, 167
Multiple sidelobe canceller, 201-202
Mutual interference
    in pseudonoise network, 58, 100
    in frequency-hopping network, 100-121

Near-far ratio, 116
Network
    encryption in, 261
    frequency-hopping, 100-121
    pseudonoise, 56-59, 100
Noncentral parameter, 275
Normalized frequency offset, 48
Notch filter, 219

One-time tape, 234
Optical fibers, 1-2, 188
Output word, 243

Permutation box, 233
Phase estimation, 180-182, 186-187
Phase modulation (PM), 6-9, 11
Phase-shift keying (PSK), 24-26, 90
Pilot signal, 215
Playback, 259
Polarization
    adaptive, 225-228
    loss, 5
Positive definite matrix, 290-291
Power spectral density
    average, 38
    of pseudonoise code, 37-38
    of random binary sequence, 40
    of stationary process, 38
    of transmitted pseudonoise signal, 39-40
Preemphasis, 10-11
Primary antenna and signal, 192-194, 217-218

298 PRINCIPLES OF MILITARY COMMUNICATION SYSTEMS

Processing gain, 28, 48
Propagation, 1-6
Pseudonoise code or sequence, 30-36
  acquisition, 53-56
Pseudonoise network, 56-59, 100
Pseudonoise spread spectrum, 23-62,
  147, 219
Pulsed jamming, 17-20, 256-259

Q-function, 268, 278
Quadratic form, 291
Quadriphase pseudonoise system,
  24-25, 28-29, 41, 50-52
Quadriphase-shift keying (QPSK),
  24-25, 28-29, 90, 115

Radiometer, 128-140
Random binary sequence, 40
Reacquisition time, 256
Reference antenna and signal,
  192-194, 217-218
Relay, 2
Repeater jammer, 85-89
Repetition code, 79
Rotating beam(s), 174-180

Scanning superheterodyne receiver,
  155-160
Session key, 261
Shift Register, 31-33
Sidelobe canceller, 192-205, 218
Signal-to-noise ratio criterion,
  209-211
Sinc function, 37
Single-channel modulation, 65
Sinusoidal frequency-shift keying
  (SFSK), 115-116
Slow frequency hopping, 66-68
Spectral splatter, 100-102
Spectrum analyzer, 147-167
  acousto-optical, 152-154
  chirp transform processor, 164-166
  discrete Fourier transform,
    149-152
Spread-spectrum system, general,
  23-24
Stationary multibeam system, 168-174

Steepest descent, 213
Stream cipher, 232-249, 251-259, 261
Substitution box, 233
Switching time, 100-101
Symmetric matrix, 291
Synchronization
  of burst communications, 60
  of cryptographic communications,
    256-259
  of frequency-hopping code, 94-95
  of pseudonoise code, 53-56
  tracking, 53
Synchronous cipher, 233-237, 243,
  249, 251-259, 261

Tapped delay line, 205, 207
Time-division multiplexing, 58
Time hopping, 58-59, 188
Trace of matrix, 288
Tracking, 53
Train, 243
Transmission channel, 68

Weights, 205
  convergence of mean, 223-224
Weighting functions, 197-200
Widrow-Hoff algorithm, 214-216
  convergence, 223-224
Wiener filter, 212
Wiener-Hopf equation, 212
Word error probability, see
    Error probability